AIDS Issues

Background Papers and Proceedings of a
Binational (Canada/U.S.) Consultation

SPONSORED BY

The Canadian Council of Churches
The National Council of Churches of Christ in the U.S.A.
The World Council of Churches

HOSTED BY THE TORONTO SCHOOL OF THEOLOGY

AIDS Issues

Confronting the Challenge

EDITED BY

David G. Hallman

The Pilgrim Press
NEW YORK

The biblical quotations in this book are from the *Revised Standard
Version of the Bible*, copyright 1946, 1952, and © 1971, 1973 by the
Division of Christian Education, National Council of Churches, and
are used by permission.

Library of Congress Cataloging-in-Publication Data

AIDS issues

"Background papers and proceedings of a binational
(Canada/U.S.) consultation sponsored by the Canadian
Council of Churches, the National Council of Churches
of Christ in the U.S.A., the World Council of Churches;
hosted by the Toronto School of Theology."
    1. AIDS (Disease)—Social aspects—Congresses.
2. AIDS (Disease)—Religious aspects—Christianity—
Congresses.   1. Hallman, David G.   II. Canadian Council
of Churches.   III. National Council of the Churches of
Christ in the United States of America.   IV. World
Council of Churches.
RC607.A26A3476   1988   362.1'969792   88-25508
ISBN 0-8298-0793-4 (pbk.)

The Pilgrim Press, 132 West 31 Street, New York, NY 10001

DEDICATED TO
THOSE WHO HAVE DIED OF
AND
THOSE WHO ARE LIVING WITH
AIDS

MAY OUR RESPONSE TO THE AIDS CRISIS
LEAD US TO CREATE
A MORE HUMANE COMMUNITY
AT HOME AND GLOBALLY.

Contents

Foreword

AIDS is a global problem and a challenge to us all. As of July 1, 1988, a total of 100,410 AIDS cases have been reported to the World Health Organization (WHO) from 138 countries around the world. However, WHO estimates that the actual number of AIDS cases worldwide since the beginning of the AIDS epidemic is closer to 250,000.

Available data suggest that 5 to 10 million persons worldwide are probably infected with the human immunodeficiency virus (HIV). If we assume that 5 million persons are infected, we would predict that approximately 1 million new cases of AIDS will occur during the next five years.

Although the routes of HIV transmission are the same everywhere (sexual intercourse, direct exposure to blood, infected mother to infant), the global picture of HIV infection and AIDS is not uniform or consistent. Three patterns of HIV/AIDS can be described.

The first pattern (I) includes North America, Western Europe, Australia, New Zealand, and, increasingly, urban areas of Latin America. In Pattern I areas sexual transmission predominantly involves homosexual and bisexual men, although heterosexual spread is also occurring. Spread of HIV through blood mainly involves persons with self-injecting drug behavior, as blood for transfusion and blood products are now essentially safe. Relatively few children have been infected because, thus far, women are less affected than men in Pattern 1 areas of the world.

Pattern II areas include sub-Saharan Africa and parts of the Caribbean. In these areas heterosexual transmission dominates, along with spread through unscreened blood transfusion and the use of unsterile needles, syringes, or other skin-piercing instruments. Finally, because in some urban areas 5% to 15% or more of pregnant women may be HIV-infected, infants are increasingly affected by HIV/AIDS. In some areas the child health gains projected by the child survival initiatives may be tragically canceled by the impact of HIV/AIDS on infant and child health.

Finally, Pattern III includes North Africa, the Middle East, Eastern Europe and most of Asia and the Pacific. HIV/AIDS is less common in these areas, although AIDS cases have been reported from twenty-five countries in Asia and Oceania. Pattern III countries may be able to prevent AIDS from becoming the important public health problem it has already become in Pattern I and Pattern II areas of the world.

AIDS is not just a health problem in the narrow sense of the term. AIDS is a challenge with important social, cultural, economic, and political dimensions and impact. At the WHO we stress that these dimensions of the AIDS pandemic are as much a part of the problem as the virus itself.

An effective social response to HIV/AIDS requires broad discussion, including social, ethical, and theological issues. This book is an important contribution to this debate, the quality of which will help to determine our collective future.

Dr. Jonathan Mann, Director
Global Programme on AIDS
World Health Organization, Geneva

Contributors

Ron Bayer is co-director of the AIDS Project for the Hastings Center, New York, a research institute dealing with ethical questions in the medical field.

Carl Bean is with the Minority AIDS Task Force of Los Angeles and has been a leading spokesperson in the United States, calling attention to the underlying causes and implications of the high proportion of racial minority persons with AIDS.

Gene Copello teaches medical ethics at Vanderbilt University School of Medicine, Nashville, Tennessee, and is director of the Vanderbilt AIDS Project. He was recently elected president-elect of the International Society for AIDS Education.

Mark Mosher DeWolfe served as minister for the Unitarian congregation of South Peel, Mississauga, Ontario, and was diagnosed as having AIDS in October 1986. He was a founding member of AIDS Support, the social service and counseling arm of the AIDS Committee of Toronto. He died in July 1988.

Eilert Frerichs is the United Church of Canada chaplain at the University of Toronto. The Rev. Frerichs represented the United Church at the WCC Consultation in Geneva in June 1986 and was part of the program-planning committee for the October 1987 consultation in Toronto.

Chris Glaser served for nearly a decade as director of the Lazarus Project, a ministry of reconciliation between the church and the lesbian/gay community in Los Angeles. Now a full-time writer, he is the author of *Uncommon Calling: A Gay Man's Struggle to Serve the Church,* (Harper & Row, 1988).

Kevin Gordon is a Roman Catholic lay theologian teaching human sexuality and biomedical ethics at Brooklyn College, City University of New York. He is president of the Consultation on Homosexuality, Social Justice and Roman Catholic Theology (which recently published his book, *Homosexuality and Social Justice*) and was the moderator of the World Council of Churches Consultation on Ethics and AIDS in Geneva in June 1986.

Nicholas Gray is a writer living in Vancouver, British Columbia. He is editor of the newsletter of the Vancouver Persons with AIDS Coalition and has been diagnosed with AIDS.

Douglas Graydon serves as a chaplain at St. Michael's Hospital in Toronto and has provided pastoral care to many persons with AIDS.

Bonnie Greene is director of the Office of Church in Society for the United Church of Canada and formerly was the denomination's Program Officer for Human Rights.

André Guindon is Professor of Christian Ethics at St. Paul University, Ottawa, Canada.

David Hallman is program officer for social issues and justice for the United Church of Canada. In that capacity he has provided leadership on AIDS in his church and acted as coordinator for the October 1987 ecumenical consultation on ethical and theological issues related to AIDS.

Mary Hunt works with the Women's Alliance for Theology, Ethics and Ritual, based in Silver Spring, Maryland, and has written and lectured extensively on human sexuality.

barb m. janes is the minister for two United Church of Canada congregations in northern Ontario and has been actively involved in issues related to theology, feminism, and human sexuality.

Annette Johnson is a Management Fellow for the New York State Department of Health and formerly served as an AIDS educator for the State Department in New York City.

Abbyann Lynch is director of the Westminster Institute for Ethics and Human Values in London, Ontario. She is a frequent speaker and writer on bioethical issues.

Gary McClelland is a practicing physician working in Los Angeles and is actively involved with the Metropolitan Community Church. He was diagnosed with HIV infection in November 1985.

Patrick Morin is a sculptor with a Master of Visual Arts degree. He is a participating member of the Metropolitan Community Church of Edmonton. He was diagnosed with AIDS in 1986 and has been doing public education work on behalf of the AIDS Network of Edmonton.

Janet Pierce is a minister with the Metropolitan Community Church in Nashville, Tennessee, and is active in AIDS support work in Nashville.

Adele Resmer is a Lutheran pastor employed as a researcher in the Division of Social Ministry Organizations of the Evangelical Lutheran Church in America. She has been a member of the Task Force on AIDS of the National Council of Churches.

David Roy is director of the Center for Bioethics of the Clinical Research Institute of Montreal. In that capacity he has been involved extensively in assisting professional, public, and private organizations explore the implications of AIDS for their work.

Ron Russell-Coons is a minister with the Metropolitan Community Church in Seattle, Washington, and was diagnosed with AIDS in December 1986.

Stephen Schell was a market research consultant and is currently studying theology at the University of Toronto. He was diagnosed with AIDS in January 1987.

Gerald Sheppard teaches Old Testament Studies at Emmanuel College in Toronto. He was previously on the faculty at Union Theological Seminary in New York where he had an article titled "The Use of Scripture Within the Christian Ethical Debate Concerning Same-Sex Oriented Persons" published in the *Union Seminary Quarterly Review* (Vol. 40/1&2, pp. 13–36, 1985).

Mervyn Silverman is president of the American Foundation on AIDS Research. He was the director of health for the city of San Francisco from 1977 to 1985, during which period he provided leadership in helping the city to recognize the dimensions of the AIDS crisis.

Tom Sinclair-Faulkner teaches in the Department of Religious Studies at Dalhousie University, Dartmouth, Nova Scotia, and is a contributing editor to *Christian Century*.

Margaret Somerville is director of the McGill Centre for Medicine, Ethics and Law in Montreal and is a member of the Canadian government's National Advisory Committee on AIDS.

Cécile De Sweemer works with the International Development Research Centre as coordinator of their Health Services Division of West and Central Africa. Previously she was a special adviser on AIDS for the general secretary of the World Council of Churches.

Acknowledgments

There are many people to thank when a project like this book actually sees the light of day. I will start with those who were involved in the planning of the October 1987 Consultation in Toronto on which this book is based. The vision, commitment, and hard work of the planning committee made the event possible. The group included Sr. Ann Anderson, Dr. Lee Cormie, Fr. Michael Fahey, the Rev. Eilert Frerichs, Dr. Ray Hodgson, Dr. Roger Hutchinson, Dr. Richard Isaac, Dr. Bill Lord, the Rev. Arch McCurdy, Dr. Gerald Sheppard, Ms. Jenny Silcox, the Rev. Peter Thompson, and Mr. Art Wood.

Many of these people are associated with the Toronto School of Theology (TST), which graciously acted as host for the event. Other TST personnel who helped before, during, and after the Consultation were Dr. Ray Whitehead, Dr. James Reed, Mrs. Jane Jeffries, Ms. Veronica Vallentine, Ms. Barbara Sanderson, and Ms. Sandra Deaves. Appreciation is also due to a number of volunteers, who contributed a great deal of time and energy, in particular, Mr. Richard Chambers and Mr. Bill MacKinnon.

Ms. Janis Traquair, my secretary at the time, spent at least as much time as I did helping with all the logistics related to the Consultation, and I am much in her debt.

Valuable assistance was received during the planning process from Ms. Cathie Lyons and other members of the National Council of Churches (U.S.A.) Task Force on AIDS. Ms. Edith Shore of the Canadian Council of Churches, Dr. David Gosling of the World Council of Churches, and Dr. Bonnie Greene of the United Church of Canada provided sound advice along the way.

The Consultation was cosponsored by the World Council of Churches (AIDS Working Group), the Canadian Council of Churches, and the National Council of the Churches of Christ in the U.S.A. (AIDS Task Force and Division of Church and Society). These councils exhibited courage and vision in being prepared to lend their support to a Consultation on a controversial subject like AIDS.

The resource people and participants at the Consultation deserve the credit for creating reality out of the vision. Those who made specific written contributions are identified in the book, but there were many others who helped to shape the thinking and collective challenge that emerged from the event.

When it came to transforming the Consultation experience into a book that could be more widely shared, Ms. Janis Traquair, my secretary, spent innumerable hours typing and retyping manuscripts. Ms. Barb Scott transcribed some of the proceedings. Ms. Laurice Mahli, my present secretary, has helped in the later stages of the book preparation. Dr. Gerald Sheppard assisted in some of the coordinating with The Pilgrim Press.

I am very grateful for the patience, diligence, and good humor of Ms. Marion M. Meyer, Senior Editor of The Pilgrim Press, who guided the book to its production stage.

The United Church of Canada, for which I work as a Program Officer for Social Issues and Justice, was very generous in providing a considerable amount of my staff time and that of my secretary to the planning of the Consultation and the preparation of this book. The Church's commitment to ensuring that churches respond effectively to the AIDS crisis has resulted in its giving considerable leadership on this issue in Canada and internationally.

The Consultation and this subsequent publication would not have been possible without financial support from many Canadian denominations and religious orders and from several American denominations. Special appreciation is due to the Canadian government which, through the AIDS Centre of Health and Welfare Canada, provided a very generous grant.

Finally, to my friend William Conklin I owe a special word of thanks for his constant support and practical assistance over the many hours of planning for the Consultation and preparation of the book.

Introduction

Are Christian churches going to be a constructive or divisive force on the subject of AIDS? The reviews to date are mixed. On the positive side, we find some churches beginning to provide compassionate pastoral care to persons with AIDS and their families, partners, and friends. Less encouraging are the churches' efforts at education. Missing almost completely have been any serious intensive attempts to struggle with the range of difficult ethical and theological issues that AIDS is precipitating.

In the near absence of constructive leadership by churches on these issues, the public has been left with the judgmental theological attitudes voiced by some conservative church spokespersons and TV evangelists that AIDS is God's punishment of homosexuals and IV drug users. With the churches largely remaining silent, society can hardly be faulted for assuming that this perspective is representative of the total Christian community.

The consequences of such silence could be disastrous. The logical conclusion of the line of argument about AIDS being God's punishment is that those with AIDS deserve it, and therefore society has no obligation to care for them. It divides the population into the "bad" (i.e., those who have been exposed to the AIDS virus) and the "good" (i.e., those who are not HIV-positive). People suffering from this horrible disease would be abandoned, left to die alone.

Such a dichotomy would also undermine educational efforts. If AIDS is considered part of an intentional plan of punishment by God, then those who feel morally superior to homosexuals and IV drug users would assume that they run no risk of contracting the virus. There would be difficulty generating political support for explicit education programs on means of preventing exposure to the virus. Sexually active young people could be easy victims of such a blinkered societal approach.

Christian churches can and must play a role in pushing our societies to deal with AIDS compassionately, constructively, and creatively. We must communicate the message that all people are children of God and entitled to the best and most humane care society can offer. We need to emphasize that AIDS is a disease, not a moral judgment, and that we need to treat it as the major public health crisis it is. The HIV virus must be explained as being blind to sexual orientation and that with what we know about the means of transmission, all who engage in unprotected "risk behaviors" leave themselves vulnerable.

Origin of the Consultation Idea

Challenging Christian churches to grapple with such ethical and theological issues was the rationale for sponsoring the consultation that is the subject of this book. Leadership is needed in order to help society respond effectively to the crisis. The credibility of churches regarding their concern about the well-being of humanity is also on the line. A major effort to move churches toward constructive involvement was the goal of the event.

The idea for the consultation originated in the fall of 1986 when a number of us in Canada were reflecting on the World Council of Churches'(WCC) Consultation on AIDS held in Geneva in June 1986. The WCC Consultation had called for churches around the world to become involved in responding to the needs of persons with AIDS and others affected by the disease. (The final statement from the WCC Consultation is attached as Appendix A.)

As we analyzed how churches in Canada and in the United States had responded to AIDS to that point, we concluded that progress was being made on several fronts. Denominations were starting to make educational material available to their congregations to counteract some of the myths and misconceptions about AIDS. Chaplains and other churchpeople involved in health care were taking leadership in helping their churches provide compassionate pastoral care for persons with AIDS and their families, partners, and friends. Liturgical events to acknowledge the suffering and deaths and to celebrate the lives of the increasing number of people dying of AIDS were being sponsored by some churches.

Our assessment of this progress did point to a serious gap. There was a wide range of theological and ethical issues related to AIDS on which the churches had, to that point, been largely silent. Serious illnesses often provoke profound theological questions on an individual basis. With the initial association of AIDS with marginalized groups like homosexuals and later IV drug users, these theological questions took on social and political dimensions. How persons with AIDS would be cared for, what measures would be taken to reduce transmission of the virus, and what resources society would provide for dealing with the disease were all linked to attitudes toward those with AIDS. Those attitudes in turn often had religious overtones.

There were probably a variety of reasons why churches had not addressed those issues. The issues were complex and would require disciplined, hard work. They were also controversial, and churches have a tendency to want to avoid controversial subjects. The historic difficulty in dealing with issues related to human sexuality, particularly homosexuality, was no doubt a major factor.

Whatever the reasons for this avoidance, it was our assessment that it should not be allowed to continue. Providing pastoral care would be a losing battle if our societies started to become extremely polarized and persons with AIDS were denied adequate care. The churches needed to provide leadership on fundamental values, attitudes, and ethics that would underlie the kinds of public policies that would be adopted regarding AIDS.

Planning and Process of the Consultation

We concluded that one way to give the churches a push in this direction would be the convening of a consultation. It was our intention not to deal with the whole range of the churches' response to AIDS, but specifically to focus on the difficult theological and ethical issues. To be successful, we would need the commitment of the churches to support it, we would have to have participants with a variety of skills and experiences equal to the task, and we would require a process that allowed for intensive, disciplined discussion and analysis.

Although the United Church of Canada was the initiator of the concept, we recognized that it should be ecumenical. Thus we approached the Canadian Council of Churches and got their agreement to act as a sponsor. It was also decided that the event should be binational, involving churches and participants from Canada and the United States. Although our cultures and sociopolitical systems are very different, both countries were experiencing some of the same problems related to AIDS. The idea of the consultation was raised with and supported by the National Council of Churches of Christ in the U.S.A. (NCC) through their Task Force on AIDS and their Division of Church and Society. Because we saw the event as a Canadian-U.S. regional follow-up to the World Council of Churches' June 1986 Consultation, we approached the WCC AIDS Working Group with the request that they be the third co-sponsor, and they agreed.

With the focus of the consultation being issues of theology and ethics, it was important to have people trained in those disciplines active in the planning and involved as resource people and participants in the event itself. The Toronto School of Theology (TST) seemed like an appropriate institution to assist and to act as host for the consultation. TST is a federation of Protestant and Catholic theological colleges in Toronto and would provide the kind of expertise and credibility that the event would need. Their agreement to act as host and the support they consistently provided were critical factors in the consultation's success.

Churches in Canada and the United States were invited through their respective councils of churches to appoint participants. Representatives of the Universal Fellowship of Metropolitan Community Churches were also invited from Canada and the United States because of their intensive involvement in addressing religious issues related to AIDS. Invitations to apply to participate were sent to a wide range of individuals and networks representing the kinds of skills and experiences needed for the consultation: social ethics, theology, persons with AIDS, health care professions, community service organizations, public policy formation. In order to keep the consultation small enough to allow for intensive debate and hard work, it was agreed to limit the number of participants to no more than 150. Selection of participants was done by the Program Planning Committee in conjunction with the NCC Task Force on AIDS.

Through the planning, a process was developed to maximize the potential for detailed discussion and concrete results. The overall theme of "grappling with theological and ethical issues related to AIDS" was broken down into three distinct, although interrelated, streams. Stream A would focus on "social consequences of AIDS," including the range of public policy issues like access to health care, testing, quarantining, and the impact of AIDS on women and persons of color. Stream B was entitled "illness and health" and was to adess theological issues related to suffering, the nature of healing, the accusation that AIDS is God's punishment of homosexuals, and some of the ethical dilemmas faced by health care professionals. "Sexuality" was chosen as the theme of Stream C and included concerns about the difficulty churches hcave in dealing with human sexuality, biblical analyses, and options for the future.

Three resource people for each stream were invited to write background discussion papers to help focus and prompt discussion on issues related to their respective themes. These papers were circulated to participants in advance and are included in this book. All those attending the consultation were expected to have read and reflected on the papers before the consultation. The papers were not the subject of presentations at the event itself. In fact, there were only two plenary addresses, one by Dr. Mervyn Silverman, providing an overview of the AIDS crisis (chapter 1), and another by Dr. Cécile De Sweemer, on the global aspects of the problem (chapter 2). Most of the time in the first two days was spent with participants working in the stream that they had chosen, discussing issues raised in the background papers, debating various perspectives on those issues, and deciding what recommendations and statements to draft regarding them. The reports from the streams were presented and discussed in plenary sessions on the third day. They are included in the chapters on each theme in this book.

Although this was largely a by-invitation-only consultation, we thought it imperative as a planning committee to do our theological work in as public a context as possible so that the impact of the discussions could be experienced far beyond just those attending the event. In order to accomplish this, an extensive media strategy was developed that included pre- and post-consultation news conferences. Secular media were not allowed into the working sessions of the consultation, but a number of representatives of religious journals were invited as participants. This book represents the most detailed aspect of our strategy for sharing the discussions and reflections of the consultation with a broad audience.

Successes and Limitations of the Consultation

We believe that the consultation worked well for several reasons. The range of participants allowed for rigorous intellectual discussion on social ethics and theology, combined with the reality of personal experiences directly related to AIDS. The process facilitated intensive work on these issues, although sometimes it was hampered by the inevitable limitations of time and the pressure to produce a report.

The participants worked remarkably well together in their streams. It was a risk bringing together such a broad spectrum of people with widely varying backgrounds, differing attitudes toward organized religion, and dissimilar experiences related to group process like that of the consultation. Although there were difficulties at times for the streams to achieve a sense of identity as to who they were as a group and to whom they would be speaking in their recommendations, they nevertheless surmounted those problems and were able to produce significant and provocative statements.

The consultation suffered from lack of sufficient representation of persons of color and those involved with AIDS as it affects people other than homosexuals (e.g., IV drug users and hemophiliacs). The incidence of AIDS among persons of color and IV drug users is much higher in the United States than in Canada. Although Annette Johnson of New York, author of one of the background papers in Stream A, and the Rev. Carl Bean of the Minority AIDS Task Force in Los Angeles provided excellent leadership, the underrepresentation of persons of color among participants was felt, and the adequacy of the consultation to address such issues was consequently hampered. In order to compensate for that weakness, we have added Appendix B, AIDS and Substance Abuse.

There was not a comparable underrepresentation of gay and lesbian people, another population group that has suffered disproportionately from AIDS. The gay and lesbian communities in the United States and in Canada were the first in our countries to come to grips with the reality of AIDS in the early 1980s. Long before many health care professionals, politicians, the general public, and certainly the churches recognized the seriousness of the problem, the gay and lesbian communities were actively supporting those dying of AIDS and initiating vigorous education programs on prevention.

Christian gay and lesbian people have been anxious to see their churches constructively address the issues of AIDS. Many have been active in providing pastoral care on behalf of the church to persons affected by AIDS and simultaneously encouraging their church as an institution to become involved in AIDS-related education, pastoral care, advocacy, and ethical and theological issues. It was thus natural that denominations appointed some of these gay and lesbian people to be participants in the consultation.

Although a minority in terms of the number of participants at the consultation, gay and lesbian people made significant and articulate contributions to the discussion. Ironically, some people have suggested that this involvement undermines the credibility of the consultation statements. Homophobia is pervasive and often insidious. No one would expect the churches to address issues related to women or Native people without their active involvement. However, when it comes to issues of homosexuality, the participation of gays and lesbians is too often seen as "biasing" the discussion.

That is not to say that opinions of gay and lesbian people in relation to AIDS should go unchallenged. As churches, we need to learn how to have open and dynamic discussion without people becoming either oppressive or defensive. Debate at the consultation was often difficult. It was a new experience for many of the participants to be in a church context in which gay and lesbian people were visible and articulate. People struggled to find how to respect everyone's life experience and yet be able to disagree with one another's opinions.

Consultation Statements

Many ethical and theological issues did not get addressed at the consultation. With some of those that were tackled, we just began to scratch the surface. But it was a start.

The statements that emerged from the event were drafted by each of the three streams and represent a consensus of opinion within that stream. They were not voted on by the entire consultation. They are intended as a stimulus for and contribution to debate on ethical and theological issues related to AIDS. We hope that you will find them provocative and challenging and that you can use them to spur discussion in your setting.

I would like to comment briefly on a number of the issues raised in the statements.

No one is expendable. In the strongest language they could find, participants in all three streams emphasized the value of each individual. All people, including persons with AIDS, are children of God and loved by God. Furthermore, persons with AIDS are among us and part of the human community. Any attempt to separate them into a distinct class and impose a we-they dichotomy not only misrepresents reality, but also restricts our capacity to respond effectively to the AIDS crisis.

This is an important message for the churches to communicate loudly and clearly. In some ways it is not an easy task for them. AIDS has largely been associated with homosexuals and IV drug users, two groups of people with whom our predominantly middle-class churches have not had much of a positive history of relationship. Indeed, many Christians would still maintain that homosexual behavior and drug use are sinful. The best of Christian theology nevertheless upholds the importance of "the least of these," and churches in their better moments do exhibit courage and love in supporting people who are oppressed or marginalized. AIDS is one such occasion. We pray that the churches will respond to the challenge.

Attempts to link the AIDS crisis with the wrath of God are irresponsible, seriously harmful, and misrepresent the character of God. The theological arguments about any possible relation between AIDS and divine intention are central to the churches' response to the crisis. It is on this question that the general public associates the churches with AIDS.

Following up on their assertion that all people are children of God, the consultation participants clearly stated their position that God has not selected out homosexuals or drug users for punishment with AIDS. It is scandalous that, in the name of Christianity, some religious leaders have expressed such a perspective. Consultation participants were convinced that the AIDS-as-punishment theme is unbiblical and theologically inaccurate.

The churches have an uphill battle on this one. The conservative judgmental religious voices were quick off the mark, and their statements were given a lot of publicity, adding to the early hysteria about AIDS. The public probably believes that that is the "Christian" position on AIDS. But we are giving too much credit to those religious voices if we credit the entire public perception to their effectiveness as communicators. What they did was primarily to articulate and reinforce an underlying attitude that many people hold, whether actively religious or not. Homophobia is alive and well (sick) in our societies among church and secular folk alike. It is no surprise that AIDS should be seen as God's punishment of homosexuals. There is a long history of interaction between religious attitudes and social intolerance of homosexuality.

In some ways the situation of IV drug users is even worse. At least with homosexuality there has been a vigorous debate in churches and society over the past twenty years attributable primarily to the self-acceptance, liberation, and initiatives of gay and lesbian people themselves both within and outside the church. Measurable progress has been made in the acceptance of homosexuals. By and large, there is no comparable movement to articulate the situation and needs of drug users. They are much less present in our churches. They are separated from others in society and the church. Poverty, discrimination, and class form walls over which few in society or the church are prepared to reach. The addiction of the drug user usually disables him or her from being much of an articulate presence to argue against the AIDS-as-punishment theme. Those who work with drug users have little energy left after battling our societies' preferences to ignore the problem.

To create a viable alternative position identified as Christian within the public mind will take some hard theological work. At the consultation, participants were clear that AIDS was not God's punishment of homosexuals and drug users. We did not get very far, however, in exploring and articulating biblical and theological understandings of how God does act in history, in our personal and social lives. We acknowledged the loving presence of God as personified through the selfless commitment of the many chaplains, care-givers, health workers, and medical researchers involved in AIDS. But more is needed.

This will be necessary theological work, but in and of itself it will not be sufficient to have a profound effect on our social attitudes toward AIDS. Society will be more influenced by actions than by words. The example, multiplied many times over, of Christians caring for persons with AIDS as well as their partners, families, and friends will communicate stronger than words that these are people loved by and not being punished by God.

One can be healed without being cured. The consultation participants underlined the issues of the nature of suffering, healing, and wholeness as a priority for further theological work. We only scratched the surface. We entered, in a tentative and superficial way, the suffering related to AIDS through the witness and sharing of the persons with AIDS who were participants. But there is much more to do. How do we help persons with AIDS who are dying at a prematurely young age to believe in the existence of a God who is loving and just? How do we minister to suffering that has both physically and spiritually personal dimensions and social and political dimensions?

The consultation statements do refer to some understandings of ways in which people with currently incurable diseases can experience some aspects of healing. The love of God as expressed through the actions of caring people can help where medical science is still impotent.

These questions are not new. People suffering many diseases have asked them for centuries. The emergence of AIDS as a socially high-profile disease gives us an opportunity to address them anew. As a culture, we have had a horror of disease, suffering, and death. Our usual personal and social response has been one of denial and avoidance. Maybe AIDS can help us crack that barrier and develop new understandings that will be of use for us all, regardless of the source of our suffering.

We have failed to respond to the global health crisis, especially the concerns of those people living in conditions of extreme poverty in developing countries. Planning for the consultation began early in the fall of 1986. In the subsequent months it became clear that we could not address AIDS only as it manifested itself in Canada and the United States. During 1986 and 1987, the global tragedy of AIDS became increasingly apparent. It would be an act of considerable narcissism, racism, and insensitivity to ignore the AIDS-related problems being encountered in African and other developing countries.

One of the blessings experienced by people who attended the consultation was to be exposed to the compassionate, challenging witness of Dr. Cécile De Sweemer, who is currently working in Africa. Her insights and passion moved us all. Whether that response had depth will be indicated by the way in which we seek to educate our churches to the problems and needs of developing countries in the face of this crisis and how successful we are at moving from awareness to action.

In some ways there are distinct differences between how the crisis is being experienced in developing countries in comparison with Canada and the United States. By far, the majority of persons with AIDS in Africa are heterosexual and the capacity of the health system to respond to the needs is a fraction of what it is here. There are also many similarities: discrimination against persons with AIDS and education efforts hampered by social difficulties of discussing sexuality and by religious attitudes that reinforce a response of denial and judgment.

Perhaps the greatest challenge and opportunity related to AIDS in developing countries is how the disease is emerging at a time of an increase in other diseases, a growing economic crisis, and the deterioration of their health systems. Malaria, yellow fever, and malnutrition are posing renewed threats to the populations. The Third World debt burden and changes in the international economic order had already undercut many of the advances in development made in the previous few decades. Now AIDS is threatening to be a debilitating body blow to an already fragile situation.

In this context the response to AIDS cannot be a single-disease-oriented campaign. Certainly specific AIDS-related needs must be addressed, such as access to sterilization equipment to ensure that needles used in immunization and other programs do not inadvertently transmit the virus, blood testing to avoid the use of contaminated blood in operations, and ready availability of inexpensive condoms. But for a successful attack being launched on AIDS, it must be in the context of a vigorous effort to provide general development assistance that will improve the health system as a whole. A new partnership is needed. Perhaps the realization of the global nature of AIDS will bring us together as an international community. Perhaps we will see ourselves as partners working together and not as donors and recipients. It is in everyone's interests to have a healthier global population.

Many other issues were addressed within the streams and are reflected in their statements. Recommendations were made about:

- the importance of church support for explicit preventive education programs;
- the effectiveness of voluntary testing over mandatory testing;
- the destructiveness of quarantining proposals;
- the need for the church to support health workers and at the same time emphasize their responsibility to provide care for all persons, including those with AIDS and those who test HIV positive;

- the urgency for active governmental support for research, education, and care both nationally and internationally.

A three-day consultation can only go so far in exploring the dimensions of such issues. We did achieve consensus on many points, as the statements reflect. Much more work will be needed to test these positions within the complexities of AIDS-related situations as they develop over the next years.

AIDS is a dynamic crisis. It is evolving as it progresses. The consultation papers and discussion reflect the context of the pandemic as it was experienced by the resource people and participants in the fall of 1987. By the spring of 1988, in New York City, the number of newly diagnosed persons with AIDS who are IV drug users surpassed for the first time the number of newly diagnosed persons with AIDS who are gay or bisexual men. The nature of the crisis in the future may be very different than it has been during these early years. Some of the ethical and theological issues related to AIDS with which we will have to deal as societies in coming years may vary from those represented in this book. Many of them will be the same.

This book can be an important contribution to helping churches and broader society identify and respond to the ethical and theological issues related to AIDS as we understood them in the fall of 1987. Learning from those understandings will be critical if we are going to be able to respond to the AIDS crisis in the future. Indications point to the pandemic growing much, much larger. God help us all if we are not better prepared than we have been to date.

David G. Hallman

Part 1

Facing the Challenge

1

AIDS: The Challenge of a Lifetime

Dr. Mervyn Silverman

The title "Challenge of a Lifetime" might sound like hyperbole, but it really isn't. When I was getting my Master's degree at Harvard, we used the "case study method," where you go over a true-to-life case of a public health problem and discuss it. Later you look at what resulted to see whether the way you would have handled this public health issue was the way it was actually managed. If someone would have asked me, "Could you design the quintessential public health problem for a case study?" I don't think I could have come up with one any more complete, complex, challenging, and frustrating than the issue of AIDS. It certainly challenges every aspect of public health: medical, social, ethical, and legal. AIDS truly challenges all of them.

Six years ago there were a few cases of a new disease in New York and Los Angeles. In fact, we didn't even know it was a disease; we called it a syndrome that was affecting previously healthy gay men and seemed somehow to result from an immune system compromised for no apparent reason. These individuals were not being given drugs to suppress their immune system for transplantation, yet some of the conditions—the pneumocystis pneumonia, the Kaposi's sarcoma—were similar to what had been seen in people whose immune systems had been artificially compromised. Because the disease was primarily found in the gay community, it was called the "gay plague" or "grid—gay-related immuno-deficiency." We began to realize that it was somehow related to behavior and probably the behavior had to do with sexual activity (this was before we were even seeing it in IV drug users). In a short time, in 1983, we had determined the causative agent. It was a retrovirus (HIV) that was attacking the T cells in the immune system. These cells perform like a conductor of a symphony or the general leading the troops—the symphony, the immune system; the troops, the defensive mechanism of the body. The destruction of this one type of cell throws the immune system into chaos. Other infections can then overwhelm the body and ultimately kill the individual.

By 1985 a test had been developed that could detect antibodies produced by the body in the blood of an individual infected with the virus. By 1986 one drug, AZT, had been developed that showed hope of slowing down the progression to death by inhibiting some of the intercurrent opportunistic infections that often occur. Unfortunately it has many toxic reactions: at least 40% of the patients get bone marrow depression and 50% of those, or 20% of the whole group, require regular blood transfusion. AZT is not a panacea, but it certainly offers some hope.

Especially important was the epidemiology of AIDS, the study of the epidemic in human beings. This has been a rich and complete study, telling us how AIDS is spread and how it is not. We know that it's predominantly spread through sexual contact and IV drug use, and, of course, from mother to child through pregnancy—but basically it's spread through sex and drugs. The reason I stress this is that as we go out into the churches and into the general public, we find a constant fear that AIDS is spread through casual contact. People do not seem to want to believe that the disease is sexually transmitted or transmitted through the blood.

If you look at how quickly we've learned important information about this disease, it becomes evident its spread has been more rapid than any other disease in medical history. Unfortunately the public doesn't appreciate this because we haven't discovered a cure, we haven't developed a vaccine.

It took 3,000 years from the first recorded history of the plague to find out how it was transmitted. It took ten years more to identify the agent and another thirty-five years to come up with treatment. Look how far we've come with AIDS. Certainly we don't have the cure, we have no definitive treatment, we don't have a vaccine, but we have come a long way and we shouldn't be defensive about our knowledge of AIDS. We know a great deal about this disease and will know a lot more in the near future. As of October 1987, in the United States, we have approximately 43,000 cases of which 24,000 have already died, and there are 600 children who have been diagnosed with AIDS. It's been estimated that 1 to 1.5 million persons in the United States may be infected, most of them unknowingly at this point. In Canada there are about 1,500 cases of AIDS, about 1/30 of those in the United States.

In the United States and elsewhere at least 50% of those who are infected go on to get AIDS. I say "at least" because unfortunately that percentage is going to grow. In the United States, 74% of the persons infected have been homosexual or bisexual men, 16% IV drug users, 4% heterosexuals (from sexual spread), 2% transfusion recipients, and 1% hemophiliacs. The last two groups, as a percentage of the whole, will diminish because of the testing being done on donated blood and the treatment being given to blood products used by hemophiliacs. This is the last time that I will use these categories here, although they have been helpful for epidemiological purposes. It is obviously not who you are, but what you do. There are no high-risk groups as far as I'm concerned. There are only high-risk behaviors. The constant referral to high-risk groups further separates us and encourages denial: "If I'm not this and I'm not that, then I'm not at risk." This is not the case.

Tragically, 90% of infected persons are between the ages of twenty and forty-nine. In the States, among those who are adults, 60% are white, 25% black, and 14% Hispanic. That's a representation of blacks and Hispanics at twice their representation in the general population: blacks about 11%, Hispanics about 8%. With children, we see a far different picture. Instead of 60% white, there are only 20% white; instead of 25% black, there are 54% black; and instead of 14% Hispanic, 25% are Hispanic. Thus the disease in infants is predominantly a minority disease in the United States.

5

Internationally, there is hardly a country that hasn't reported a case. Certainly the situation in Africa is absolutely tragic. It's tragic in Canada, and it's tragic in the United States, but I think the numbers pale by those that we see in Africa!

The cost for treating persons with AIDS in the United States runs anywhere from $35,000 to $100,000. The $35,000 figure is based on the San Francisco experience, where the average length of stay is twenty days at $850 a day with $3,000 of outpatient expenses. Canada has a different health care system, but the costs are not a great deal less. The total direct and indirect costs in the United States are about $1.5 billion, which represents approximately .3% of total medical care expenditures. The U.S. government is spending about $700 million. Most of that is spent in research, little of it in care, and almost nothing in education.

To look at AIDS today, we should look at the epidemics of the past. Nearly every major disease produces not one, but two epidemics: the disease itself and society's reaction to it. Generally, what we see when we look back in the Dark Ages and the Middle Ages is initially denial and then hysteria and a search for a scapegoat—someone or something to blame. The fear of being infected and ignorance about the cause have often led to bizarre behavior and at times barbaric acts. In 1100 B.C. the plague at its worst killed more than 500 people a day; instead of being concerned about providing care to its victims, society spent its time deciding how deep to dig the graves to protect those who were still alive above the ground. It was determined that a depth of six feet was safe and that still is the depth to which we bury people today. The difficult cases, those who failed to die or failed to recover, were bound together in cathedrals to die or to allow faith healing to cure. In the thirteenth century in Europe, lepers were cast from society and isolated. They were not even allowed to touch their children. In the fourteenth century in Germany and Switzerland, the Christians blamed the Jews for outbreaks of bubonic plague, believing that the Jews were poisoning the water (interestingly enough, the same water that the Jews themselves were drinking). As a result, entire communities of Jews were slaughtered.

Syphilis started to spread around the world, killing many in its path. The Italians called it "the French disease," and the French called it "the Italian disease"! In the flu epidemic of 1918 and 1919, 20 to 50 million people between the ages of twenty and forty died, and San Francisco's citizens were required to wear masks. One form of therapy was cabbage baths. It may not sound like a bad idea to jump into a tub with lots of cabbage, but that was not how the baths were produced. The baths were made by feeding patients cabbage, having them urinate in a tub, and then putting them into the tub! I don't know if this therapy reduced the spread of the flu, but it probably kept people away from those who were infected, so it may have had some indirect effect.

Looking again at the plague, we see that it took more than 3,000 years to get to where we are right now with AIDS. Yet today, despite all our scientific technology, our electron microscopic know-how, we really haven't gotten far from the plague.

Denial? In the early days gay men in the United States and elsewhere thought that AIDS was some form of conspiracy. Others thought that some form of germ warfare had leaked. Today we see heterosexuals practicing denial: "If I'm not gay, if I'm not shooting drugs, then I don't have a problem." We see a lot of emphasis on prostitutes. I try to get away from that—one reason is that from all the studies we've done, we are convinced that the virus doesn't know whether you've paid for sex or not. The reason I mention this is that sexually active women don't see themselves as prostitutes and may not see themselves at risk. Yet in San Francisco sexually active women and prostitutes have been tested and their seropositivity rate is the same—very low, but the same.

The anxiety that occurred in the past we certainly see today, and in fact if we didn't see it, I would be surprised. At least six elements are related to this disease, any one of which could cause anxiety. The *first* is that it is a sexually transmitted disease. We certainly didn't deal with this very well in the past—witness the Italians and French—and we don't deal with it very well today. We often hear people say, "Boy! Did I have a terrible case of the flu last week" or "I had a cold." How many times have you been in a social setting when someone said, "Boy! Did I have a terrible case of gonorrhea. I had burning and the drip . . ." Well—stop and think about it. It is caused by a germ. The AIDS virus didn't decide that it's more fun to be transmitted sexually than to be sneezed like a rhinovirus. The reason these diseases are spread this way is because they need a warm, moist environment to survive. So, simply stated, it is an infection. Yet, because it's an infection that has been transmitted through sexual activity, it is something we don't feel comfortable dealing with or discussing.

The *second* issue is that AIDS has predominantly occurred in homosexual and bisexual individuals, and unfortunately, throughout the United States and Canada, there are many people who are still uncomfortable about homosexuality. That causes some dis-ease about the whole problem.

Third, the incubation period is long. People say, "How do I know what you're telling me today makes any sense because I may not get AIDS for five or ten years. So what you're telling me now probably doesn't mean anything." Of course, we know that antibodies to the virus can be detected much sooner than that—within weeks or months. But people ignore this and doubt what we say, and that causes more anxiety. *Fourth,* we don't have a cure and certainly that's enough to cause a great deal of anxiety. *Fifth,* we have no vaccine—likewise scary—and *finally,* the most alarming element of all is that AIDS seems to be almost universally fatal.

Now, you add to these elements misguided or just bigoted physicians making untrue statements. We have some in Belgrade who are saying that AIDS is spread by mosquitoes. Others, in Houston, Texas, are telling everyone not to shake hands with strangers because they could get AIDS through sweaty palms. We have politicians who have been pressured to do something, sometimes innocently doing the most visible thing, whether it's calling for testing or for isolation. We have some politicians who are not so good-willed and definitely bigoted and homophobic using AIDS as a method to somehow isolate or segregate certain individuals. I don't know if you have them in Canada, but we certainly have them at the national level in the United States. There is the religious community, some of those in the extreme—the fundamentalists—who are making it clear that the problem is that certain individuals have sinned, and therefore God is getting back at them. They have a little problem dealing with infants who are born with the AIDS virus and with transfusion cases, but as in most similar situations, such people don't

8

want to be confused with the facts. One of the reasons for this consultation is that few churches, synagogues, or religious organizations have really been in the forefront with reason, rationality, compassion, or sensitivity.

And what about blame and search for a scapegoat? It was a short search this time—instead of the Jews, it has been the gays and those who are shooting up drugs. Africa believes that the accusing finger has been pointed at it by the West, and a lot of denial has been practiced there. In fact, denial was a significant factor in the growth of the disease in Africa. When a country spends only 50¢ to $5 per capita for health care and denies that there is a problem, then the odds that there is going to be any education, any information, any prevention activity are very, very slim. In short, the disease gets out of control.

Today we also see bizarre behavior. We're not putting people into cabbage baths, but we do see health care workers in hospitals sliding food into the doorway for patients who have been diagnosed as having AIDS. In Colorado a person getting a physical examination for insurance was asked by the doctor, "Why don't we get an antibody test on you?" The applicant agreed and was tested. The test results were negative, but the applicant was turned down for insurance. When he asked why, the insurance company said that his agreeing to take the test indicated that he had something to worry about, and if he had something to worry about, then the insurance company had something to worry about—so they were not going to insure him.

Unfortunately there have also been barbaric practices. We know of people being thrown out of their homes and fired from their jobs. Another tragic situation was depicted in a photograph of a baby in a crib that appeared in a U.S. newspaper about a year ago. On the crib was a sign that said, "AIDS—do not touch." This hands-off type of reaction is seen not only with infants, but all the way up to adults. We also see a lot of commercialization and exploitation. AIDS is a growth industry, and people are jumping in to make money with all kinds of quack cures. I'm not saying that there aren't some good alternatives to traditional medical treatment that people are turning to, but a lot of people are trying to profit from the fear that exists. An example is the "negative" clubs. You go to your club and get tested, and if you are negative, you can join the club. Then you meet someone at a bar and you show each other your cards indicating that you're both negative and go off into fantasyland. What this does is diminish the kinds of preventive actions you should take, like the use of condoms and spermicide. The use of such cards gives people a false sense of security because they don't know what the person did the day after the test, or whether the test itself in fact was accurate. And the charge for this service is anywhere up to $600 or $700!

It is hard to believe that quarantine and isolation are being considered today. Although they seem extreme, these options have been offered by some legislators in the United States. Again, we are responding in similar ways as in past epidemics.

Certainly the number of cases and the number of deaths are not as high in North America as they were during some of those other epidemics, and we hope we'll never see millions die. We may, however, see such numbers globally. It is estimated that more than a quarter million cases will be diagnosed in the United States alone within three years. The death toll from AIDS will equal what we are seeing on the highways (over 50,000 per year). In the United States and in Canada we are getting caught up on the morality of whom do we teach and what do we tell them. It is my feeling that the church has had something to do with this. I personally believe, however, that there is nothing more immoral than letting our youth die out of ignorance.

Obviously we want to talk about abstinence. You don't get sexually transmitted diseases if you are abstinent. But we have to be aware, at least in the United States, that more than 800,000 to a million teenagers are getting pregnant every year. We also know that a female can get pregnant only three or four days out of a month, and yet the virus is there all the time if one is infected. If it gets loose in our young populations, it is going to spread like wildfire. Are we still going to be avoiding the issue and wondering what we're going to tell our youth, or are we going to look at our communities and determine at what age our youngsters may be sexually active—and are we going to decide to tell them to wait and just say no! Parents saying no has not been effective, as we all know—with ourselves and with our children. So are we just going to tell them to say no, or are we going to add, "If you can't say no, learn how to help protect yourself through the use of condoms and spermicides"? If we are afraid to do this, then we must not be afraid to let some of our youth die.

Unfortunately, among some of the minority communities, this has been seen as a "white" disease, and it has essentially been treated the same by local jurisdictions as well as the U.S. government. We can no longer do that. We must work with the communities using the language and culture of the communities, and get the necessary information disseminated.

Looking at the financial implications for the future, we are going to see expenditures of probably $8 billion to $16 billion three years from now. Those will be only for the medical costs involved, and they will be exceeded only by the costs involved in caring for victims of automobile accidents. This will represent only 1.5% to 2% of all medical costs. I mention this because we hear insurance companies saying that they can't do anything because it's going to "break the bank." Two percent of medical costs is not going to break the bank. It may "break some banks" in some local communities, and that's why the burden must be spread among all insurance companies, all public providers. A different situation exists in Canada, but in the United States, some people are not getting the drugs they need because they can't afford them! In other words, health becomes not a right, but a privilege, and it's going to be costly. Even these small percentages don't mean that it's not costly. Yet it is something that can be managed, if we are willing to spread the risk.

Having discussed society's response to the epidemics of the past and to AIDS today, what will be *your* response? I think that's going to depend on how educated about AIDS you become and on whether you react with your intellect or rely on emotions and anxieties.

When we look at the evidence of transmission of the virus in health care settings, we find that it has been incredibly consistent and extremely rare. In the United States 1 million to 1.5 million persons are infected, and many of these people are coming in contact with health care workers, knowingly or unknowingly, in dental situations, clinic situations, or in the hospital. Probably

11

hundreds of thousands to a million contacts take place every day between health care workers and people who are infected. Yet only thirteen instances of people having been infected as a result of being stuck, scratched, or splattered with blood have been reported.

The National Institutes of Health has studied more than 300 health care workers who have had more than 400 cumulative exposures to persons with AIDS through needle sticks, cuts, and splashes, and not one has tested positive. Of more than 800 health care workers monitored at the San Francisco General Hospital, only one person has been found to be infected. One person in this group of 800 has accidentally stuck himself eleven times. Now there may be a klutz factor involved, but even this person has not become infected. More than 1,200 dentists have been followed, and only one has become infected. I think we can acknowledge that a risk exists—and the health care setting is by no means a risk-free environment—but it's easily dealt with by adherence to basic infection control guidelines, following body fluid precautions regardless of your knowledge of the patient's condition.

Yet with all this knowledge available, we hear medical societies calling for mandatory testing. We hear similar calls by politicians. What is the issue? It isn't whether or not to test, but mandatory testing versus voluntary testing. I encourage people to be tested who think that they may be infected, are considering marriage, are planning to have children, or may be examined for sexually transmitted diseases. I encourage such testing with three qualifications: that it is voluntary, that it is anonymous if possible, and that there is intensive counseling before and after.

In fact, I believe that the much more important issue is counseling. We need to try to get people into counseling situations and, if they are HIV positive, to convince them that they have a problem and help them deal with it. Or if they are not positive, they need to be advised of how to protect themselves from becoming infected. You may use the test as an adjunct to further influence their response to what you are trying to convey. The counseling is what is important, yet everyone talks about testing! We have people calling for pre-hospital testing, supposedly to protect the employees. But because some people will test negative but be positive, there will be a false sense of security. Health care workers who treat people coming into the emergency department feet first are not going to have time to wait for the results of the test, and that's where the most exposure can take place. The real tragedy occurs when surgeons refuse to operate on people who either are infected with the virus or refuse to take the test. This practice is going to spread throughout the country and the continent and, unfortunately, the world. How are we going to convince parents to send their children to school when surgeons are afraid to treat patients who are infected? I'm afraid we are in for far greater problems than we have had thus far.

There is also the call for pre-marital testing. In the United States most public health officials are trying to get away from pre-marital syphilis testing because it costs $250,000 to find one positive result for syphilis. My education tells me you get syphilis the same way you get AIDS, which means that you're not going to find many people with HIV-positive results through pre-marital testing. It would be tremendously expensive unless you're not going to do any counseling, which would be unethical and immoral. One state has already passed a law that if one of the two parties tests positive, they can't get married. Think of the ramifications! By not getting married they can go out and spread the virus in the community instead of keeping it contained in the household! Obviously we want to prevent babies from being born so we want to make sure people getting married have the information. I don't know any couple who would willingly want to have an infected child. Certainly if you provide the information, they may decide to get tested, but if you make it mandatory, it is likely some would not get married.

A different approach to testing has been used in San Francisco, where there are alternative testing sites. The testing is anonymous. In one study more than 400 persons who had taken the test were asked, "Would you have come in and taken the test if it were just confidential and not anonymous?" (Mandatory testing would not be anonymous.) Of the 400, 60% of the gay men said, "Absolutely not"; 34% of the heterosexual men and women said, "Absolutely not"; 22% of the gay men said, "Might not"; 34% of the heterosexuals said, "Might not." One can see that at least 50% of people who, on their own initiative, came in to be tested because they believed they have engaged in some behavior that may have been risky would not have come in to take that test if it had not been anonymous.

Now, if our goal is, as the U.S. government says, to have people who don't know they are infected, tested and, when their seropositivity is determined, to act accordingly, it seems to me that we are going about it in a backward way. The study in San Francisco is a classic example. If our goal is truly to bring people in who may be infected and get them counseled and tested, we ought to do everything in our power to encourage them to do so. Mandatory testing and having names put on a list are not the way to do it.

Immigration policies on testing are going into effect soon in the United States. There is historical precedent for this. No infectious diseases are supposed to be brought into the United States. But it's interesting that our country, the country that has given more AIDS to the world than almost any other country, now says, "We're not going to let you in if you have it." I guess we think that it's better to give than to receive. It's interesting because we have a new policy regarding aliens who have been living in the United States who want to become legal residents. If they test positive, they probably got the infection in the United States. So we tell them, "You must leave—because you got it here you must take it and spread it somewhere else." This is obviously not logical. What's going to happen is that we will start seeing barriers erected by countries. I don't think that you can get into Saudi Arabia or Iran even now as a tourist if you are HIV positive. Now that may not be a big problem for most of us. But, conceivably, if you decide you'd like to visit other countries, they may say, "Let's see your test before you can come." In fact, in Japan today if you look as if you come from America, you may not only be shunned, but you may also not be allowed in certain places out of fear of AIDS.

The impact of AIDS on our society and on humanity generally is going to depend on our governments' response. Certainly the response in the United States has been anything but ideal. The response has to be in the areas of education, care, and research. At the local level there has to be a collaborative and cooperative relation between the church, civic groups, private

14

groups, nonprofit groups, the government, and persons who have been infected. They all have to come together to plan and work in a collaborate and cooperative way.

What is your response going to be as clergy, as care-givers, as health care workers, as educators, as role models? How we as a society deal with this crisis will tell us a lot about ourselves as individuals. It is truly the challenge of a lifetime. A challenge that, if not taken seriously by all of us, will devastate humanity.

Discussion Following Speech by
Dr. Mervyn Silverman

Question: Just a point of clarification. You talked about the plague going back some 3,000 years. Is this plague in the generic sense or AIDS?

Response: I was talking about the black plague. I now call AIDS the plague of the '80s because our response to it has been not much different than our response to other plagues. I'm talking about how society has responded to the plague, to influenza, to syphilis, to many others that I didn't even speak about. We are not doing much better today. We don't have all the superstitions, or shouldn't have because we have the germ theory. What is more disappointing to me than anything else is the medical response. When people were running out of cities because of the plague in the old days, probably some physicians were leading the way, but I would like to believe that physicians today come into the profession because of a concern that transcends the risk. I remember in my internship, which goes back unfortunately quite a while, there were few drugs for meningitis. I was scared to death. I had a baby at home. But I decided that this was what I was going to do. If I don't want to have high risk, I could become an accountant. That's probably not terribly risky, but the health care field is. Radiologists may be exposed to radiation; anesthesiologists have a higher risk of cancer because of the gases they use; psychiatrists sometimes get shot by their patients. There's a risk involved, and you decide whether or not you want to do it. If you decide you want to do it, then, by damn, you take care of everybody. Today it's AIDS. What is it going to be tomorrow? I believe that we have an obligation. If not, let's get into some other field.

Question: I wonder if you would care to comment on the recent proposal by Stephen Joseph, New York City Health Commissioner, to institute mandatory information to contacts—a program more or less parallel to other venereal diseases.

Response: I haven't seen the proposition, but I'm familiar with the concept. I don't like to use the term contact tracing. I prefer to use the term partner counseling. The reason I do is that contact tracing has the connotation of the Nazis torturing a person with thumb screws, asking, "Who's your partner?" The person says, "OK, it was George, it was Sally," and then the authorities go out in the middle of the night and forceably remove the named person from the home and test him or her. As you know, contact tracing, or partner counseling, was basically used when you had a person who had a sexually transmitted disease and you tried to convince that person to bring in his or her contacts. Sometimes they might say, "Well, I'm embarrassed. Would you do it for me?"

In San Francisco, while I was still director of health there, we set up that program. However, we set it up only for low-prevalence populations. The purpose is to inform someone who is probably ignorant of the fact that they could be infected. Obviously a woman sitting at home thinking about having a baby who doesn't know that her husband is "playing around" and has brought her the infection would need to know her status even to understand that she could be infective before deciding to get pregnant. However, to have contact tracing in the gay community in San Francisco would be sheer idiocy. First of all, there's not a gay man in San Francisco who can't out-debate any physician on the facts about AIDS. (I'm always amazed at the sophistication of the community.) You don't have to tell gay men in San Francisco that they may be at risk. With one out of every two men in San Francisco infected, they know. So it doesn't make

16

any sense to use contact tracing with this group—it's not cost-effective.

But in a low-prevalence community, where people may be ignorant that they could be infected or at risk, I think it makes some sense. That's my position on it. Not everyone agrees with that, but I think that the ideal is to have such rapport with the patient that the patient makes the contact. It is something of a failure if you have to go and do it.

Question/Comment: I think this opens up a very interesting and problematic area. When the project that Merv was describing in San Francisco was first proposed by Dean Echenberg for infectious diseases, Echenberg was denounced as a Nazi and a fascist, as someone who was trying to create a list of sexually active Americans. In fact, contact notification was established in virtually no city across the country for many, many years, and we have to ask ourselves why they weren't established. What limitations did we place on ourselves in order to respond to AIDS, and were they appropriate limitations? I raise this because I think, in our legitimate anxiety about invasions of privacy and in the way in which the state misused all of this, there have been times when we have tied our hands in ways that might have been extremely effective. Especially in areas of infection and especially in populations in which individuals had no reason to believe that they were infected. Just two weeks ago I suggested the option of sexual contact notification for female partners of bisexual men. A well-meaning physician asked me, "What right do you have to invade that woman's privacy by giving her that information? She didn't ask for it." Now I may be naïve, but I asked in return, "Don't you think that woman has a right to that information?" And the physician said, "It is more important to protect her against information that she didn't seek." Now that's a clash of perspectives we ought to be aware of because it may form an enormous amount of the debate.

Response: In so doing it backs some of us into corners. It makes it more difficult to deal with the real issues. We are constantly criticized for being more concerned about civil liberties than public health, but in reality I think they are consonant with this

17

disease. The way public health is dealing with this is also appropriate for civil liberties. Whenever there is a conflict, a true conflict, between public health and civil liberties, public health wins. Now, what I've heard also in the debate over contact tracing is "Well, sure, the person who comes in is anonymous, but the person they point to is no longer anonymous." From my perspective, if I were sitting there unaware that I might have the virus, I would want to know about it rather than be kept ignorant of it because I would not want to infect others.

Question/Comment: I'd like to make a brief remark about the physician who wants to protect the woman against information she didn't seek. It may also be apropos to protect her against an illness and a death that she doesn't desire.

To the speaker, I'd like to ask one or two questions that deal with numbers. There are about 40,000 diagnosed in the United States over the past six or seven years, and you mentioned that over the next three that will rise to about 250,000. I'd like to know what ideas we have on what's the basis for that prediction and how solid it is. How much do we know about seroprevalence study? And the second question has to do with health care professionals' refusal to treat, for instance, surgeons requesting a routine pre-surgical testing. There have been stories of some that are refusing to treat. Do we know how extensive these refusals are?

Response: Let us look at the statistics in the United States that we do know. People who are giving blood, one can assume, are in the "clean" category. People who are enlisting in the military may not be because of prior IV drug use or other reasons. You find that in those donating blood, about .04% are positive; in those joining the military, about 1.5%. If you extrapolated both of those to the general population, you'd average out to about 200,000. One of the unknowns is the number of drug users. In fact in most cities the way they determine the number of IV drug addicts is to count the number of heroin deaths and multiply by a certain factor, which is somewhat less scientific than we'd like to be.

We also don't know how many gay men there are and what is

the average infected rate. We cannot take San Francisco and rubber-stamp that on Des Moines, Iowa, or on Toronto. We really don't know what those numbers are.

As I start looking at the drug-user problems in New York, 1.5 million is probably within the range; some would say it is higher. The federal government is going to do a seroprevalence study, but I understand that they are not going to ask questions like "Are you gay? Or are you shooting drugs?" If you don't ask that, I don't know what results you're going to get. Of course, they're afraid if they ask those questions, people will stay away. So you have a real conundrum there.

As for health care workers refusing to treat persons with AIDS, I don't know how widespread it is. I tell you I was shocked within the past two weeks when I sat in a room with the chief of orthopedic surgery of a major hospital in the United States. The place has a reputation for having some of the most compassionate, sensitive, and creative care. She told me that not only was she not going to do elective surgery if the patient refuses to be tested or the patient is positive, but that she knows of other surgeons who are doing the same thing but not talking about it. They just decided that it's too great a risk working with persons with AIDS. We're trying to develop a policy at that hospital and it's getting to be difficult. One could argue that in some surgical procedures, if you knew the person was HIV positive, you would cauterize bleeders rather than tie them off, something that might create a little more risk, but that also would significantly reduce the risk for the people in the operating room. There's some argument for that, although there's always going to be somebody lying on that table who may be positive but tests negative. You could argue for the usefulness of testing as long as you still did the surgery. My feeling is, if there is a clinical reason for not doing the surgery—in other words, it will not benefit the patient or it would cause more harm—then it shouldn't be done. If you've decided before the person has been tested that he or she should have the surgery, then I think you must proceed. People were talking about double-gloving in the operating room. However, if you cut yourself, you can cut through two layers of latex as well as one. It's going to happen and it's scary. I don't think we can ignore the reality of that fear. I think what we have to do is say yes, if you get infected, you will get AIDS, and if you get AIDS, you will die. That is a very real fear, but what is the relative risk of getting infected? There's a pulmonary specialist at San Francisco General who has been broncoscoping (putting tubes down into the lungs of patients) long before we ever knew there was AIDS. He has been repeatedly splattered with saliva, sputum, and blood and has never gotten infected. He stuck himself with a needle that was used for a person with hepatitis and AIDS. He did get hepatitis but did not become HIV positive. That doesn't mean he couldn't have, but it's probably in the range of one in a thousand. It certainly is not a high risk, but I think we have to understand the fears or we are in for a real problem. Another concern (and it's the reason I have tried to secularize this disease) is that this fear of not getting treatment is not a gay issue. Although there may be homophobia, AIDS phobia is far surpassing it. Whether you're gay or straight or whatever, if somebody knows you are positive, you are in trouble!

Question: At the press conference this morning your colleagues described you as humanistic rather than religious. I wonder if there's anything in your experience, by way of concrete instances, in which you felt what you saw as religious faith made a difference to the way people were living through the experience.

Response: As was mentioned this morning, I think a number of people have come back to the church or temple in a state of crisis. I guess some of us get a little more religious as we look more closely to our impending death. I have always been impressed at how well people who have a good sense of religion can deal with adversity. I guess it's the reverse of God's wrath, making it God's will. I have seen people who have gone through incredible tragedy but seem somehow to survive with some equanimity because they say it's God's will and they put their faith in God. I think that's wonderful, and probably that is happening with AIDS, although I don't know of concrete instances. I know of other people looking to religion and being turned away, and again I can't think of anything more a-religious, if there's such a word, as that kind of action. I guess what it comes down to, whether we're physicians, clergy, or whatever, is that we are all human beings.

Question: I want to ask a question relating to sex practices, particularly as it relates to those people who are presumed to be negative but may not be and as it relates to those who are already HIV positive or who even might have AIDS. It's my experience when I talk to people who are HIV positive or have AIDS and who are sexually active and practicing safe sex as far as they know about it that often they get criticized for having a sex life even while they're using safe practices. On the other hand, those people out there who are presumed to be safe but may not be are encouraged to have sex and are encouraged to have few safe sex practices. Many of these people tell me this is all a sham— there really is no such thing as safe sex and certainly it's not allowed for people who are HIV positive or who are AIDS patients. Yet one of the important things for people who are HIV positive and who are AIDS patients is that they have some quality of life. I think that having intimacy with people that they love is certainly part of that life.

Response: If we are talking about penetrative sex, there is no such thing as safe sex. There can be safer sex, and I think that's one of the things you are alluding to. If you don't have penetrative sex, there's a lot of sexual activity that can take place that is perfectly safe. I have talked to a number of people with AIDS, and they say they feel obligated to tell their partners that they are positive and, in so doing, have not had any intimacy because no one wants to have sex with them. I think, though, if one is talking risk, relative risk, one has to be honest in saying if you have sex with someone from the general public, you're going to have less risk of encountering the virus than if you were having sex with someone who is definitely carrying the virus. We can't ignore that fact. You see, what I'm saying is not that people shouldn't have that intimacy; I'm saying that the reality is not the same. It's why I never got into this whole idea (and I'll have to clarify it, so please let me get through the sentence) of monogamy. People were saying in the early stages of the disease that if gay men would just be monogamous, there would be no problem. However, if they were monogamous with someone who was positive, they were running more risk than not being monogamous. So I think we have to be much clearer in what we say.

Now I have problems with some of the education programs. Even though some of the production quality of what they are doing is great, they emphasize the use of condoms. That's all it says! The New York public service ads are really great from a production value, but they give you the idea that if you just use a condom, you are safe! I think that's a mistake. It's being hit by the Far Right and they are right on this one. We have to be a little more honest and say it will help to reduce the spread of the disease. We also have to add use of spermicide because that is another way to add to the protective barrier. But it isn't absolute.

Question: You made some comments about our need as a race to find a scapegoat. Can you comment further?

Response: There has been some recent publicity about a "patient zero" who is supposed to have been the originator of the spread of the virus in North America. There's always going to be a patient zero somewhere. Obviously, in the early days of the infection, with gay liberation and the kind of freedom that was felt in places like New York and San Francisco and elsewhere, there was a tremendous amount of sexual activity. We all know that. If there had been that level of sexual activity among heterosexuals, it might have been a heterosexual disease probably faster than it was a gay disease. If you look at the way infectious diseases spread, you don't have to have all that many contacts. You have a relationship with two persons, and each of them has relationships with two persons, and so on. Before long it's spreading widely. So there's lots of patients zero. Whether that was the one, who knows? It's very nice with the retrospectiscope to look back and talk about everything that should have been and how it should have been and who did what. One of the problems with this publicity about patient zero is that it further focuses on the fact that it was a gay, that the gays caused this disease. I don't think that helps very much. It doesn't help in dealing with the issue.

22

Question: What do you think of the actual mortality cases of 100% of persons with AIDS?

Response: Well, we have some people who have been diagnosed with AIDS as long ago as five or six years, so one wants to believe, and I think we all have to believe, that some people, somehow, will overcome this. Unfortunately we have to assume that most will not. When I was at the Names Project before the march in Washington, there were a number of people there who represent a long survival. We have to acknowledge that once we get infected, we are infected for life. I don't think there is any way we are going to be able to pluck the virus out and leave everything else intact. Hopefully we will be able to come up with something that will suppress the virus. It may not be AZT; it may be the next generation of drug that we can take at the point of infection so we can prevent the destruction of the immune system. If we do that, quite possibly many people who get infected won't move along the continuum to AIDS, and very possibly those with AIDS may go into remission. But right now, it is not an optimistic picture. It would be dishonest to say it is.

Question: Dr. Silverman, I agree with the comments you made regarding voluntary testing and mandatory testing. I'm currently dealing with an issue, and I would like your comments regarding freezing blood samples of employees at the initial time of employment in areas of high levels of care regarding AIDS patients. I'm a little concerned about the other outside factors that might prove positive after employment, and I am beginning to think that it's a useless consideration.

Response: The reason people are doing that—if they're doing it—is for workers' compensation so that you can say, "I didn't have it when I got here; I've gotten it since I've been here." I don't even know that the thirteen health care worker cases that we talk about were obtained in that way, although I'm willing to accept them all as professional exposure. But if someone was in a situation where one could have been infected, get cut, get splattered, get stuck, it is a good idea to get tested then. So that, in fact, if you do get infected as a result of that exposure, you have

23

some financial recourse as a result of it. It doesn't mean you still couldn't have gotten infected on the outside after the stick, but it adds a little more credence.

Question: I was talking to a number of physicians last week who have made a commitment to caring for people with AIDS. But the problem lies at doing mouth-to-mouth resuscitation on their patients or somebody in the street who had a heart attack. Would you speak on that?

Response: Now that's a difficult issue. In fact, we tried to deal with it about four or five years ago when we came up with the first infection control guidelines at the University of California, San Francisco. We have said that in health care settings—and I extend that not only to clinics and hospitals, but also to fire-fighters, police officers, paramedics—you can use plastic airways that work very well, are inexpensive, and utilize one-way valves so you can breathe in and the air from the patient goes out the side. If you do mouth-to-mouth resuscitation and you do it right, you're probably going to have bleeding, and there's a risk. We don't know of anyone who has gotten infected, but I don't know if anyone has done a study. We also encourage the use of Ambu-bags [hand-held resuscitation device], especially in hospitals and in emergency vans, so that no one would think twice about attempted resuscitation.

Question: I'd like to know if you have any comments about the heterosexualization of AIDS in terms of statistics.

Response: I've always tried to walk the line between Chicken Little's "The sky is falling!" and apathy. I don't think everyone who has been sexually active who is heterosexual has to run out and get tested. Some might. But by the same token, if heterosexuals continue to think of this as not their problem, we'll look back four or five years from now and see a problem not necessarily equal, but not dissimilar to the gay problem now.

What I try to tell heterosexuals is, we have a luxury. We can look back and see what has happened—a luxury that the gay community didn't have. In 1981, when we saw the first case, we

24

were already five years too late. So we have a chance now, and we know without question it can move from male to female, female to male, not only in Africa, but also in the United States. We know this is true from studies in Florida and elsewhere.

Question: Dr. Silverman, you talked several times today about doctors refusing to treat patients, and I certainly can identify that with health care providers potentially doing the same thing. It would seem that we have expended a great deal of energy teaching people how to protect themselves clinically and the kind of treatment program you want to have in place. But it appears that health care providers are rather remiss in giving time to our staff to deal with some of their feelings, whether it's fear or the morality issue or anger or whatever. I'd like you to comment on your own experiences in California on what kind of impact that has had.

Response: Well, I think a word will be used over and over again this weekend and in the foreseeable future—that is education. In fact, we need to do a lot more education. At San Francisco General Hospital I was initially opposed to a dedicated inpatient unit. I thought that it would further isolate persons with AIDS. I'm glad I was persuaded otherwise. We had people serving in the unit who wanted to serve there. This has been a positive experience with little burnout. To prevent burnout, we have had to have support groups. One of the things that has kept the dedicated inpatient unit going as long as it has and as well as it has is what I call a horizontal hierarchy. It's doctor, nurse, aid, clerk messenger working together as equals. It breeds a camaraderie, a sense of support for one another. But it has also provided a kind of emotional support that people need. Burnout is high among AIDS providers except in this dedicated unit. There has been very low turnover in staff because all those forms of support were in place.

Question: I would like to return to the issue of people who are treating a person who actually has the virus. I am a person with AIDS. If I'm in an emergency situation, what would be my responsibility to that person who is coming to help me?

Response: You raise a very interesting point. In the best of all possible worlds, you should tell them and then they might take a little more care. In the best or an even better world, they would be taking the same level of care to protect themselves from being infected by you or by someone whose status they don't know. The difficulty you may face is one that a man in northern California who was going in for a hernial repair faced. He happened to tell the nurse when she was drawing his blood, "Oh, by the way, be a little careful; I am infected with HIV." All of a sudden he was no longer a candidate for a hernial repair! They thought he ought to go to San Francisco because they could do the surgery better there. This is not esoteric surgery we're talking about! So, in the best of all possible worlds, you definitely should tell your health care providers, but to be honest, I'd be a little reluctant to do so if you really needed to be cared for and your health care community tended to respond to seropositives by refusing care. It is also well accepted by the experts that health care workers should treat all patients as if they might be infected with the HIV and that if they do so, the risk is very, very small.

I hate to caution you, and I probably would not have a year ago. But with the kind of response by some health care workers that I'm seeing now, I would be worried about the kind of care you may or may not get as a result of that information. Hopefully, if we can educate the health care community, we won't have to think twice about providing this information.

Question: Our discussion so far about education, information, and decision-making has all been at the cognitive thinking level. Yet you are suggesting that it's not working. I wonder if you've got any comments about what role the churches might have because of their judicial role of really approaching more of the symbolic level and the noncognitive, not so much simply that thinking process. What could they do to influence those factors that influence our decision-making about AIDS?

Response: Well, historically, the church has been there for the lepers and for a lot of people in Africa with many contagious diseases. The church has quite often cared for people, and that

26

is certainly where a lot of support should come from. The way in which you can somehow help that is to educate the clergy before they have to deal with AIDS. In many instances we are too late. In this case, obviously too late.

The church can play such an incredible role because people are looking to it for spiritual counseling. When we don't hear it from the pulpit, that silence becomes deafening. It's non-action that causes a very strong re-action, I think.

Question: What should we be saying to our colleagues in the church about this disease? What criteria, what objectives would you want us to have uppermost in our minds about shaping our work for the next thirty-six hours? What is there that we say about ourselves in relation to the disease that ought to be distinctive for organized religion?

Response: I don't necessarily think it should be distinctive. I mean, we are talking about humanity, and it's not only the church's purview. And there are people who don't go to church who are the most humane, and there are some people in churches and probably some people in the cloth who are very far to the other extreme. What I'd like to hear come from this conference is not platitudes (there are enough of those around), but some action steps. Ideas that people can take back to start moving churches and religion to take a pro-active role. To really do some soul-searching, to really look within ourselves and see how we, as religion, as religious leaders, have behaved in the face of one of the most tragic epidemics that we've had to deal with in modern times. There need to be strong, unambiguous statements of what you believe the role of organized religion should be. Then there should be some action steps, not just, as I say, the platitudes, but action steps so that you can come together next year and talk about your progress and what areas need to be reinforced.

2

AIDS: The Global Crisis

Dr. Cécile De Sweemer

When I was given an honorary doctorate at Carlton College, the president called me and said, "Look, the faculty and the students have proposed you for the application of humanistic values to research, service, and teaching. In some sense, you are the next best thing to a Third World person." I feel a little bit like that now—the next best thing to having here a real African medical person, committed Christian working in AIDS. And, in spirit and thought, I have been assembling my friends who I know do that work in Zaire, in Nigeria, in Senegal. There are many very hardworking, very committed, very competent people working there.

To try to bring to you what the AIDS crisis means in the African situation is difficult unless I try to bring to you what Africa means. It's really hard to do that in Toronto in October! But let me try.

When I went for the first time to Zaire, I went to visit in Vanga. Probably none of you has even heard of Vanga—it's a small Baptist mission in Bandundu, 500 kilometers to the west of Kinshasa. You reach it by a little missionary plane because there is no road that goes from Vanga anywhere. When I came to Vanga there was great tension between the mission and the local population. Because I had been the teacher of several of the doctors who were there, they expected that I would somehow find the solution for this tension. I asked to go first and foremost

28

to the village. I stood in a clearing of the forest. This was 1973. Everyone had forewarned me that whites were hated, that whites were feared. I stood as the only white in that clearing in the forest, and I could see women coming from different sides. As soon as they would appear, they would withdraw when they saw me. But there were a few women at my back who were softly singing, so I tried to capture the rhythm of it, and I started swaying to it, and then started singing with them. They all came out of the forest, very curious about what was happening. They formed a big circle around me and the song got bigger and bigger, and the women started dancing more and more. One woman after another would come to me and give me her baby, and we would dance a few dance steps. She would take the baby back from me and withdraw and then the next woman would come, until finally the oldest woman came, and here we were dancing face to face. I thought, this is not the moment for an anthropological enquiry of what I should do! Who of us has to stop?—because this seemed to go on and on and on forever! I thought, if this were Nigeria, I could not stop; it's the oldest woman who has to stop. So I bravely went on imitating all her movements. Finally, we were both so tired, and the ground was so worked, and we fell into each other's arms. That was for everyone the blossoming of the total dance.

For me, it's one of the loveliest memories of Africa, of the tremendous willingness to open to love, the tremendous spontaneity that at the slightest chance will leave behind hostility, will leave behind suspicion, and will find a way of expressing that we are all human. We are all together in protecting the new life of those little kids.

Africa is also, for me, the continent of South Africa. I can say that, through the South African struggle, and through many less well known struggles throughout Africa, I have learned qualities of courage that I have never seen equaled on any other continent. Courage that, for example, has meant that in Nigeria, when the army attacked civilian people, sixty-four witnesses went to court, specifying who the officers were, who commanded the army, who did what, knowing full well that each witness was putting life on the line, but determined that they would not cower down to that kind of violence. Each one of us can probably name a thousand examples of the struggle in South Africa, where blacks, Indians, so-called coloreds, and white democrats have shown the same kind of deep commitment to what they understand justice to be.

If I have devoted more than twenty years of my life to Africa, it's not out of pity. It's because there are such strong forces of hope within Africa that I have learned a lot from it. Having said that, I want to say also that it's one of the continents where you need the most courage and coping because the problems are beyond belief for people who have not seen them.

Let me try to give you an idea of the general context. The crude mortality rates in Africa are among the highest in the world. They are anywhere from 20 to 25 per 1,000 persons, which means that you have life expectations somewhere between high thirties to low fifties. Now I hope you have enough imagination to know what it means when you live in a constant environment of death. At all moments you are reminded that death is just there, and it can hit anyone—it can hit a small child, a young adult, a middle-aged person, or an old person. This dominance of very high mortality in Africa explains a good deal of the cultural mechanisms of coping with that.

One of the most striking things in Africa is that as long as things are not as bad as they possibly could be, there is a reason to rejoice. The most difficult thing is when you see the women with big loads on their heads trying to cross the streets in Lagos, and they barely escape with their lives, running between the cars. When on the other side, they stand there, "Ah! We made it!" It's a real joy to look at them in their triumph of having made it alive across the street! Also, some deaths become good deaths—those of the older person, because at least the person has lived a full life. You can celebrate that.

In that context there are high-risk groups. Some of you may remember that I had a hard time understanding the objections of North American gay activists against the term "high-risk" group. As an epidemiologist, I have used the concept for the past thirty years and, to me, a high-risk group is a group that I know needs special protection. It's not a group that is to be blamed for what is happening to it because it's mostly what society does to the group rather than what the group does to itself that makes it high risk, particularly within the African context. But I would submit, even in the North American context, you should think more of that. The high-risk groups within society, first and foremost, are the women and children. For almost any disease you can dream up in Africa—malnutrition, any of the infectious diseases—will primarily hit women and children. There is some biological reason for that, notably that the woman who is in reproductive cycle needs more protein and needs more calories in order to perform, and that the child that is growing needs more for the same weight than an adult. But I would submit that, over and above any biological reasons, there are social reasons. Women and children are just not the priority of these societies.

Having just come back from travel through Zaire, where I lived with the villagers for the past month, I can honestly say that my impression was that children lived like scavengers. They were getting the leftovers of the leftovers. It was, to me, a miracle that they were alive because it often meant that they got a minute amount of rice with nothing, and I mean nothing—no oil, no vegetables, no fish, no meat, nothing—or that they got a little piece of bread with nothing. Women were a little bit better off but not much. This may be worse than it has ever been because all over Africa there is a strong economic crisis. There is not only the debt crisis, but the debt crisis has provoked higher unemployment, the higher unemployment has provoked migration back into rural areas, even at times that they cannot be productive. So everyone has less than they ever have had, and they are just scraping by.

Within that context, for the past thirty years, many other colleagues and I have developed over the years the idea that the only way people could possibly help themselves and be empowered is to have an integrated development effort directed by local groups, not directed by governments, not directed by outside groups. Within that integrated development effort there should be a strong factor of prevention, linking the agricultural production and the marketing with the nutrition, for example, and making sure that people have not only the knowledge but also the skills and access to credit wherever that is needed. Linking preventive measures and knowledge through the whole

31

chain and trying to give them the minimal skills and the minimal knowledge that that will take—that's how the primary health care movement was born.

Now, before the primary health care movement has been able to really go beyond decision into real empowerment of large groups of people, we have a number of health crises coming in. The one that we are all interested in is AIDS. Within Africa, it is mostly within central and southern Africa that AIDS has taken on real epidemic proportions, visibly. When I say central and southern, I refer to Zaire, Ruanda, Burundi, Uganda, Kenya, Zambia, Zimbabwe, Malawi. For many of the smaller countries we don't have even a beginning of an estimate, so there may be some missing on that list. Some of the countries in western Africa we know are at the beginning of an epidemic. For example, Nigeria has eleven recognized cases.

Now what are the people in Africa to make out of this crisis? The first thing is they have great difficulties getting the figures straight. The number of cases reported to the World Health Organization (WHO) is almost meaningless. At a time when I knew in Zimbabwe that sixty-four patients were in the university hospital, the report to WHO said zero cases. There was a political directive that no medical doctor could notify the cases. But, without willingly falsifying the reports, let us take Nigeria. Eleven cases reported, approximately 100,000 persons tested. When I was shown that figure for the first time, people said, "So we really have no problem." I said, "Now wait a minute. If you have 11 for 100,000, and you have roughly 100 million persons, then you would have roughly 11,000 cases." They sat back and said, "Oh, yes! That's right!"

One of the things we have to remember is that the clinical syndrome of AIDS looks very much like the clinical syndrome of immunity depression, which physicians like myself have dealt with ever since we started practicing in the developing world, when malnutrition and infection combine to start destroying a person's immunity. That is another confounding factor because people look at an AIDS case and say, "This is nothing new. We have seen this forever. Why are you telling us that there is an urgency about this one now? We have seen it! It's very sad, but what's the urgency about it, and what makes you think that this is anything different from what we used to see?" So there is a big problem about whether Africa should and can recognize AIDS as a priority problem.

I think Africa *has* to act now. And that was my undivided advice, for example, to the Minister of Health in Nigeria, Professor Ransome-Kuti, an old colleague of mine with whom, for the past twenty years, I have been struggling to build up primary health care in Nigeria. My reason is that AIDS is different from most of these other conditions in that it has a long latency time. It is a time bomb where waiting means that the problem will increase, where not informing the population means that the problem will increase, and basically the people will become victims of their own lack of knowledge and have no choice in how they live or die because they don't know what the consequences are of different choices.

It is also very different from the other diseases because you cannot, after the fact, come and hope to do a lot of good. We all know that even within the developed world, AIDS still does not have a credible treatment and that AIDS has no vaccine. We also know that the average survival in the North American and European contexts is about one year. The average survival in the African situation is a couple of weeks. One of the more recent Zairean studies shows eighteen weeks as the average survival from the time of diagnosis. That might have many reasons. One might be that patients come late to the hospital, and therefore diagnosis is very late. But I would think that there are other reasons, one of which is that there is already a lot of immune depression because of malnutrition and heavy infectious load. There is also the quality, or lack thereof, of the health care that patients can get once they actually get to the health services.

I would like you to get some idea of the clinical context. In 1984 I did a ten-day spell of running a hospital in Zambia. During those ten days we had something like 200 deliveries, out of which better than 80% of the women came in with severe vaginitis. At the same time I saw about 300 clinical cases of sexually transmitted diseases in the same clinic, some of which presented with gonorrhea, syphilis, and lymphogranuloma venereum, all at the same time. Now most of the health services in Africa are not geared toward care of sexually transmitted diseases. The very same hospital where I made all these observations had gone years without any specific drugs for these diseases. It means that the general level of health of the mucosa of either the vagina or the penis is very bad, so that the terrain is completely prepared for transmission of viral diseases.

It means much more than having to educate people. It means, for example, that you have to educate the administrators of health services. It means that you have to educate the educators of the nurses so that they start paying attention. Part of it is that the sexually transmitted diseases are considered a female problem, and as females are low priority, those problems are low priority. So it connects also with the status of women.

I know there is a problem of empowerment of women there. I'm not sure how to get at it immediately, but it is definitely a problem. Within that setting I lost one woman who had had a series of pneumonias. I'm convinced that she was probably an AIDS case, but I have no proof that she was because there was no way I could have her tested. In fact, in that same hospital, there was no soap, there were few syringes, and so one of my first tasks was to get soap from the market and syringes from the closest possible place. That's not an exceptional situation. When I traveled through Zaire in the past month I asked in each and every dispensary how many syringes they had. People gave me a lot of hemming and hawing. "You know how expensive it is, how difficult it is to maintain, how difficult it is to get." I used to say, "Yes, I know all of those things. Now tell me, how many do you have?" Usually they would come down to telling me they had three or four, and when I asked them to show me, I would see one or two. So you have health services that basically don't have the equipment.

Within that context, to make a lot of demands on focusing on one disease is not realistic. It's not going to work—nobody is going to listen. So I think if we are truly interested in the global situation and we are truly interested in people, not just in diseases, but in people, then we need to start taking development aid seriously. We need to start focusing on what it is Canadians as individuals, or Canadians as organizations, and Americans as individuals, or Americans as organizations, can do better than has been done in the recent past to shore up not just the health

34

services, but any organization that can do meaningful health education and empowerment. I would submit that within the African situation, the health situation feels like the highest priority at this point. All the other tasks are so formidable that they are going to take a lot of time.

We all know that in Africa, AIDS is heterosexually transmitted. It is not a homosexual disease in Africa. It is a disease that is heterosexually transmitted and transmitted from the mother to the child. It would therefore look relatively simple, in order to try to slow down the epidemic, to talk to people about having fewer partners and using condoms. There are a couple of problems with that, and I hope I have set enough of the context that you understand it. If people don't have enough money for one square meal a day, you can't seriously expect them to have enough money for condoms. And that is a question I haven't yet solved. I remember I raised that question in June 1986 at the World Council of Churches Consultation, and I asked people to reflect on what this means. Does it mean that for the richer half of the world, we can say you can practice safe sex, use condoms, use spermicides, and that to the poorer half, the only choice we have to offer is strict monogamy and otherwise abstinence? Is that realistic? Is that fair? If neither one, what are the options? I don't know, I don't know. But I know for sure that we need to start a discussion with the local community. It doesn't do that either the local professional elite or we decide that there is no solution; therefore, let them all die. One needs to engage the local communities in the discussion and see what they come up with as potential approaches and how they start solving the problem once they understand the nature of the problem. I need to stress that the nature of the problem isn't clear to the local population. And there is no reason it should be. It's a disease we have only started to understand—there has been no health education done of the general population. There is no reason why they would understand it.

Similarly, you end up in a paradoxical and difficult situation when you start thinking about what a woman who is HIV positive and an African is supposed to do. Think of the women I was talking about who were dancing around me. They all had babies except the very old woman, who probably had had a long

35

series of babies. A woman within the African situation is the major tool in fighting the high mortality, and her tool is to have as many babies as she can. Therefore, the whole status of the woman is bound up in her being a mother. If she is HIV positive, and you would have the courage to say, "Look, you have this danger of transmitting AIDS to your child; therefore I think you should have no further children," you could just as well tell the woman to jump off the bridge. It means sure divorce and, if people start understanding what it's all about, it may also mean accusations of sorcery.

So far, most of our physician friends have therefore said nothing to the women and nothing to their husbands. That is also no solution because it goes back to the basic principle that ignorance is bliss. What do you do when this woman repeatedly has children who are infected? Or when she dies immediately after the next childbirth? So there again, I don't think we have solutions coming from our North American/European context because our context—socially and culturally—is so different. But I believe that the only reasonable way of approaching this question is to start talking with women, particularly women who have the problem, and try to get them to form groups to start trying to solve this problem.

There are heart-rending problems to face, but I think Africans in general are very resourceful people. Their greatest resource is that they have been able to cope with life and death questions most of their lives without losing their vitality, without losing their joy. This is not a minor challenge, but neither is yellow fever a minor challenge when you can lose in one country 18,000 persons in six months. But besides their own psychological and spiritual resources, Africans have little to call on. Most of the countries try to run primary health care at $1 per person per year, or even less. So you definitely cannot do a lot of technological stuff with that kind of physical resource. And that is where people like ourselves need to start thinking very, very hard. What is a good input coming from the North American side that is going to support and not overwhelm primary health care that would probably be the major vehicle for meaningful health education, meaningful support groups for people who are already infected? How can we form partnerships across the

36

continent that do not come out of the feeling of pity? I think we will all come out of it quite enriched if we can truly form partnerships with Africa. The more we are able to enter the forest with them and sing with them and celebrate life with them, the more we are likely to actually assist in important innovations that can mean a major sign of hope for this continent that, at this point, is one of the most deeply suffering continents in the world.

I have tried to give you those facts, those experiences that I think are most meaningful so that you can get an idea of what the human context is within which the AIDS crisis is happening, what the total health crisis is within which the AIDS crisis is happening. Perhaps one point that I want to stand out is that there is much misinformation about Africa. I recently saw a write-up by a church group that had many outrageous statements; one of them was, "In Africa, AIDS is a disease of prostitutes and their clients." I felt so outraged that I was speechless, and that doesn't happen very often! Two stories may help you recognize how inaccurate those stereotypes are.

I want to leave you with two vignettes of people whom I met on my last trip to Zaire. One was a young, probably twenty-three- or twenty-four-year-old nurse, who had given birth to a baby two weeks before. She had been perfectly healthy, very happy. She had left the nunnery to marry a young medical graduate and this was their first baby. Soon after the delivery she developed a fever and chronic diarrhea and started to lose weight. She had AIDS. She assured everyone that she had never known another man than this medical graduate. He was even more frantic in swearing up and down that he had never known another woman beside her. The only thing people could find out was that four years ago she had had a blood transfusion. She died the day I left. Her husband basically went out of his mind and kept repeating that he had not meant to kill her because he was convinced that her leaving the nunnery had set off God's wrath.

A few days later I went to Bas-Zaire and wandered into one of the areas that is so remote that there have been basically no conversions to Christianity there. Any one of you who knows Zaire knows it's a confederation of missions, so to find an area in which the missions have never gone was a big amazement to me.

Here I was in this very remote area with an agricultural group that has tried to start simple health posts in the small villages. Let me assure you those villages are small—200 to 300 persons. In one of those villages I talked with a trained nurse, which is another exception. I asked him how much of a problem was anemia. He replied that he was seeing quite severe anemia, and I asked him to show me some of his case records. He pulled out a record of a young woman, whom he had noted as twenty years old, with 55% hemoglobin. I asked to see her. It so happened that he had hospitalized her, although hospitalization meant having her in a little hut to the side of the dispensary. So we went in there in the dark, and the first thing that struck me was the stench, and I couldn't see very well in the dark. I asked if we could carry her outside so that I could see her a little bit because there was no window in the hut. He carried her and the baby that was with her outside. The young woman was almost a child herself, I think thirteen or fourteen years old. Her husband had been killed by a crocodile two months before the birth of the child, so she was now a widow. She had delivered the baby three weeks before. When I examined her I found that she had metritis (inflammation and infection of the uterus). When I questioned the young girl, I was able to get pieces of medical history. Basically, since delivery, she had had fever and diarrhea and had been losing weight. She could not tell me for sure whether she had had all the time any flow coming from the uterus. The more I talked with her and the more I looked at her, the more I became convinced that this might be another AIDS case. And I was torn about what to do. To get the diagnosis for sure, we had to take her 200 kilometers to the nearest hospital with our car because no other car ever passes there.

This meant breaking the link with the family. I kept thinking, am I sure enough of the diagnosis to say, no, it's better to leave her here, let her die here? Or do I feel sufficiently hesitant about the diagnosis that it's worth taking her all the way and having a slim chance that she can pull through? We finally decided to take her, and before I left I got confirmation that she was another AIDS case. She had never left the village before her illness. Probably the father of the child was truly her first and only partner. It's too late to ask him where he would have picked it up. The only thing you can worry about now is whether the child is positive. And if it isn't, is it dangerous to continue breastfeeding or not?

The church paper put both those women under the category of prostitute. And both partners in the category of clients. You have probably all been aware of the stereotyping that has happened in North America about who gets HIV and who develops AIDS. I hope you fight equally ferociously the whole stereotyping that is happening about the African people who are getting the disease. In Africa it's basically a disease that is rampant in the general population now, and there are the usual transmission methods that we all know—heterosexual contact, syringes, blood transfusions. But syringes and blood transfusions in Africa pose a much bigger problem because of the state of the health services so that any stereotyping anyone comes up with on African people having HIV is only reflecting their own prejudices.

When I was with those two women one of the things that struck me most was how both were most worried about their children. They had by and large accepted that, for them, this was the end of the game, but they wanted their children to live.

Panel of Responders and Discussion Following Speech of Dr. Cécile De Sweemer

Panel of Responders

Mervyn Silverman, San Francisco: I think it's very difficult to say anything after that presentation. Obviously those remarks and the information that was given do not diminish the tragedy we face in North America, but it does give some idea of how horrendous the situation is in Africa. I can't speak for Canada, but the United States has been very insular in their approach to AIDS, not only with their lack of support for the World Health Organization from which they withdrew funds several years back, but also by just not being terribly concerned about the problem. If a country has 50¢ or a few dollars per capita for health care, the HIV antibody test is out of the question. If one wanted to impact the crisis very directly, one could provide testing so that at least the blood supply could be cleaned up. I don't know what statistics you have, Cécile, but what I've heard is that in Zaire and some other places, one out of every five or six units of blood is contaminated. In the United States, the percentage of people who are positive and donate blood is .04%, which is about 4 in 10,000.

I was also sitting here thinking in what ways we could do something. One thing came to mind. San Francisco has sister cities all over the world for trade purposes. Maybe we could have towns and villages throughout Canada and the United States adopt a town or village in Africa. It wouldn't take much. Several thousand dollars would be such an incredible infusion into each community and wouldn't be any great sacrifice for any American or Canadian community. That might be one way we could help. I'd like to talk more about creating that kind of a situation. I think it would give a sense of well-being and a sense of doing something and wouldn't diminish our efforts here to deal with the problems we face.

I guess the only thing I would say in closing is that I wish we could clone Cécile many times over because she is obviously a superb individual and we need many, many more like her.

Cécile De Sweemer: I thank Mervyn. On the testing, I think very definitely the blood screening is one of the tests that absolutely needs to be done and can only be done with international help. It's far beyond the financial means of any of the developing countries. WHO has convinced a couple of the countries to have a few testing centers. It's a good beginning, but it's only a beginning. For example, for 100 million persons in Nigeria, there will be four testing centers; that's one for 25 million persons. It's obvious that under those conditions, blood transfusions that should go on either will not or will go on without testing. So one could improve on what is being started by WHO. I would say similarly the question of syringes and needles is something that needs outside help. We cannot expect the governments alone to solve it. Neither is it a one-time expense.

Your idea of trying to create partnerships I fully applaud

because it might also give a new dimension to development work in general. It might stop being the quarter that you throw at the beggars to make your conscience feel good. It might become a real partnership between communities that start seeing each other in a real sense, recognizing that the other is a full human being, a full community. Things can be done together that will improve life tremendously, in AIDS, but also in other aspects.

Eilert Frerichs, Toronto: When Cécile was speaking, whole sets of conflicting emotions went through me. At certain points the most overwhelming one was that I really am quite ashamed sometimes to be a Christian. Then, when Cécile was finished, I thought how proud I am to be a Christian to have her and a whole bunch of other people like her as my sisters and my brothers. Then I thought maybe what we should do in the Canadian churches is a project related to condoms, sending them all over the globe. Then I remembered the talk on AIDS I gave to a church youth group one Sunday evening. I was going to talk about condoms as a means of protection from the AIDS virus, but the priest asked me not to: "My job is on the line if you do that." So I think the condom project probably won't work because it has to do with sex, and we have some difficulties in the churches with that particular issue. Also, it would be far too divisive ecumenically, I think, to send condoms. Catholics and Protestants have different attitudes toward that little device, which is not only preventive in terms of birth, but also preventive, obviously, in terms of health for AIDS and other sexually transmitted diseases. So in terms of the North American churches, a sense of helplessness began to overwhelm me as Cécile talked.

One of the papers that we have for this particular consultation talks about AIDS being an illness, a disease of the human community. I think precisely because it's an issue of justice and precisely because AIDS is a disease for "disposable" people, it's a sign of how sick the human community is. We have to come to grips with this disease and our relationships at so many levels all at once. The task may seem overwhelming, but it is extraordinarily exhilarating and exciting and extraordinarily hopeful.

Ron Russell-Coons, Seattle: Well, I also was challenged and felt a sense of this as an overwhelming problem. Yet I will go back to my local church and we will take up an offering for condoms for Africa! I believe it's time for pastors and churches to get over being afraid to talk about things like that. I appreciate the fact that you have shared with us the global issue. I listened to people this afternoon talking about their communities in which they've had only one or two cases of AIDS. Yet those people are here because they know the crisis is coming their way and it's no longer just San Francisco or New York or Seattle; it's the entire globe, and the church needs to find a way to reach out.

I've also read some of those articles by church leaders that you referred to. I have found that some North Americans in the area of religion have been able to ease their conscience when it comes to Africa by talking about coping wth life and death issues—after all, those people are used to dying, they're used to seeing death around them. I've read articles that have used that premise to ease our conscience and say it's not our problem—they're used to it! And I would submit that death and dying issues are also global issues; they affect all of us whether we're in the United States or Canada or in Africa, and we can't hide behind that.

I also appreciate the fact that you shared some stories with us, Cécile, and I would like to ask us as a group, meeting in this consultation, to focus on two of those stories and perhaps make them part of what we are doing this weekend. One was the story of going yourself and the circle of people around you and the fear. Some of us here this weekend are persons living with AIDS, and we see the church as those who are hiding out, kind of fearfully not knowing whether they can move toward us or not. I submit it's time for us to begin dancing together and that the only way we can understand one another is for us to get in movement together. I shared, and others shared in our group this afternoon, that the church needs to hear what persons with AIDS are asking for, rather than to say in a group like this, "This is what we can do for you." You need to hear what we need from the church.

The other story that was meaningful was the story of the women crossing the street and that small triumph was cause for joy and exhilaration. I tell you that our triumphs, the small ones, are also cause for joy, and for those of us who are here, even though we don't feel like being here, this is a major triumph and it's exciting to know that we are together. I would also ask that we begin to think of the AIDS crisis not in terms of "us" and "them." The church is sort of "us," and the "them" outside there somewhere are persons with AIDS. Of course, some persons within the church have AIDS, and we need to begin to think globally as "*we*" rather than as "us" and "them." We are here together and so I thank God for you.

Carl Bean, Los Angeles: This has been kind of difficult for me, but I have to be honest because it's one of those times when you must be honest. To listen to her talk was to listen to my talk in America, very little difference. I say the same things when I speak to blacks with AIDS in the United States. I've done it so long now, three years till I shared with somebody outside today, I wonder if this is real anymore. I wonder, are we really coming together to change things anymore? Because nothing seems to change when it comes to my people with this disease in America. Right now, we deal with people in the black community who have no insurance in place, who have little or no work history, who don't get to the hospital until they are so very sick they don't know anything else to do, who've learned how to work with headaches and heartaches and all the other aches because they've had to just survive. One of my cases in Newark, New Jersey, is a woman who lives in a tenement that no one else lives in except four families. When we went in to deal with her case, the legs of her baby's crib were in paint cans and the cans were filled with gasoline. We didn't understand it and she explained that they were in the cans because she greases the crib legs with the gasoline so the rats can't eat her baby at night! That's the kind of thing we're dealing with right here. A lot of my clients in Los Angeles who say, "Before you came to see me at hospital, I slept on a piece of thin cardboard between me and the concrete and I covered with newspapers, Rev. Bean, but now I have no immune system, I can't return to that."

We opened a house in October in the black community for people who were homeless with AIDS. It's a seven-bed facility and we had forty-five referrals the first night, and yet nothing is changing right here. It's the same story, same poverty, no real intent to empower our people, fighting over monies, considering that we do not have a piece of the pie! Very little change. I've been speaking to church groups for three and a half years. Once someone took an offering to help me feed the poor. Once out of three years! Talking to my own community of faith!

People have to deal with the reality of poverty. Deal with the illiteracy. To develop brochures and posters and pamphlets for people who can't read still doesn't make sense!

Six years into this crisis the Centers for Disease Control finally had the *first* conference to even speak to minority issues, in 1987, in Atlanta, Georgia. I don't know what to say anymore. When I go back to my community now, the feeling is, "We have to take care of our own because, Rev. Bean, you've been out there three and a half years and there's no real concern seemingly. So we'll have to go after it the way we've always had to go after it because the other way never works for us as a people right here in this country."

Cécile De Sweemer: Listening to the last three responses I felt that people were basically reinforcing what I had tried to convey from my own experience, so I won't try to embroider on it. I will, though, take up where the Rev. Bean left off. It's true that we are talking about the same things and some of you may have heard me say that there is a very high correlation between what people do about AIDS and what people do about South Africa. There's a very high correlation between what people do about AIDS, South Africa, or justice in general.

I see two light points in what is basically a very long agony that I think several of us are living through. *One* is, in human terms, some people may be defined as disposable, but who cares? In God's view nobody is, and in the end that's the point of view that will win out.

The *other* thing I see as a very strong point is that people suffer, people struggle, and through it many of them grow into such spiritual strengths that when one struggles with them, one just doesn't have the courage to say, "I'm sorry, I'm giving up," because they are still out there struggling. So I think we have no

44

choice. Whether it is for love of God or love for the other human beings, we can only go on struggling.

Questions from Audience for Cécile De Sweemer

Question: In Africa, how many cases are we talking about potentially and what is the relationship, do you think, between those AIDS cases and the related infections that you talked about, like yellow fever and malaria?

Response: In terms of numbers at this point, WHO has roughly 3,000 notified cases in Africa, but that strictly means nothing. I'm willing to give you my own estimate, which is that it's probably closer to 50,000, and that guesstimate is probably worth anybody else's guesstimate on how many the numbers really are at this point. I want to point out that this numbers game, particularly in AIDS, is not very rational. It's a little bit of voodoo almost because if the numbers are small, it means that we are at the beginning of the epidemic, and therefore, if we start acting now and start being able to spread the necessary information and empowering people to make their own decisions on how they are going to tackle it, there is more likelihood that we can slow down the epidemic before many thousands upon thousands die. If the numbers are big, it means that we are much later in the epidemic. In either case we can't sit on our duffs and say, "Oh, so be it! Let us see what it will be next year." We know next year it will be double because it is a geometric progression that roughly doubles every year. So it is not like with an acute disease, where the incubation period is short, where you can say, "Now we have the epidemic and two months from now we won't have it." What you are saying is, "Now I see so many cases I know that must mean there are so many more hidden, and that must mean that my action either is a heroic struggle against almost the impossible, or it is doing what we can do at the time when it's still timely."

In terms of total numbers, you can safely presuppose that they are roughly the same as in North America, so, roughly about 50,000 at this point. Another reason the numbers are not very meaningful is that you cannot reach those 50,000 persons;

45

there's no way. The little girl I found in Emvoicie—there's probably only one such visitor every five years in that village, and there are many such villages. So you cannot reach all the people who at this point are suffering with the disease.

In the African setting the best thing you can hope is that people learn how to stop the spread of the disease. There's not the slightest hope that you can have big-scale treatment at this point of cases in Africa.

Now, the relationship to the other diseases. AIDS, as we know, suppresses immunity against almost any disease, and in the African situation the AIDS syndrome does not present itself clinically the same way you see it in North America. You do not necessarily see Kaposi's sarcoma; you do not necessarily see *Pneumocystis carinii*. What you see much more frequently is tuberculosis that suddenly starts being resistant against all treatment, or chronic diarrhea that does not respond to any treatment. So AIDS in Africa presents itself under the garb of the most frequent, most destructive diseases that are already around there. It presents itself even clinically, I would say, in the garb of poverty.

The body does not get destroyed by opportunistic infections. It gets destroyed by the infections that are mostly around in the community and that also attack other people who have immune depression, for example, for malnutrition reasons. The most obvious interaction is between malnutrition and AIDS. There are no good research studies that show it so far, but all of us who have worked in malnutrition know how much immune depression is part of the overall presentation of malnutrition. At this point, chronic malnutrition—and I'm not talking about famine situations, but about chronic malnutrition because of poverty, unemployment, bad distribution networks—is becoming more and more widespread, even among the adult population. Many of you may know the descriptions of marasmus and kwashiorkor among children. Well, in the '80s, I have seen kwashiorkor and marasmus among adults, free-living adults, and if I tell you that my doctoral work was in malnutrition and infection, you know that I know what I'm talking about when I say I see kwashiorkor in adults.

I know it has not yet been described in the literature, but any clinician has seen it. In those kinds of circumstances, very obviously when the HIV virus comes on top of it, all hell breaks out! One factor we did not talk about that is an interesting scientific factor but changes very little the whole development and human context is the fact that there are two HIV viruses around in west and central Africa—HIV 1 and HIV 2. HIV 1 is the classic one. HIV 2 also seems to be perfectly capable of producing AIDS in these populations. Whether it would in well-nourished populations is anybody's guess. But it seems to have a longer latency period and seems to be much less virulent. In the long run, we don't know what's going to give. These two viruses seem to be competing within the African context. It may be a blessing in disguise. It may be that, in fact, the HIV 2 is slowing down the spread of HIV 1. But it may also be a further complicating factor because, as it has a longer latency period, your time bomb effect becomes even much stronger.

Question: One of the difficult areas that we're working on within the context of the consultation is sexuality. How are discussions of sexuality going on or how can they go on within the African context? What are African churches teaching about sexuality, and what is their involvement? Can changes in sexual behavior be integrated into general health care planning and education?

Response: OK, if you permit, I will stand up for that one. I need to get rid of a little bit of energy on that one.

African churches fall into three categories: at one extreme there are the mission-dominated churches and at the other extreme, the African native churches. In between there are those that are derived from missions but are now directed by Africans. Strangely enough, the one item on which the three categories of churches do equally badly is sexuality. Some of you have heard me say I don't know how missionaries were selected, but that I have a strong suspicion they were selected for not being able to handle sexuality. It is amazing. It really is amazing. You know, I gave you the little vignette of me in the forest with women? I should really end it with how it ended because I went back to the mission and to my ex-student. I was so full of what had happened, and I said, "You know what happened today?" And so I told him, and he went gray. And I said, "What's wrong?" He said, "We are trying to teach them that dancing is sin!"

Now, when you look at that, you can see that we aren't even talking about sexuality or condoms. Most of the churches can't touch with a ten-foot pole anything that comes anywhere close to sexuality. Now some churches are trying very hard. The Kenya Council of Churches asked me to come in August '86. They asked me because no Kenyan doctor would try, and I was disposable politically. All the same, they were willing to put me forward and try to get going. The first thing they did was have 1,500 pastors and 25 bishops to enter in dialogue with me on AIDS. When I came to the point, finally, of saying, "Listen, I think we need to understand that there is not only a hierarchy of truths, but there is also a hierarchy of sins, and killing somebody with sex is worse than simply sleeping with someone. So, if we want to avoid the killing of someone with sex, then we need to teach condoms. We need to teach everyone who is anyhow going to be sexually active how to use condoms." There was a little pastor waving at the back. He said, "Doctor, I agree with you, I fully agree with you, but I think we should teach this only to married couples." I stood there and thought, "Man, how do I tell you what I think?" I finally said, "OK. Now just tell me with which partners are they going to use that?" I have also worked with an African native church. They have the same hang-ups on dancing. In fact, they play beautiful music in their churches, and when people collect money, everybody walks up and there's a natural tendency to walk up and swing one's hips. Sure enough, they have special guards who stand there with a long stick. Usually it's a woman who does it. They hit the hip if they detect swinging. The woman often slips and drops the collection!

I know most of their high-up people, and in private they will say, "Yes, we need to do something." But when it comes to going out in the community to discuss sexuality and discuss biologically explicitly what we are talking about, they don't have the courage for fear that the Catholics will get on their backs and say, "We have always known that these guys aren't real Christians," or that the Baptists will get on their backs and say, "Haven't we always told you that these are really renegades?" So the whole spectrum of African churches has terrible difficulties with the subject.

I have been overwhelmed with those problems. Truly, the bishops and the others were kind of holding me from the back, to be sure I wouldn't give up. Some of the bishops were even tugging my dress when I was in public and saying, "Don't forget the condom." But I could feel that the moment I would disappear, they wouldn't have anybody they could say to "Don't forget the condom," and they wouldn't have the political courage to come out with it themselves.

So I did what I so often do in Africa—I sat down with women and I said, "Where do we go from here?" The women said, "Don't worry, the men are really ignorant on this whole thing and it's really bad that you mostly have to deal with them. But we women, we are very proud of you and, you know, we will carry this on." They haven't been able to—the political situation has not permitted it. But I think that maybe here is a clue which way one can go because culturally, within the African context, the woman is the one who is most biologically honest. She is the one who is most directly concerned with health, with death, with birth. Maybe through the churchwomen we can start getting a serious discussion of sexuality within their own community: what is really going on, why is it going on, what could be done about it, who can we talk to, how do you talk to these people? There must be a way, but I sure haven't yet found a foolproof way of helping African churches to actually deal with sexuality.

Now let me swear by all that is dear to me that all these taboos have nothing to do with traditional African culture. If you go back to the pagan village, you can discuss anything you want! And you will get honest answers and knowledgeable answers, and you can discuss it particularly with the women as a woman and with the men as a man. It's the moment you get into the Christian environment, a Westernized environment, that things just don't work.

Question: Can you comment on the effectiveness of global efforts, like those through the World Health Organization? How effective are those approaches, and how much support should we be providing to them?

Response: I have great admiration for Dr. Mann of the WHO and for his team. I personally feel that AIDS is one of the subjects the WHO has tackled most efficiently and most effectively. They have their own limitations, so it's not that we can say, "Here's the package and now run with it" because, as an inter-governmental organization, they can only do what the governments let them do. Some of you have heard me mention that the WHO was the one who invited the World Council of Churches to involve itself officially and openly in the debate because they could not handle the many constraints that were being put on them by the governments. The governments were putting on the constraints because they thought the churches were putting on constraints.

Now, having said that, I think particularly our Canadian friends can help very much because there's a willingness through the Canadian government to work with the WHO. With our American friends, the problem is very different. President Reagan, thanks to Heritage Foundation, has decided that the WHO is really a leftist commie outfit and has cut the subsidies for the past three years. This has harmed not only the AIDS work, but also the work on the sleeping sickness, also the maternal and child health work—you name it, the whole lot. I would very much ask from our American friends that they put up a much stronger lobby effort than so far has happened in order to at least restore the support the WHO was receiving and, if possible, to provide special support for AIDS. That will require that you document yourself very well on what the WHO does and document yourself very well on what the Reagan administration so far has been doing against the WHO. I personally think that the American administration's actions very much stem from an attitude that the rest of the world are disposable people!

Part 2

The Social Consequences of AIDS

3

The Duty to Prevent, the Duty to Care: Social Challenges of the AIDS Epidemic

Dr. Ronald Bayer

At the conclusion of his magisterial history, *Plagues and People,* William McNeill asserted:

> Ingenuity, knowledge and organization alter but cannot cancel humanity's vulnerability to invasion by parasitic forms of life. Infectious disease, which antedates the emergence of human-kind, will last as long as humanity itself, and will surely remain as it has been hitherto one of the fundamental parameters and determinants of human history.[1]

Written ten years ago, these observations seemed, at the time, somewhat overdrawn, especially with reference to the advanced technological societies. Now, in the seventh year of the AIDS epidemic, as American political and social institutions seek to fashion a response to the HIV retrovirus, McNeill's observations seem prescient.

Since 1981, when the Centers for Disease Control determined that a pattern of extraordinary illnesses had begun to appear among young gay men on the West Coast of the United States, North Americans have been compelled to confront a challenge that is at once biological, social, and political. What some had believed might be a short-lived episode, like toxic shock syndrome or Legionnaire's disease, has proved to be quite otherwise, and no end is in sight. Predictions as to the ultimate toll over the next decade range into the hundreds of thousands. However this modern epidemic is brought under control, it is clear that no critical dimension of social and political life will remain untouched. AIDS has become a "fundamental parameter" of contemporary history.

Like the epidemics of prior eras, AIDS has the potential for generating social disruption, for challenging the fabric of social life, the more so since it has been identified with those whose sexual practices and use of drugs place them outside the mainstream. As the disease spreads more rapidly among heroin users, the color of those who fall victim will darken, thus adding another dimension to the perceived threat to society posed by the bearers of the HIV retrovirus.

In the face of an extended microparasitic siege, will our social institutions respond on the basis of reason guided by a scientific understanding of how HIV transmission occurs, or will anxieties overwhelm the capacity for measured responses? Will the threat posed by AIDS elicit Draconian measures, or will fear of such measures immobilize those charged with the responsibility of acting to protect the public health? Will our capacity for social reason allow us to traverse a course threatened by irrational appeals to power and by irrational dread of public health measures? Will reason, balance, and the search for modest interventions fall victim to a clangorous din? Will we meet the medical, social, and psychological needs of those who fall ill, or will we treat them overtly or subtly as a pariah class? At stake is not only the question of how and whether it will be possible to weaken, if not extirpate, the viral antagonist responsible for AIDS, but the kind of society we will become in the process.

The Duty to Prevent

In the face of the AIDS epidemic, the pre-eminent ethical standard against which all proposed public health strategies must be judged is: How will the proposed strategy limit the further spread of AIDS infection? How will it alter the tragic trajectory of illness and death?

But if the protection of life and the limitation of suffering is the pre-eminent ethical standard against which we must judge our actions, it is not the only standard. In the United States both national and presidential commissions over the past two decades have underscored the importance of informed voluntary consent to the practice of medicine. This ethical norm derives from both cultural and constitutional traditions and must inform even the aggressive pursuit of the public health.

Screening and prevention. The antibody test for HIV deficiency has been mired in conflict since it was first developed. At first, the conflict centered on the clinical uncertainties as well as on fear about how the test could be used to create a pariah class denied employment, insurance, education, and housing. Because the population that had so clearly borne the brunt of the epidemic—gay and bisexual men, intravenous drug users—was already socially vulnerable, the issue of whether testing would be conducted under conditions of strict confidentiality appropriately assumed great salience.

Because of these fears of how the test and its results might be misused, most gay leaders and some public health officials expended considerable effort in discouraging the use of the test. Since modification of behavior was the sole route to halting the spread of HIV infection, what need was there to take a test when the adoption of safer sex practices was the task at hand?

Much has changed in the past year. Gay leaders have begun to recognize that for some, taking the antibody test will reinforce the counseling message and so will help modify sexual and drug-using behavior as well as decisions about having babies. Those health officials in cities who greeted the HIV antibody test with trepidation have begun to recognize that making testing widely available is required by the public health crisis with which we are faced. New York City, for example, which for a long time restricted testing almost exclusively to doctors' offices, has just opened its first test sites—long after such had been available throughout the United States.

If the most central public health task before us is to foster the modification of behavior that may spread HIV infection, and if such change requires the encouragement, at times even aggressive encouragement, of testing, then testing itself must not place those who are screened at risk. Whatever is done by the insurance industry or by employers, results produced in clinical settings must be shielded by regulation and statute from disclosure except under the most circumscribed of conditions bearing on the public health. This requirement is placed on us not only by an ethical commitment to privacy and respect for persons, but by the practical necessity to act in ways that advance the public health.

If we are to make the test broadly available, and if we are to encourage the testing of those who are fearful but who ought to know their antibody status, it is a matter of public health importance to preserve a system of publicly funded sites where testing is done anonymously. Such sites were created as a way of discouraging the use of blood banks for obtaining antibody test results. These centers must now be preserved to protect the public health itself.

Because antibody testing can play so critical a role in the future, the move—already successful in six or seven states—to make test results reportable to public health authorities must be viewed with concern. The logic of antibody test reporting flows naturally from the logic of reporting AIDS itself. If AIDS is end-state HIV disease, and if all antibody-positive individuals are presumed to be infectious, why should they not be reported to public health authorities? Why should HIV infection be treated differently from other infectious reportable diseases?

The answer should by now be clear. If our goal is to encourage asymptomatic individuals to come forward for testing, anything that may subvert that important goal subverts the public health. Thus, even in Colorado, the first state to mandate the reporting of positive antibody test results, no effort is made to require individuals at testing centers to show proof of their identities. Indeed, many individuals who volunteer for testing in that state do so under pseudonyms.

So far I have focused on the problems raised by voluntary testing. Let me now turn briefly to the issue of whether HIV screening ought to be made mandatory and, if so, under what conditions.

On October 3, 1986, my colleagues at The Hastings Center,

Carol Levine and Susan Wolf, and I published an article titled "HIV Antibody Screening: An Ethical Framework for Evaluating Proposed Programs" in the *Journal of the American Medical Association*.[2] In that piece we concluded that the invasion of privacy that would be represented by mandatory screening could be ethically justified only where it could be shown under "stringent standards of scientific evidence" that such efforts would halt the spread of HIV infection. We raised no objections to, and indeed supported, the screening of all blood donors, semen donors, and organ donation.

We found, however, that proposals for mandatory universal screening were ethically unacceptable, given the marginal public health benefit that would flow from the massive system of surveillance that would be necessitated by such a program. Further, we found all proposals for workplace screening ethically unjustified; we were troubled by the military decision to undertake such testing. The additional moves on the part of the U.S. government to screen all foreign service personnel, applicants, and their dependents, as well as applicants for the Job Corps, have no true public health justification and are therefore without ethical foundation.

Based on this ethical analysis, I do not believe that recent proposals to mandate pre-marital screening—given the pattern of the disease and the pattern of pre-marital sexual relations in the United States—can be justified either on ethical grounds or on grounds of the rational use of public health resources.

Nor do I believe that universal hospital admission screening can be justified. Given the age distribution of those admitted to hospitals, such screening must be viewed as a thinly disguised maneuver to begin universal screening, to begin using every encounter between citizen and the health care system as an occasion for testing.

Both proposals, mandatory pre-marital screening and universal hospital admission screening, must be viewed as representing a lurch into compulsory public health measures that will do little to interfere with the spread of HIV infection either within those populations where infection levels are already high or within the heterosexual community. Such testing is not necessary to provide public health officials with the picture they need to plan their strategies for interventions. If invasions of privacy must be justified in terms of the public health benefits they can produce, these proposals must be viewed as without practical or ethical warrant.

We are at a critical point in the epidemiological curve of AIDS. There can be no doubt that the rising toll in illness and death will place great strains on our commitments to the principles that define a liberal democracy. We should not subvert those principles by interventions unlikely to alter the course of the AIDS epidemic.

Prevention and the duty to warn. Wherever antibody testing is done, and whether confidentially or anonymously, it will be vital to counsel individuals who are antibody positive about the importance of notifying current and past sexual partners whom they may have infected. When they make clear that they cannot do this, and especially when their sexual partners may have no reason to believe that they have been exposed to an HIV-infected individual, it is the moral obligation of the public health authorities to develop systems for informing those partners of exposure and to provide sexual contact notification services.

Contact notification has been a long-accepted public health practice in the effort to control the spread of sexually transmitted diseases. Through notification programs health officers request from those reported to them as suffering from venereal diseases the names of those with whom they have had sexual relations. Health officers attempt to elicit cooperation with a well-honored promise that the identity of the reported—or index case—will not be shared with the named contacts. When found, contacts are treated, if infected, rendering them noninfectious. Contact notification programs thus serve two purposes: they cure the infected; they break the chain of disease transmission.

Yet, with some notable exceptions, contact notification programs have not been relied on in an effort to control the AIDS epidemic. Contact notification is no panacea. But it has an important role to play under carefully defined conditions in any strategy to limit the spread of HIV infection.

Opponents of sexual contact notification services do not deny that HIV-infected individuals have a moral obligation to inform their sexual partners. They oppose governmental involvement, however, fearing grave violations of privacy and the diversion of resources better spent on "safer" sex education campaigns for the general public. Each of these objections contains a *partial* truth. But in the end the moral and public health claims for contact notification have been obscured by its critics.

When San Francisco announced that it would attempt to contact the past female partners of bisexual men with AIDS, because they would have no reason to believe that they were at risk, the plan was denounced as Orwellian and as a thinly disguised attempt to create a list of the sexually active. The American Civil Liberties Union has declared its opposition to "any measure designed to compel involuntary disclosure of sexual contacts and any unconsented disclosure or unauthorized use of such information when voluntarily provided."

But contact notification does not rely on coercion. Ultimately the index case must be willing to provide the names of those with whom sexual contact has been engaged in. Often the index case is reluctant to undertake notification because of fear and shame. In the case of AIDS, it is not difficult to imagine why a "closeted" bisexual male would want to avoid such embarrassment. For such individuals the existence of contact notification programs, bound by law to confidentiality, presents the opportunity to warn the unsuspecting past partner through an intermediary.

It is a strange conception of civil liberties, confidentiality, and privacy that would deny to the potentially infected individual the right to such information.

But even some who support contact notification for venereal diseases in general have opposed its use in the case of AIDS because no treatments are available to those whose privacy is invaded. True, there is no cure for AIDS; there is, however, prevention. Contact notification, especially when it involves those who would have no reason to believe that they have been exposed to HIV, has a part to play in preventing the further spread of this lethal infection.

Finally, opponents of contact notification have asserted that efforts to reach past sexual partners directly would simply be impractical. In cases where the infected have had large numbers of anonymous partners, this is a strong argument. In cities such as New York and San Francisco, where the level of infection among gay and bisexual men is very high, contact notification programs would be literally impossible to undertake.

But AIDS is not simply a disease of those with many anonymous partners. Nor is it restricted to a few tragic and geographically self-contained cities. Where the level of infection is relatively low, contact notification accompanied by voluntary antibody testing and counseling could play an important role in affecting the course of the epidemic, as part of a strategy of containment. It would be most effective where the epidemic has just begun to make itself felt.

But if contact notification is to play any role in the struggle against AIDS, it will be necessary for such programs to seek out, under carefully defined provisions designed to protect confidentiality, the partners of those who are the asymptomatic carriers of HIV as well as those with AIDS. To develop such programs, while preserving both the options of testing under conditions of anonymity and strict confidentiality, will challenge the ingenuity of public health departments. The challenge is not insurmountable.

What stands in the way of implementing programs of contact notification are not practical problems, but a failure of moral vision: those who have unknowingly been infected by HIV have a right to such knowledge. Public health departments have the duty to provide the appropriate warnings.

Protection against the infected. It is not surprising, given the threat of AIDS, that the epidemic has provoked calls for quarantines, sometimes of the most far-reaching kind. Although such proposals have typically come from the most extreme right, and have often been based on disregard for our scientific understanding of how AIDS is transmitted, they bear attention, if for no other reason than because they appear to retain some popular appeal. A recent proposal for such total control was published in the *American Spectator:*

> There are only three ways that the spread of lethal infectious disease stops: it may be too rapidly fatal, killing off all its

victims before the disease can spread; the population affected may develop natural or medically applied immunity; it may not be able to spread because uninfected individuals are separated sufficiently well from those infected. [At this point the only way] to prevent the spread of the disease is by making it physically impossible. This implies strict quarantine, as has always been used in the past when serious—not necessarily lethal—infections have been spreading. Quarantine in turn implies accurate testing.[3]

The authors then lament the failure of nerve on the part of Americans: "Neither quarantine nor universal testing is palatable to the American public where AIDS is concerned, yet both have been used without hesitation in the past."[4]

What is so striking about such proposals is that they would enforce a deprivation of liberty on vast numbers for an indefinite period (the duration of HIV infection) because of how infected individuals *might* behave in the future. Unlike the transmission of some infections, where one's mere presence in public represents a social threat, the transmission of HIV infection requires specific, well-defined acts. Hence the quarantine of all HIV-infected people would rest on a willingness to predict or assume future dangerousness and would be the medical equivalent of mass preventive detention.

Rarely do those who propose quarantines suggest how all antibody-positive individuals would be identified, how they would be removed to quarantine centers, how they would be fed and housed, how they would be forcibly contained. Indeed, it is one of the remarkable features of proposals for mass quarantine as a public health response to AIDS, and an indication of the profound irrationality of such suggestions, that they treat with abandon matters of both practicality and history. Because proponents of quarantine speak of mass removal as if it were an antiseptic surgical excision, they can assume that their ends could be achieved without grave social disruption. A vision of benign quarantine measures is informed by recent memories of health officers imposing isolation on those who suffered from diseases such as scarlet fever. Even were such a vast and thoroughgoing rejection of our fundamental constitutional and moral values tolerable, and even if it were possible to gather

61

broad-based political support for such measures, the prospects for so enormous and burdensome a disruption of social life make mass quarantine utterly unlikely.

Of a very different order are proposals for the quarantine of individuals—male and female prostitutes, for example—who, although seropositive, continue to behave *publicly* in a way that exposes others to the possibility of HIV infection. Both criminal and health laws provide ample authority for the control of such individuals. Although the moral, legal, and constitutional impediments to the imposition of state control over all antibody-positive individuals do not arise in such cases, it is abundantly clear that the strategy of isolating such people could have little impact on the spread of HIV infection. Such efforts, directed as they are at the most obvious sources of infection, would fail to identify and restrict the many hundreds of thousands of infected individuals who, in the privacy of their bedrooms, might be engaged in acts that involve the spread of HIV infection. If the quarantine of all antibody-positive individuals is over-inclusive, the quarantine of public recalcitrants is under-inclusive. That is the price of living in a constitutional society committed to the rudimentary principles of law, privacy, and civil liberties. It is also a restriction placed on us by reality.

Prevention and education. Confronted by the legal, moral, and practical costs of mass quarantine and the limited possibilities of selective quarantine, there has been an understandable embrace of education as the way of seeking to meet the social threat posed by AIDS. Teaching members of high-risk groups about how to reduce the prospect of infecting others, or of becoming infected, is viewed as the appropriate social strategy, one that is compatible with our legal, moral, and political institutions. Education must produce the critical and dramatic alteration in the sexual and drug-using practices of individuals, it is argued. What well-funded and aggressively pursued education might attain it is still too soon to know. Despite the paeans to education, governmental efforts have been limited by profound moralism. To speak directly and explicitly about "safe" or "safer" sexual practices would require a tacit toleration of homosexuality. To speak about the sterilization of the addicts' "works" would require a tacit

62

toleration of drug use. For those committed to a conservative social agenda, such a public stance is intolerable.

The turn to education is, of course, compatible with the liberal commitment to privacy, to voluntarism, and to the reluctance to use coercive measures in the face of behavior that occurs in the private realm. But the commitment to education in the case of AIDS occurs against a background of controversy about the efficacy of efforts to achieve the modification of personal behavior by health-promotion campaigns. The shock wave sent through the gay community by the rising toll of AIDS cases, coupled with the extraordinary and inventive efforts by gay groups at reaching large numbers with information about "safer sex" and the transmission of HIV, has, however, apparently had a dramatic effect, at least in the short run. Anecdotal reports, quasi-systematic surveys, and, most important, the declining incidence of rectal gonorrhea, all have suggested to some that in the face of AIDS, an unprecedented change has occurred in sexual behavior in a relatively brief period. Not only have gay men reduced the extent to which they engage in sexual activity with strangers, but so, too, have they reduced the extent to which they engage in anal receptive intercourse, the riskiest of risky behaviors. Nevertheless, epidemiological studies suggest that substantial proportions of gay men continue to engage in "unsafe" sex at least some of the time. We know almost nothing about how education might affect the sexual and drug-using behavior of intravenous drug users, even were such efforts to be undertaken. In the absence of a natural social support constituency, the provision of education might well be utterly ineffective.

Faced with a fatal illness that has the potential for grave social disruption, the appeal of coercive state power as an approach to the interruption of the spread of HIV infection is understandable. But to yield to its seduction would be socially catastrophic. Confronted with the unacceptable specter of gross violations of privacy and civil liberties, many have embraced the promise of education. Here, the risk is that the politically attractive will be confused with the socially efficacious. The illusions of both power and voluntarism must be rejected. Instead of the grand vision of stopping AIDS, we must settle for the more modest goal of slowing its spread. As we attempt to fashion policies directed at that goal it will be important, at each juncture, to acknowledge the fundamental limits of our capacity to fight an infectious disease like AIDS.

The Duty to Care

In the absence of a major therapeutic breakthrough, we are bound to face in the next years a stunning increase in the number of individuals who require the attention of the health care system and of the full range of social support networks. Here I want to restrict my remarks to the issue of medical care.

Early in the course of the AIDS epidemic there were anecdotal reports of some health care providers and support staff refusing to care for hospitalized AIDS patients. With the conquest of the initial social hysteria and the more adequate understanding of the routes of transmission of the AIDS virus, reports of refusal to care became less frequent. Dentists, however, provided a contrary picture. At least in the United States there were widespread reports of the refusal to treat symptomatic AIDS patients. In some instances gay men, regardless of their health status, began to report refusals of care by dentists.

There has recently been a remarkable and disturbing resurgence in reports about the refusal of physicians to care for those with AIDS, as well as for those who are assumed to be HIV infected. Now, however, noted surgeons and sometimes entire departments in hospitals have made it clear that they will not—except in life-threatening circumstances—provide needed care.

We are witnessing, at a critical moment in the AIDS epidemic, the public subversion of the ethos of medicine that has required of physicians that they care for patients if such care entailed some personal risk. It is important to be clear about the duty to care in the context of AIDS. Were we confronted with a highly contagious illness with an almost always fatal outcome, it would be difficult to demand that all health care providers place themselves at risk. Such would require of all an ethics of heroism. But that is not the situation with AIDS. Although there are risks to health care workers, they are extremely small. Failure to care under such circumstances does not represent a refusal to adopt the stance of the hero. Rather, it entails a simple dereliction of professional duty. Professional societies as well as the broader community must make it clear that such behavior is antithetical to the practice of a socially responsible medicine. By education, by persuasion, by intraprofessional regulation, and by statute, if necessary, it will be necessary to underscore a commitment to those in need of care.

But if physicians and other health care providers are duty-bound to care for the sick, society has a moral obligation to guarantee access to appropriate levels of care to those who need it. This will present a greater problem in the United States than in Canada. The failure of the United States to provide universal health insurance protection to all has produced, in the case of AIDS, a remarkable set of controversies about how the care of AIDS patients ought to be financed. A system that is unique among those in the advanced industrial world because of its inequities has generated a unique set of problems for the polity. Confronted with AIDS, it is possible, perhaps probable, that a solution will be found through the development of a categorical program targeted to those with HIV-related diseases. A more far-reaching solution would see in the crisis generated by AIDS an opportunity to undertake a thoroughgoing reform that would at last guarantee to all a right to health care.

By way of conclusion: AIDS in Africa. I cannot undertake here a discussion of the moral responsibilities generated by the AIDS crisis in Africa. The advanced industrial world commits so very little to meeting the basic needs of the Third World that it would take a radical break to make available the kind of resources that would be required to care for those who are now sick or who will become sick with HIV-related diseases in Africa in the next years. Yet can we imagine a refusal to provide the therapeutic agents that will most certainly be developed to combat the consequences of HIV infection because they are "too expensive"? In the United States it took a special act of Congress to guarantee access to AZT by all who were medically eligible. What body will consider the needs of individuals in Africa when a year's worth of medication can cost approximately $10,000 per individual in societies in which other diseases much less costly to treat go unattended? Because of the stark toll taken by AIDS, this epi-

65

demic may force a recognition of international moral responsibilities thus far ignored. But if such a change is to occur, it will require a willingness to confront these issues now when we share a common fate of relative therapeutic impotence.

We are left, then, with a daunting set of challenges both within our own nations and in terms of our relations with those nations that are very poor. It is but one of the ironies of AIDS that a viral challenge has bound the richest nations and the poorest nations in a common struggle against a viral antagonist.

At the conclusion of Camus' *The Plague*, Dr. Rieux explains his decision to write a chronicle of the people of Oran by stating that he could not be silent, but had to "bear witness in favor of these plague-stricken people; so that some memorial of the injustice and outrage done them might endure; and to state quite simply what we learn in a time of pestilence: that there are more things to admire in men than to despise." How a chronicle of our time of pestilence will judge us it is still too soon to tell. Whether it, too, will reveal "that there are more things to admire than to despise" will depend on the decisions we make on the policies and practices we foster.

Notes

1. William W. McNeill, *Plagues and People* (Garden City, NY: Anchor Books, 1976), p. 291.
2. R. Bayer, C. Levine, and S. Wolf, "HIV Antibody Screening: An Ethical Framework for Evaluating Proposed Programs," *Journal of the American Medical Association*, October 3, 1986, pp. 1768–74.
3. J.F. Grutsch and A.D.J. Robertson, "The Coming of AIDS: It Didn't Start with Homosexuals and It Won't End with Them," *American Spectator*, March 1986, p. 12.
4. Ibid.

4

The Impact of AIDS on Women and Persons of Color: Ethical and Theological Problems

Ms. Annette Johnson

For many people in the United States, AIDS is not a personal reality. Rather, it is a mysterious disease that affects individuals who, in some way, have engaged in some taboo behavior and must now suffer the consequences. Too often the face portrayed is that of someone they do not readily identify with or understand. The only connection may be that of another human being. The race or ethnic group of the person, gender, or lifestyle is dissimilar from theirs and, therefore, not relevant to them. These images, although representing the human situation of AIDS, allow those who do not identify with the individual to deny their potential vulnerability.

For persons of color and women, this denial has allowed them to minimize their risk and underestimate the effects of AIDS in relation to their community. What we see is an epidemiological and sociological picture that is somewhat frightening. The denial and unintentional misrepresentation have helped to perpetuate the myths and allow the real situation to go unchallenged.

Initially, the epidemiological and scientific approaches that were used caused confusion and anxiety on the part of the larger community. The conflicting messages about who was affected and how this occurred and the possible origins of this new disease created, in many situations, a hysterical reaction and a sigh of relief that only certain people were susceptible because of their life-style or national origin. The theories advanced as to the probable origin of AIDS created even more of a false sense of security for some and polarization for others. The assertions that the probable origins were African did little to foster understanding of AIDS and the potential impact, for the black community in particular. The hypothesis that described the possible link between Haitians and the introduction of the disease to the Western Hemisphere aggravated the situation. Once again, people of color were being scapegoated as a cause of something perceived as negative and life-threatening.

Similar reactions were voiced by women, who found themselves implicated in the spread of the disease to the heterosexual population through prostitution.

Statistical Overview

In looking at the statistics, we are faced with a serious situation. Of 41,825 reported cases in the United States, approximately 14% are Hispanic, 24% are black, and 1% are considered "other," which comprises Asian, Native American, and unidentified race/ethnic groups. This means that approximately 40% of reported cases in the United States are people of color. This, in contrast to the 18% they make up of the entire population, represents a disproportionate number of cases.

For women, especially for women of color, the statistics depict an even more disproportionate situation. Of the 3,160 cases reported, 21% are Hispanic women and 31% are black women. The "other" category comprises 1%, indicating a need for concern here also. Of the 575 pediatric cases reported, 24% are Hispanic children and 54% are black children.[1]

In large metropolitan areas, like New York City, where the number of cases is well into the five digits (11,513),[2] AIDS ranks number one as the leading cause of death for men between the ages of twenty-one and twenty-nine and number two for women in the same age-group. Again, we see a disproportionate representation of Hispanic and black cases.[3]

Those individuals making up the "other" group—mainly Asians and Native Americans—are now beginning to have statistics generated, individually by group, in areas in which their numbers are becoming statistically significant. It is important that these data be made available and that members of these communities be informed of the potential risks and preventive measures.

Ethical/Theological Problems

To understand the implications of AIDS in an ethical and theological context, we must first look at the sociological situation into which AIDS has been introduced for women and people of color. For significant numbers of these population groups, socioeconomically, they are in the lower strata. There are many barriers that may impede access to the means by which they could improve their quality of life, in particular education and/or increase in economic level. This subsequently impacts on their ability to attain other resources that affect the quality of life, like health care.

When it comes to health care, the issues of equity, in terms of access to care, are exacerbated, even more, by other barriers. Health care may be viewed as more of a privilege than a right because of the costs and the process for obtaining services. For those in the lower socioeconomic group there may be inadequate or no resources to meet the costs of care. When care is available, it may be fragmented and of poor quality. This represents for those individuals in receipt of these services a lack of concern for their well-being. In other words, the system does not work for them. Even though there are specific guarantees and protections under the law addressing their right to such care, there is a perception that their needs will not be met, given their place in society. This perception may be reinforced by the way in which they are dealt with by the providers they come into contact with. The unspoken message that they are undeserving of service or being done a favor perpetuates this.

The effect of this treatment can be alienation from any part of what is perceived as the "system," with inherent mistrust of any service or intervention offered by that entity. It is important to note that the attitude formed in relation to one segment of the power structure oftentimes prevails for all parts, perceived as representative of the controlling structure. The concept of power brokers enters into the arena.

People of color traditionally look to the clergy in their communities as leaders and advocates on their behalf because the clergy have received advanced education and are capable of advising them on what course of action to take in a given situation. They may be the most influential members of the community, able to articulate the needs of its members, in addition to being moral trendsetters. Even where Christianity or Judaism may not be the primary religious following, the spiritual leaders may be viewed as the interceders between the community and the power structure. This has been demonstrated in numerous situations. The civil rights movement, human rights movement, right to life, and others were oftentimes spearheaded by clergy. These actions were seen as just and worthy of their support and advocacy. There was an expression of moral outrage at the existing order.

In many ways, these issues support the basic ideals of the rights of individuals to equality. However, they are also supportive of morality, family, and community concerns. The role the church has played as perpetrator of values and moral standards serves an important function for the community it represents. This means that there is a voice that could articulate the community's views and needs in the larger arena. Furthermore, it has meant a support system and place for consultation, if the need should arise. This was particularly important for members of the community who perceived themselves as powerless and unable to control their lives, or impact the system.

Consequently, when confronted with AIDS, many members of the black and Hispanic communities have turned to their religious leaders for advice and direction. This disease, however, also required an inquiry into behaviors considered immoral by many clergy. Human sexuality, particularly homosexuality, and intravenous drug use are considered as illnesses to be treated, by some, and frank discussions of how to reduce one's risk or talking to one's family about these life-styles, in addition to a diagnosis of AIDS, would present a real challenge to many clergy. In addition to the moral and legal concerns that arise, there is the issue of possessing the informational background and being fully conversant in related concerns, such as the right to appropriate care, confidentiality of medical information, and preparation of wills.

The relation of clergy to women and their role in the definition and defense of women's rights and needs raises a number of questions and issues. One of the basic concepts that has been reinforced by the clergy is that of the strong family unit, based on the traditional model. The reality that presents itself, however, is that of an increasing number of single-parent-headed households, with women as the sole supporting adults. This does present a challenge to the concept of family unit, in the traditional sense. The role of women in these new configurations is in conflict with the accepted norm. Women have assumed more responsibility for financial support of the family unit. They have not provided all the resources effectively to carry out this task, though.

As pointed out earlier, women may not be economically prepared to take on this role with ease. In addition, many support systems are not in place to help them successfully carry out these responsibilities. Such programs as day care, job training, education assistance, and affordable health insurance are not readily available or accessible. The lack of these resources contributes to maintenance of a significant number of women at the lower end of the economic spectrum. This means the children of these households are also locked into poverty. The fact that a large proportion of these women are people of color underscores the seriousness of the situation. This means there may be even more of a feeling of lack of control over their circumstances and a resignation to the situation.

The role of the clergy in addressing these issues has not been perceived as a vigorous one. Again, it appears that these issues have taken a back seat to those affecting the larger community. Even though the issues of poverty, access to services, and equality are in the forefront for clergy, the special needs of women are not singled out and examined separately.

Given the many problems associated with AIDS, and its introduction into this overburdened system, women are faced with yet another responsibility to incorporate and find the means to meet their families and their own needs.

In deciding what their moral and civic obligation is in relation

71

to AIDS and the many needs that may be encountered, clergy must confront their own personal fears as well as determine the impact on their community standing and the viability of their place of worship. Historically, they may have dealt with homosexuality and drug abuse as undesirable, forbidden behaviors. Now a decision must be made as to whether pastoral and compassionate care should be the primary consideration as opposed to the presenting behavior. If it is decided that this is to be a part of one's ministry, there is the risk of criticism and, possibly, censorship by one's peers. Again, the potential for negative impact on one's standing as a community leader is a concern.

An even bigger dilemma is now emerging for clergy. As community leaders, they are being sought and approached by public health officials to become partners in providing education and development of services for the communities they represent. This means that the issues of church and state as separate entities or as a joint entity must be addressed, especially in terms of the message to be transmitted. There must be an examination of the issues of prevention and what they mean for those considered at greatest risk. Is abstinence the primary message, or one of several choices, each of equal merit?

How will the congregation and the larger community view not only what may appear to be a liaison with the larger power structure, but the apparent contradiction in the current message and what the moral standard had previously been?

For the clergy, too, the issue of control over the level and type of involvement in these educational and service development efforts is crucial. In order to enter into such a relationship with an entity that they may have been in an adversarial role with at another time, the issue of control in order to provide what is most beneficial to the specified community, in a manner that is acceptable, is important.

Future Planning

The role of clergy in the future will have to be weighed carefully. For people of color and for women there is the immediate need for clergy to provide the services for which they have become best noted in their community—leadership, advocacy, and compassionate care. Further, the attitude with which clergy approach their new roles, in partnership with public health officials to provide education and develop supportive services for those affected by AIDS, must reflect a pure moral sense of duty to one's community, not a punitive and judgmental attitude.

It is also apparent that the impact of AIDS on the entire society and the way in which it affects all aspects of the system of services utilized by its members will need to be addressed by clergy. The individual concerns of a person or a family must be addressed, but the larger context must also be considered. It may be necessary to change the way these services are delivered so they can be more responsive to the needs of the community. The roles of leadership and advocacy must be continued and expanded to foster these changes and improve the quality of life for all those affected by AIDS.

Notes

1. *AIDS Weekly Surveillance Report,* Centers for Disease Control, September 14, 1987.
2. *New York City Department of Health, AIDS Surveillance Update,* September 1987.
3. *New York State Department of Health, Bureau of Communicable Disease Control—Monthly Update—AIDS Surveillance,* August 1987.

5

Social Consequences of AIDS

Dr. Margaret A. Somerville

There are so many ways in which the topic of the social consequences of AIDS could be addressed that it is extremely difficult to choose between them, let alone select the most appropriate organizational structure. This statement may seem trite, but it carries an important message. Our choice of structure for exploring and making decisions concerning an issue may not be neutral in terms of the insights it provides and the outcomes it is used to produce. This is likely to be especially true of an area as complex, difficult, and controversial as AIDS. As we are all aware, the consequences, including the social consequences, of AIDS are both serious and extensive. Most of them, but not necessarily all, involve intense suffering and can often be described as tragic.

Sometimes I have a fantasy that I would not be surprised to find is shared by others similar to myself, in the sense that we spend a large proportion of our professional working lives dealing with issues related to AIDS. The fantasy is that it would be wonderful if a miracle happened and AIDS just disappeared by tomorrow morning. It has struck us so suddenly—certainly in terms of the magnitude of spread of the disease and its potential for further spread—that it seems that if it could appear so quickly, it might be able to disappear just as quickly. Unfortunately this seems most unlikely. Perhaps this fantasy reflects the feeling that there is a certain sense of unreality associated with AIDS. However, the consequences of AIDS, including the social consequences, are often too real. One only has to read the daily newspapers to realize their seriousness and variety. Both the consequences themselves and how we deal with them will have major impact on our society far outside the immediate realm of situations directly involving AIDS.

What I have tried to convey above is the overwhelming impact of AIDS and the feeling that this can generate, that it is impossible to cope with the issues it raises. In order to deal with this feeling, in addressing the social consequences of AIDS, I have decided to adopt a somewhat disparate approach. First, I will consider a case that raises issues at the individual, personal, micro level and explore some of these. Then I will change to the macro level to consider some of the social consequences that can arise at this level and how these can be dealt with. Finally I will consider ways in which we can structure our decision-making in order to deal with issues raised by AIDS, including its social consequences.

Micro Level

Louise and Paul Johnson (not their real names) have been married for six years. They have three children: Peter, five years; Jane, three years; and Emilie, four months. Emilie had been ill since her birth and was hospitalized for treatment of an overwhelming systemic infection. It was at this stage that the pediatrician looking after Emilie, Dr. Stark, ordered an HIV antibody test. It was positive. The results were supported by confirmatory testing. This test, together with Emilie's rapidly deteriorating state of health, enabled Dr. Stark, in consultation with other physicians, to come to a diagnosis of AIDS.

Dr. Stark arranged to meet with Paul and Louise to discuss Emilie's condition. At this time he disclosed to them that she had AIDS, that it was extremely unlikely that she would live more than two years, and that it was very likely she would be seriously ill throughout this time. They, of course, were devastated by this information. Probably the most devastating situation parents can face is to be told that their child has a fatal illness. Paul and

75

Louise are facing not only this situation, but also all the other implications and consequences of a diagnosis of AIDS.

There was no readily apparent reason why Paul or Louise should be infected with HIV, as neither of them had ever received a blood transfusion and, as far as either of them knew with respect to the other, neither of them had engaged in conduct that was risk-taking with respect to the transmission of HIV. In fact, both of them had engaged in such conduct. Paul was bisexual and had had several "anonymous" homosexual encounters in gay bathhouses while he was away on business trips. Paul's last homosexual encounter had been in a gay bathhouse in New York eighteen months earlier, when he had engaged in unprotected sexual intercourse. For a short time in 1980, before her marriage, Louise had spent six months in New York after the breakup of a long-term, live-in relationship in Toronto. During this time she had had many male sexual partners and on two occasions had experimented with intravenous drugs, when she had shared injection equipment.

Dr. Stark suggested that Paul, Louise, and their other two children should be tested for HIV antibody positivity. The results were that Paul and Louise were positive and the two children were negative. It is likely, although not certain, that Louise was antibody negative at the time she gave birth to her first two children and became antibody positive subsequent to that time. The only way this could have happened was that Paul had become infected through his homosexual encounter in New York eighteen months earlier and subsequently had infected Louise.

Three months after his homosexual encounter in New York, Paul had gone to see his doctor in Toronto and told him that he was concerned about his recent risk-taking activities with respect to HIV transmission and that he was deeply concerned that he might have been infected. The physician, Dr. Black, explained to Paul about the availability of an HIV antibody test but neither encouraged nor discouraged Paul to have it. Dr. Black knew Paul was married and had two children, but he had never met Louise. He did not know, because Paul did not tell him, that Paul and Louise had at that time discussed the possibility of having another baby. They had not come to any firm conclusion in this respect, although Paul knew that Louise was going to have a "three-month rest" from taking the contraceptive pill.

After testing positive, Louise felt that she could no longer cope psychologically with the situation that had developed and went to see her doctor to ask for a certificate for sick leave from her job. Louise presented this certificate to her employer, who asked her what was wrong. Louise, in a state of great distress, explained about the baby and her own and Paul's HIV antibody positivity. Three days later Louise received a registered letter notifying her that her employment was terminated and that she would receive three months' salary in lieu of notice. Word spread around the neighborhood that the baby and the Johnson family "had AIDS," and the principal at the school where five-year-old Peter was in grade one asked that the child be withdrawn. Likewise, the day-care center where three-year-old Jane stayed while both Paul and Louise worked refused to accept the child any longer.

Louise's employer had told one of Louise's workmates that Louise's baby, Emilie, had AIDS and that Louise was HIV antibody positive. The workmate had children at the same school as Louise's child Peter and informed the principal. Parents of other children at the school, who also had children in the day-care center, learned of Peter's exclusion and informed the day-care center.

Paul was now manifesting neurological symptoms possibly attributable to HIV infection. The physician immunologist caring for him asked a neurologist colleague for a consultation, and the neurologist ordered a brain scan using nuclear magnetic resonance imaging (NMRI). However, the nuclear medicine specialists at the only hospital that had an NMRI scanner refused to accept Paul or any AIDS patients because of fear of contaminating the NMRI examination chamber with HIV.

Louise had not known that Paul engaged in sexual activity outside his marriage, and she found this extremely difficult to cope with emotionally, especially because of its homosexual nature. Louise and Paul now also face a constant, ineradicable threat to their own lives and must deal with the possibility that both of them could die of AIDS and leave their other two children without parents. Paul is self-employed and has inadequate sickness and disability insurance and no life insurance, and they are not independently wealthy. This means that they will not be able to provide for their own future care and that of their other two children, and must live with this knowledge and the fear and despair it produces. Paul and Louise and all their children will probably be subject to further discrimination and stigmatization because it has become known in their community that members of their family are infected with HIV. Whether, and if so how, to disclose the information regarding their HIV infection to their wider family and coping with their reactions and suffering are also serious problems. There is also a great deal of uncertainty in this situation, especially regarding the likelihood of occurrence of serious consequences, and such uncertainty can be difficult to live with psychologically. Another frequently encountered impact of having knowledge that one is HIV antibody positive is necessity for change with respect to sexual behavior. Even this may be required of Louise and Paul in relating to each other, although they are both infected with HIV, because repeated exposure to the virus may cause them further damage. Such a change would also be required on the part of Paul with respect to any future homosexual encounters.

Unfortunately the "snapshot" scenario described above is not far-fetched in terms of the consequences for "persons with AIDS." (This term is used to refer collectively to all persons who have been infected with HIV, whether or not they have developed HIV-related disease.) If the scene were converted into a movie that commenced at this point, we could follow the snapshot situation into all the difficult social, ethical, legal, and economic issues that arise for individuals as a result of AIDS, many of which also have major impact on the community. These include, not necessarily in chronological or other order of priority, the following:

1. Should gay bathhouses be shut down? Did the bathhouse Paul visit provide information on "safer sex" and condoms, promote "safer" sexual practices, and discourage risk-producing activities?

2. What are the moral obligations of husbands and wives to disclose to each other that they may be at risk of transmitting HIV infection? Are there also legal obligations? Could a third party, such as a physician, have a derivative legal obligation to

warn an at-risk spouse, if spouses had such legal obligations to each other?

3. What were the obligations of Paul's physician to make inquiries regarding his life-style, family, and sexual contacts, and what was the physician's obligation to warn any of these people, especially Louise?

4. Should Louise have been warned by her obstetrician about the risk of AIDS, as a routine precaution, when it was discovered that she was pregnant, and should she have been offered an HIV antibody test?

5. If it were discovered that she was HIV antibody positive, what counseling regarding abortion should she have been given?

6. Was Louise wrongfully discriminated against in being dismissed from her job, and does she have a remedy?

7. Was Louise inadequately counseled, or counseled at all, regarding HIV antibody before testing and after receiving her test results, and was this, at least in part, the cause of her disclosure to her employer?

8. Has Louise any remedy against her employer for disclosing information about her and her child's HIV antibody positivity?

9. Should the school be forced to re-admit Peter? Can it be?

10. Should the day-care center look after Jane? Can it be forced to do so?

11. Should the nuclear medicine physicians refuse Paul access to NMRI? Has Paul any legal right of access to this or other health care? If he is given care, will it be adequate and humane, and equal to that given to persons without AIDS?

12. What counseling and other support services are available for this family?

In short, at the micro or individual level, AIDS raises ethical and legal issues, including, but certainly not limited to, obligations between spouses; obligations of confidentiality; obligations to warn; abortion; wrongful discrimination; children's rights; and rights to and in health care. The range of difficult and controversial legal and ethical issues raised by the situation described provides a good example of the wide swath cut by AIDS just at the individual level. This swath is exponentially expanded when one turns to the macro level.

Macro Level

The social consequences of AIDS at an individual level can have impact at a community level as well, and some social consequences of AIDS also have direct community impact.

At a practical level, the community needs to be protected from disease. This is not only a benefit to the individuals in the community who are protected from disease, but it can also be essential to the continuance of the community itself. In this regard, it is interesting to consider that the rationale of ancient criminal law was more to protect the state, the king's army, and the community than it was to protect the individuals who constituted these entities simply for their own sakes. This explains why it was a crime of maim (mayhem) to remove a man's two front teeth but not to castrate him. Removing his two front teeth made him less able to fight because he could no longer bite the bullet, whereas castrating him was not seen as having any deleterious effect on his usefulness as a soldier.

This ancient law may provide an important insight regarding the use of law, especially criminal law, to deal with AIDS. Criminal law should not, in general, be used paternalistically to protect people from themselves, and its use to protect others must be regarded as an exceptional measure to be used only when nothing less will achieve a necessary and justified outcome, and when its use does more good than harm. This is not intended in any way to deny or ignore that the community does have certain claims, and possibly even rights, to protection. The issue is, how should these be implemented? In particular, when claims of the community to protection are in conflict with the rights of individuals, should the former ever take priority, and if so, what are the conditions for this?

Our public health protection laws recognize that the community has valid claims to be protected from disease. These laws establish structures within and conditions under which such claims can be implemented, subject to proper safeguards. Modern public health legislation tends to reflect a philosophy and policy that the least invasive, least restrictive alternative course of action reasonably available and likely to be effective in achieving a desired and justifiable outcome must be used. That is, more invasive, more restrictive measures would only be justifiable when less invasive, less restrictive measures that appear feasible have been tried and failed. A good example in this regard in the AIDS situation is contact tracing (tracing of the at-risk contacts of persons with AIDS). Requesting "index individuals" to do such tracing themselves is the least "invasive" approach; if they do not comply, the physician can request the index individual's consent to the physician making this contact; to report the matter to a public health authority and seek their assistance in contact tracing is yet a further step on a progressively more "invasive" continuum. If the first step is likely to be effective, then one is justified in moving to the second step only if the first fails, and so on. An example of such an approach in a non-AIDS, health care context can be found in the *Public Health Protection Act* (R.S.Q. c. P-35) of Quebec, and in an AIDS context, in the Recommendations on Contact Tracing of the National Advisory Committee on AIDS (CDWR 1987; pp. 13–14).

One of the important issues that needs to be addressed in resolving conflicts of individual rights and community claims to protection is, what degree of risk to the community justifies trespassing on individual rights? Stated another way, this question becomes, what degree of risk is it reasonable to ask the community to live with for the sake of upholding other values apart from that of their safety? Or in yet another way, have our communities come to expect risk-free environments, or at least as risk-free as it is possible to make them, no matter what the consequences of this? It needs to be realized that the community often acts on the basis of a perception of there being either risk or lack of risk in a given situation, rather than responding to real or demonstrated risk, and there is much literature describing the fickleness of our reactions to risk. The issue of risk is also discussed later, within the context of decision-making regarding AIDS.

Other macro-level issues relevant to a discussion of social consequences of AIDS include the increasingly difficult area of allocation of resources to and in medicine, consideration of which raises correlative issues of rights of access to care, wrongful discrimination in providing care, and distribution of resources between community care (including provision of home care) and institutional care. Although, in general, our reactions to the threatened or real denial of medical resources is that we are necessarily being harmed, this may not always be the case. It could be that AIDS will force us to develop alternatives to costly technological care that may show us ways to avoid the technological imperialism that medicine has at least flirted with in the past fifteen years, sometimes at the expense of humane and personalized care. In short, some of the responses we develop in situations of necessity created by AIDS may be more beneficial than the costlier approaches they were designed to replace.

The appearance of an AIDS industry is another macro-level social consequence. AIDS industry activities can range from using advertisements that focus on a certain magazine's reporting on AIDS to promote sales of that magazine; to marketing literature on how to reduce the risk of transmission of HIV and products such as condoms to assist in this; to producing pornographic comic books to be used as a substitute for risk-taking conduct; to producing home test kits for HIV antibody positivity; to setting up dating clubs to which only screened HIV antibody-negative people may belong. In short, the media and the advertising, financial, and entrepreneurial worlds have, with varying degrees of tact and appropriateness, responded, at least in part, to AIDS as a business opportunity. It is probably worth noting a blatantly unacceptable example of such activity because it seeks to promote fear, panic, and hysteria in relation to AIDS and to trade on these to make profit. A full-page advertisement appeared in *USA Today* on Monday, August 10, 1987 (p. 5A), carrying the headline "The AIDS Epidemic Will be a Major Economic Disaster" and including an order form that stated, "Yes! Please rush me ——— copy(ies) of 'How You Can Profit from the Panic of 1989' at $14.95 each. . . . Satisfaction Guaranteed."

Unfortunately we also need to keep in mind that unscrupulous entrepreneurs can perceive vulnerable people, such as those dying of fatal, incurable illnesses like AIDS, as a business opportunity. It has been estimated that bogus AIDS cures could cost the U.S. public $1 billion ("Costly, bogus AIDS cures flooding the market," *The Medical Post,* August 18, 1987, p. 13). There is a fine line to be drawn between providing adequate protection from such scams, which protection is clearly needed, and not unjustifiably infringing on people's rights to autonomy in undertaking any measures they perceive might be of help to them in a situation in which no effective treatment can be offered and the outcome is death.

✓ AIDS also has social consequences related to criminality, which is a macro-level societal phenomenon. The issues can range from persons with AIDS being criminally liable for engaging in risk-creating activity likely to transmit HIV; to an increase in assault and murder of people characterized as being members of a group at high risk for AIDS; to AIDS being used as an offensive weapon—for example, a syringe full of blood was used to stage a bank robbery; to problems in prisons with fear of AIDS being transmitted between inmates, or guards refusing to work with HIV-infected prisoners, or sentences being reduced because the conditions of imprisonment for HIV-infected persons are more onerous; to rape, or sexual abuse of children now carrying the additional horror of the risk of transmission of HIV; to concern about HIV transmission among young offenders in youth protection institutions; to consideration of whether addictive drugs should be legalized to promote educational and counseling access to drug addicts and to reduce spin-off criminal behavior, such as stealing, on their part to obtain money to buy drugs.

As the examples above clearly indicate, macro-level social consequences of AIDS will also include challenges to the fabric of our society. This is a fragile, intangible entity that includes what is sometimes described as the ethical and legal tone of the society. Its components and what affect it are not easy to delineate, but certainly decisions taken in the AIDS context will affect it both directly and more indirectly through their precedent-setting effect far outside the "AIDS arena."

We also need to consider the intangible factors that affect decision-making in our society regarding AIDS, and to distinguish between those that ought to be encouraged and those that ought to be discouraged. Included in the former category are "virtues" of wisdom, compassion, integrity, and responsibility and in the latter, "vices" of prejudice, failure to relieve suffering, and even infliction of harm. These intangible factors are relevant to decision-making at both the micro and macro levels. They are also part of the fabric of society and contribute to its ethical and legal tone.

Analysis of the Issues

We need to identify, articulate, and establish both substantive and process requirements for dealing with issues raised by AIDS, including its social consequences. Substantive principles are rules that guide us in what to do in a given situation to which they apply. Rarely, they may be absolute, but usually they are general principles that have some exceptions. Process requirements are decision-making safeguards that rely on "right" process, rather than on "right" rules (substantive principles), to produce acceptable responses in a given situation. Often we use process requirements when we are uncertain what the content of the substantive principles should be, or which ones should be applied.

General substantive principles that would apply in analyzing social consequences of AIDS include those of respect for autonomy (respecting people's decisions concerning themselves), non-malfeasance (avoiding doing harm), beneficence (doing good), and justice (distributing benefits and burdens as fairly as possible). The difficulty in the AIDS situation is that it is not always possible, in a given situation, to respect all these principles, and choices have to be made. Moreover, harm may be to one person and benefit to another, which can make the choice difficult, even when the benefits clearly outweigh the harms, and it is even more difficult when the choice is between competing harms to different persons or groups.

Our analysis and decision-making must start from a prima facie presumption of respect for all people, including their rights and liberties. This means that people who seek to infringe on such rights or liberties have the obligation of justifying their interventions. Such interventions will be justified only when the benefits they offer clearly outweigh the harms; when they are

84

the least invasive, least restrictive alternatives reasonably available and are likely to be effective in achieving a justified outcome; and when they are not inherently absolutely unacceptable. The most extreme example of the latter type of intervention would be to seek to eliminate AIDS from the community by executing every person who is HIV antibody positive or suffering from AIDS. But a less extreme, absolutely unacceptable approach would be to quarantine all HIV antibody-positive people, regardless of whether or not they created, through their behavior, a high risk of transmission of HIV. It probably should be noted that this is not meant to imply that if HIV antibody-positive people do engage in risk-taking activity, quarantine would necessarily be justified. It may or may not be, but it would at least need to satisfy the "least invasive, least restrictive alternative, reasonably available and likely to be effective" principle before it could be justified.

It is also suggested that our decision-making regarding AIDS and its social consequences should, if at all possible, start from a point of consensus and move out to differences, rather than starting from differences. The tone of the discussion and the content of the decisions taken may both be different if we operate in this way. Further, such an approach is likely to be more constructive and, therefore, more effective in stopping the spread of AIDS. This is to articulate the most obvious and most important point of consensus: that everyone in Canada wants to stop the spread of AIDS; no person wants even one more person to be infected. Where we start to differ is as to the means that will be most effective to achieve this outcome.

It is also worth noting that our point of consensus, that we all want to stop the spread of AIDS, also represents a concurrence of interest, which is not necessarily true of all principles. It is such perceptions that underlie such statements as that respect for people and their rights and good public health measures are in fact promoted by the same type of approaches to the AIDS situation.

We also need to keep in mind that failed interventions are not neutral in their effect; they can do serious harm. Therefore, we are not simply at liberty to try something and, if it fails, to be regretful; we have to take into account the cost of possible failure in order to determine whether or not an intervention is justified. This also means that we have obligations to do follow-up research on our interventions to determine whether or not they work, the benefits they confer, and the harms they inflict, and to take steps to modify them if any of these outcome indicia are unacceptable. In short, there is at least an ethical obligation to undertake research on our interventions in the AIDS situation. Further, we may have obligations to compensate for unavoidable harms that our justified interventions in the AIDS situation cause.

Our interventions in the AIDS situation must always be aimed at making irresponsible persons (in the sense that they engage in risk-producing conduct likely to transmit HIV) responsible, and must never cause responsible persons to become irresponsible. One of the dangers, for example, of highly invasive, intrusive, restrictive legislation such as is being suggested in some jurisdictions to regulate the AIDS situation is that it could cause persons who are infected with HIV to feel stigmatized, discriminated against, isolated, even criminalized and excluded from society. As a result, their previously responsible reactions could be affected by an overwhelming hostility that could cause them to behave in a way in which they would not otherwise behave and that is likely to increase the spread of AIDS. Not only is it a personal tragedy for these persons that we would cause them to feel and to act this way, but it is a community tragedy as well.

There is a metaphor that can be constructed from matters familiar to us in our primary school days that may be relevant to social consequences of AIDS. It is a combination of the "two times" multiplication table and the three Rs. The metaphor is "two times three Rs." First, "reading, 'riting, and 'rithmetic" are relevant to AIDS. There is much that we need to read because we must be as fully informed as possible with respect to AIDS. There is much that we need to write and to say, but there may also be much that we ought not to write or to say. It will take a great deal of wisdom to choose between what we ought and ought not to say with respect to given situations and factors relevant to AIDS. Arithmetic represents the economic problems, for the community and for individuals, presented by AIDS. These problems are linked to each other and arise, particularly

86

but not only, within the health care system. Within this context there can be economic problems at an institutional level, especially with respect to the provision of hospital care, and this raises the wider question of our obligations as a community to provide humane and appropriate environments for persons with AIDS. These vary with each person's circumstances and needs and can range from needs for hospices for dying persons to needs for ordinary housing. This in turn raises the issue of the personal, economic problems of many persons with AIDS, which should elicit our caring, supportive, and humane responses. It is not an overstatement to say that, unfortunately, it is increasingly common to be able to equate AIDS and poverty. This is true in two respects. AIDS can cause people to become poverty-stricken, for example, through loss of employment or the cost of treatment and care. And poor people usually have less opportunity to protect themselves from transmission of HIV through information, education, counseling, testing, and psychosocial support services, and when affected with HIV-related disease, they may have little or no access to appropriate care.

The three Rs also represent responsibility, rights, and reassurance, all of which are essential in the AIDS situation on the part of individuals, subgroups of the community, and the community. We all have responsibilities in relation to AIDS, whether we are persons with AIDS or persons without AIDS. These include responsibilities both to ourselves and to others. We all have rights, and to the greatest degree possible, we must respect one another's rights. When there is conflict we need to take the least intrusive, least invasive, most likely to be effective approach in terms of trespassing on rights in resolving that conflict. We all need and we all must give reassurance. The community needs to reassure persons with AIDS that they will be respected and cared for. Persons with AIDS, likewise, need to reassure the community that they will respect and care for the community. Unless this occurs on all sides, we are in danger of augmenting hostility, which will be translated into fear. Fear in response to AIDS can be looked at on a continuum from, at one end, healthy, constructive, safety-promoting fear to, at the other end, pathological, destructive, risk-producing fear. Risk creation that results from fear can occur, for example, when fear causes persons with

AIDS to have nihilistic or denial reactions and, because of these, to engage in high-risk conduct. But risk-taking resulting from fear, although often not recognized as such, can also occur on the part of the community and can cause serious damage to its important structures. For instance, to enact highly oppressive legislation to try to control the spread of AIDS could constitute risk-taking conduct by the community. It could set precedents with application far outside the AIDS situation, and that would affect the legal and ethical tone of Canadian society by detracting from, for example, the degree of real, or at least manifested, respect that we have for one another, our respect for human rights, and the symbolism that we are a caring society.

There is no doubt that AIDS will challenge us on many levels, and it is possible that this tiny virus may alter our civilization. It is even being suggested that it could "wipe us out." We hope this is highly unlikely, but it will certainly alter our relations with one another, no matter whether they are intimate or between strangers, such that they will contain fear that would not otherwise have been present.

AIDS may alter our intimate relations through changing, for example, our perceptions of the connection between "sex" and life (which connection may be desired or undesired in any given circumstances; one can compare an infertile couple and their longing for children with unwanted teenage pregnancy) to perceptions of connections between "sex" and death. We have no evidence as yet of the likely effect of such changes on the psychosexual development of young people. Moreover, we can question whether attitudes, including attitudes to sexuality, govern behavior, or behavior gives rise to the formation of attitudes. In the latter case the changes of behavior that have resulted from the threat of AIDS may not yet have given rise to the full expression of the accompanying changes in attitudes. In trying to determine the likely effect of AIDS on our relations with one another, once again, we find ourselves in a situation in which there is great uncertainty regarding multiple factors relevant to what we might face as individuals and as a society as a result of AIDS.

It is also likely that our proclaimed respect for human rights could be affected by AIDS. Respect for human rights is often

88

implemented through law in our contemporary Western societies, which is the mechanism we use to govern our relations with one another as "strangers." Juxtaposing human rights, law, and "stranger relations" provides an insight relevant to AIDS. It is that even as strangers an intimate bond is present because we are all human beings and must respect one another as such. Further, because we all are human beings we are much more similar to one another than we are different. It is well to remember this in many of the contexts in which human rights are relevant, but particularly in the AIDS situation. Respect for human rights as a distinct and identified component of legal-political systems has been largely institutionalized in modern times, and in Canada articulated in a dramatic form in the new *Canadian Charter of Rights and Freedoms.* The reality as compared with the theory of this respect will be confronted with a major challenge by AIDS. It is easy to be an advocate of human rights when one does not perceive that there are any *personal* harms or risks involved in doing so, which is true for many human rights in Canada. AIDS may be the first real test of the strength of such advocacy in the sense that it presents a situation in which the majority of the population perceives that it must choose between upholding human rights for persons affected by AIDS and taking some minimal, although additional, risk for themselves, their children, their wider family, or the community.

This leads to the consideration of the concept of risk. It seems that in modern Western societies we have increasingly come to believe that we are owed and to demand an environment that we perceive is as risk-free as possible. The word perceive is important here because in fact it is rarely the case that our environments are as risk-free as possible, and yet we find these acceptable. One possible explanation for this inconsistency is that there are certain factors that, when they are attached to risks, make these risks unacceptable, even though they have less serious consequences and are less probable than other acceptable risks. It is likely that a risk will be found to be unacceptable at a lesser degree of seriousness and probability of occurrence when the risk is clearly identified; when the "agent of harm" (for example, HIV) is identified; when the potential victim is identified before infliction of the risk; when an act, as compared with an omission, is involved in inflicting the risk; or when some choice is present as to whether or not the risk is inflicted. It is highly probable, if we are to retain our humanity and compassion in relation to AIDS, that we will all have to learn to live with a greater degree of perceived risk than we automatically feel is comfortable. The alternative is to act in an inhumane, disrespectful, uncompassionate manner.

Concepts relevant to uncertainty and our psychological reaction to uncertainty are also related to risk perception. Many individuals, and probably most, within a modern society are uncomfortable living with uncertainty. But, again, this is true only of perceived or recognized uncertainty, not the ever-present reality of uncertainty. Life is an uncertain matter, but most of us do not recognize this most of the time. Situations like AIDS bring us face to face with the necessity to live with uncertainty, and we are at least uncomfortable, and sometimes highly anxious, having to accept this. Again, we are likely to think that we have a right to have uncertainty related to the AIDS situation reduced to its minimum possible level. But the measures that would be necessary to do this almost certainly would cause more harm than confer benefit. Consequently we will have to sacrifice some of the comfort of living with the least degree of uncertainty that we perceive it is possible to achieve in order to respect other values and other important principles.

Our modern societies also have a reaction that when there is something wrong, we should pass a law and this will remedy it. There is almost a Pavlovian response to the effect that if we pass a law, this will remedy the problem we are trying to deal with and do good, when in fact the opposite might be true, in that the law could well do harm. This possibility is rarely sufficiently investigated. The fact that increasingly we have become a legally governed society may or may not be connected with a failure to perceive that passing laws can cause harm. It is interesting to contemplate, with respect to the increased use of law, that historically law has been used to govern relations between strangers, while nonlegal mechanisms, such as moral obligations, have generally governed relations between intimates. In particular, what would the application of such an analysis reflect about cries for legal intervention in regard to AIDS? Do these cries imply in some way that persons with AIDS are strangers to each of us individually and strangers in our society? If this is the case, we should not be surprised if people who are affected by such legislation are estranged and have hostile reactions both to its passage and beyond this more generally. As with all interventions in the AIDS situation, if we enact legislation, we have a moral obligation to monitor its effects, including carrying out research in this regard, and to ensure that benefits outweigh risks and, even when they do, to reduce the harms that our legislative interventions cause to the minimum possible level. This is to raise another important point. Even when infliction of some harm is justified, it is unacceptable to inflict any more harm than is necessary, or to fail to take steps to minimize adverse consequences of a justified, but harmful, intervention. We can too easily forget when we are justified in intervening that this does not mean that we are justified in leaving present all the harmful consequences that flow from such justified interventions.

The many political issues raised by AIDS are also a social consequence of its presence in our community. As a political issue, homosexuality can be compared with abortion, in some respects. Politicians are "damned" if they support either "side," in the sense that no matter which "side" they support, they will offend certain persons or groups in the community and, as a result, lose those persons' votes. To a large extent, politicians have chosen to ignore homosexuality as an issue, which has been possible because part of the ethos of the gay movement has been to ignore, or to be opposed to, traditional institutions such as government and politics.[1] AIDS has altered the relationship between the gay movement and politicians in two directions. Politicians have been forced to take notice of the gay community because of the threat that AIDS represents to homosexual men and the wider community, and the problems that this threat presents. Similarly, the gay movement has been forced to approach government to seek help and sometimes protection. There is still, however, more than a residue of suspicion, often on both sides.

This leads to a consideration of what could be called "jurisdiction" in relation to matters involving AIDS. Initially most of the response to the AIDS situation, especially with respect to persons with AIDS, was community-based and carried out in an individual, nonformalized, noninstitutionalized way. As AIDS has been increasingly recognized as a major problem for society in general, all these factors have changed, including government becoming involved in AIDS, and more formalized and institutionalized structures, often traditional ones that have long been in existence, taking over some of the governance of the AIDS situation. This has caused a loss of power on the part of some of the "early workers" in the AIDS situation, and some of their reactions have been those of being threatened by, and somewhat hostile to, the new participants. They can feel, and rightly, that when nobody else was prepared to help, they made quite extraordinary efforts to establish mechanisms for caring and supporting persons and families who were afflicted with AIDS and that this deserves continued recognition and support. Moreover, unlike these "early workers," some of the people who are now becoming interested in the AIDS situation are not necessarily doing so for purely or even predominantly altruistic reasons, but for reasons such as career advancement and opportunities for power and influence. We need to keep all this in mind when we are deciding how to "move" (for example, to distribute funding) in any given AIDS situation. There are legitimate claims and legitimate grievances on many sides. One factor that needs to be kept in mind is that an overly strong claim on the part of the gay community, for example, to retain sole jurisdiction in relation to AIDS in areas of Canada where homosexual men are a large community and the most affected subgroup of the population could well cause a fear reaction on the part of the general community that could become hostile and destructive. Likewise, an overly strong reaction on the part of the general community to controlling the gay community could cause such a reaction on its side. In many instances an enormous amount of care, concern, good will, and, above all, compassion toward persons with AIDS has been generated on the part of the Canadian population, in general, by persons with AIDS, especially by their courage and concern for others and by those helping and supporting them. This is an extremely valuable asset, and great care now needs to be taken not to destroy it. It is one of the most important contributions made by those who responded in the early stages of the infiltration of AIDS into the Canadian society. Moreover, it should be recognized that some of the responses that were devised out of a situation of necessity, for example, the "buddy system" to offer support to persons with AIDS, especially those who are dying, has much to teach and to offer the community as a whole with regard to devising more effective, caring, and humane, and at the same time less expensive, responses for analogous situations outside the context of AIDS.

We also need to keep in mind that in our Western societies, where there has been a large decline in adherence to organized religion, medicine now carries some of the symbolism once carried by religion, in particular the symbolism that we are caring individuals and a caring society. Medicine also performs some of the functions traditionally associated with religion, for instance, provision of charity in the form of socialized, universally accessible health care. AIDS will put medicine to the test in these respects, just as it will put to the test the reality, as compared with the theory, of a respect for human rights in our society. If medicine proves not to care for persons with AIDS, this will create a symbolism of a lack of caring not only for medicine, but also for society as a whole. Medicine will not be caring if it refuses access to care to persons with AIDS, or refuses to treat them when they are already in care, or gives persons with AIDS a lower level of care than it gives other persons. Any such lack of care may be somewhat concealed. A survey of attitudes of physicians to two persons who were described as having similar clinical manifestations of disease, but where one was dying from leukemia and the other from AIDS, found, among physicians, less caring, more hostility, and more negative perceptions toward the person with AIDS than toward the person with leukemia.[2]

In a similar symbolic vein, we need to recognize that certain illnesses can serve as metaphors in our societies and that AIDS seems to have taken on this role in a dramatic way. In effect, it has taken over from the other two illness metaphors that have been used this century, tuberculosis from the 1920s to the mid-1940s and cancer from then until the 1980s. Susan Sontag elaborates on what it means to use an illness as a metaphor in her book of that title, *Illness as Metaphor*. Among other consequences, when a disease is sexually transmitted, has moral connotations, is associated with punishment and guilt by some people, and has disproportionately afflicted minority, discriminated-against groups in our communities, there is a wide open field for dangerous opportunities for use of that disease as a negative metaphor in order to impose blame and to justify adopting seriously harmful conduct toward people afflicted with it.

It is also worth considering whether health, as well as illness, has become a metaphor in our late-twentieth-century societies and whether in part our reactions to the AIDS situations are reactions to a threat to this metaphor. Just as personal disease can be a metaphor for a sick society, the personal health of individuals and, probably more so, public and community health can be a metaphor for a strong and viable society. The development from an illness metaphor to a health one can be traced in a correlative change in the focus of medicine. We have moved from seeing medicine as being only interested in disease, treatment, and, if possible, cure to its having a preventive health care role, to, recently, having a task of health promotion. The language and analogies used in promoting health are also interesting with respect to its possible functioning as a metaphor. One hears of *national assaults* on a disease, usually cancer, that could indicate that the community has an interest not only in protecting its members from cancer, but also in ridding *itself* of "cancer." Comparisons are made between, for example, the U.S. space program and its success in putting a man on the moon and finding a cure for cancer, and the World Health Organization's aim of "health for all by the year 2000." These approaches are of positive content, optimistic, and at least imply that control of our health and well-being is possible. They may reassure us unconsciously, or even consciously, that because we have been successful in other seemingly almost impossible endeavors, we can maintain our health as individuals and the health of our communities. That is, we can control any disintegration of our society and maintain or promote its viability.

If this analysis has application to our society, one can identify yet another threat that AIDS can be perceived as presenting. It can threaten the functioning of "health as a metaphor" as one of the bases on which our society operates. That is, AIDS is not just a threat to society because persons infected with HIV may become sick and die, or infect others who, likewise, may become sick and die, and in doing so, diminish our society and make large claims on its resources. AIDS is also a threat, at the symbolic level, to our vision of ourselves as a healthy society and, therefore, threatens the damage that loss of this vision would cause.

Metaphors regarding illness may not only be used for external purposes, as discussed above, but also our communities can use metaphor as part of organizing their responses to, and in order to deal with, some illnesses. Probably the most common metaphor used with respect to dealing with AIDS is that of war; for example, Canadians have been urged by the Canadian Public Health Association, with the support of the federal government, to "join the attack on AIDS." Appealing to public health as a governing principle or justification of conduct, which would otherwise be unacceptable or illegal, can be compared with appeals to national security for similar purposes; this is to bring up a link between dealing with AIDS and national defense. Security from the enemy can translate to security from a virus, and needs and rights to be protected are present in both cases. Some descriptions or analogies used regarding AIDS are reminiscent of nuclear war. AIDS in Africa has recently been described as a bomb that went off five years ago and we are now seeing the fallout (*Time* magazine, July 6, 1987). In a similar vein, it has been suggested that, because of AIDS, we may now need to consider the "half-life" of nations (the time taken for the population of a nation to be reduced to half of its current numbers), whereas previously we only considered the "half-life" of radioactive isotopes (the time taken for the radioactivity of a given substance to fall to half its original level).

Finally, premature death and the threat of this are also a social consequence of AIDS. Large numbers of young or relatively young persons—those who are HIV antibody positive—now must live their lives with an immediate shadow of premature death hanging over them. For many this threat will become a reality. It is a tragedy for them, their families and loved ones, and our society. We are not used to having large numbers of young people die except in major wars—yet another way in which a war analogy is applicable to the AIDS situation. What will it mean to our society to lose a large number of its most artistic and creative minds? What will it mean years down the road not to have a full complement of mature actors, lawyers, psychiatrists, filmmakers, artists, for example, to contribute to our generation and to guide the next generation of such people? The answers, as with so many of the questions raised by AIDS, whether they be scientific, medical, legal, ethical, social, or political, is that we do not know.

Conclusion

The social consequences of AIDS can probably best be summed up in the words loss and suffering. The consequences can range from a person's loss of himself or herself, when he or she commits suicide on being given a diagnosis of HIV antibody positivity, to loss of one's mental self, when HIV attacks a person's brain, rendering him or her incompetent; to loss of life through manslaughter, when a person learns that his or her sexual partner has AIDS and kills the partner, and loss of liberty for the aggressor who is convicted;[3] to loss, through death, of one's baby, spouse, or partner; to loss of emotional and financial support, employment, insurance, housing, access to education, or to medical care. Suffering, tragedy, wrongful discrimination, isolation, and loneliness can all describe the social consequences for persons with AIDS. For the general community, AIDS represents a threat, first, of infection and, second, of catastrophic claims, for example, on the health care system, insurance and pension industries, and even on our collective pool of compassionate emotional response.

The problems presented by AIDS can seem so overwhelming that individual or communal burnout can easily ensue. Recently, on the same page of the *Montreal Gazette*,[4] the headlines informed us that 10,000 babies born each year in the United States are infected with AIDS, and that "AIDS could cost U.S. insurers $50 billion by year 2000." The magnitude of the personal suffering, on the one hand, and the economic impact on the community, on the other hand, of AIDS represented in these headlines has an almost fantasy-like (in fact, nightmarish) quality. Yet right next to these two articles was one titled "Blind sailor tries crossing Atlantic alone." It is well to remind ourselves of the strength, courage, indomitability, and beauty of the human spirit. We are all in some sense on a blind voyage on an unknown sea in the AIDS situation. Just as we sail in spirit with this blind sailor as we read about him, we must also sail in spirit with one another, especially with those of us who are persons with AIDS. Many of our covoyagers currently require help, perhaps more than we bargained on having to provide. There are many unavoidable disasters involved in AIDS, but there are also avoidable disasters. Courage and wisdom are needed on all our parts if we are to turn the avoidable disasters that AIDS could result in into opportunities for growth in our humanity, which is also a possible social consequence of AIDS.

Notes

1. Dennis Altman, "Legitimation Through Disaster: AIDS and the Gay Movement," in *AIDS: The Burden of History,* ed. Dan Fox and Elizabeth Fee (Berkeley: University of California Press, 1988).
2. See Kelly, St. Lawrence, Smith, et al., "Stigmatization of AIDS Patients by Physicians," *American Journal of Public Health* 77:789–91, 1987.
3. *ABA Journal,* June 1, 1987, p. 69.
4. *Montreal Gazette,* August 5, 1987, p. B-8.

6

Report from "Social Consequences of AIDS" Stream

I. We acknowledge the following:

The Christian churches have failed in their response to the AIDS crisis, although we acknowledge the caring response of many people of faith.

We have failed to provide a supportive environment for people with AIDS, their partners, families, and friends.

We have also failed to provide an accepting environment in which reflection on AIDS, mortality, sexuality, intimacy, and related social issues can take place.

We have neither trusted God nor one another. We acknowledge that we have displaced our fears about sexuality and mortality onto others.

We acknowledge that the fear of AIDS has further revealed the basic problems of homophobia, racism, and sexism in North American society. Our silence and passivity have fostered prejudice and isolation. Some people have even sought to lay blame on those who have been marginalized and considered disposable by society.

We share the responsibility for the failure to disseminate information about AIDS and its prevention.

We also share responsibility for AIDS information that has been inadequate, biased, and distorted.

We have also failed to encourage dissemination of AIDS information that is accessible to people of diverse languages, cultures, and socioeconomic backgrounds.

We have failed to respond to the global health crisis, especially the concerns of those people living in conditions of extreme poverty in developing countries.

As a result, we are putting at risk the lives of many people, including our families and communities.

II. The following "Informing Principles" should guide our actions:

We believe that the attempts to link the AIDS crisis with the wrath of God are irresponsible, seriously harmful, and misrepresent the character of God.

We believe that all people are created in the image of God and are equal before God.

We affirm that all people are sacred, and that there are no expendable people.

We believe that everyone has the right to knowledge that will empower them to make informed choices.

God calls us to be in relationship with God and with one another, exercising both freedom and responsibility.

The gospel compels us to care for people who are sick, oppressed, or dispossessed, to seek justice, to show mercy, and to be present with those who suffer.

As people of faith, we believe that faith sustains us in the face of uncertainty.

III. We recommend that the following actions be taken:

The church must engage in dialogue with people living with AIDS, both within the Christian community and within the wider society, so that we all may be empowered to confront the social challenges presented by AIDS.

The church must lobby for the passage and application of laws that protect the human rights of all people and protect against wrongful discrimination in any situation involving AIDS. The church must also lobby for the repeal of existing legislation that in principle or application violates human rights, including sodomy statutes.

The church must allocate resources appropriate to the gravity of the AIDS crisis with which we are confronted. This must include the allocation of staff, facilities, and financial support.

Christian churches must encourage dialogue and work with those people without a formal church affiliation who are actively confronting AIDS, for example, community-based groups.

There must be cooperation among religious bodies in the distribution of up-to-date information and the development of pastoral care ministries.

Christian churches must be supportive of care-givers and provide pastoral care, including helping them deal with their fears, grief, and mortality.

Christian churches must encourage the development and provision of explicit and nonjudgmental educational materials regarding both drug use and sexual behavior within the framework of the educational system.

Churches must encourage the dissemination of AIDS-related information even when it relates to behavior that may be in conflict with church teachings, in order to save lives. Examples are "how-tos" of correctly using condoms and using non-contaminated needles.

Congregations and church groups should become open and inviting to those who are marginalized because of their sexual orientation, gender, race, criminal record, or economic status.

Governments must allocate sufficient resources to meet the needs for AIDS education and care, in addition to allocations for medical and scientific research. This must include adequate funding for minority groups in order that they may be empowered to care for and educate their own community.

The Canadian and U.S. governments must ensure universal accessibility of health care for all individuals and groups. No person should be denied health care because of his or her HIV status.

Voluntary HIV antibody testing must be made available in both a confidential and, for those who desire it, an anonymous/non-nominal manner. This must include appropriate pre-counseling and follow-up counseling. We oppose nonvoluntary testing of any individual or group, for example, the military, hospital admissions, prison populations, and prostitutes. Screening of blood and blood products, sperm banks, and donated organs is appropriate.

We also oppose any form of quarantine for individuals or groups on the basis of their HIV status, as quarantine is socially destructive and will have no positive effect on this type of epidemic.

The U.S. government must fulfill its contractual obligation to the World Health Organization and also make an adequate contribution to the special fund for AIDS.

North American churches must be encouraged to develop partnerships with African churches, to address their specific needs in the worsening health crisis.

7

Reflections on "Social Consequences of AIDS" Stream

A Movement in Search of a Platform

Dr. Bonnie Greene

The people who attended the working group on the social consequences of AIDS were very much like people who come to any other conference. They were deeply involved in the issue— often more than they wanted to be. Working on the issue of AIDS takes a toll on everyone involved, although it is nothing like the toll taken on those who have AIDS. Many introduced themselves as people who felt isolated from the mainstream of their denominations, employers, or professional organizations. The atmosphere of a movement-in-the-making quickly emerged.

This characteristic became the overwhelming force, driving the course of the workshop. The facilitators ran headlong into the needs of the individuals in the group when they proposed the agenda for sessions. They suggested that the group list the issues of social consequence raised by the three papers. We would then quickly list those on which we already agreed and spend most of our time on those on which we needed serious debate to reach consensus. This proposal sparked a heated debate on "process" that lasted for an hour and a half. The facilitators finally had to withdraw their proposal and turn the workshop into a committee to draft a statement for public release at the end of the conference. The exercise therefore became one of finding words for those issues on which we who attended had taken a stand before we arrived.

The size of the workshop made it difficult for the group to do more than develop lists of general points to be made. Those who worked closest with persons with AIDS or with the gay and lesbian communities were most vocal, as one would expect. However, the group's decision to do everything in plenary rather than in small groups meant that people concerned about some of the ambiguous issues raised by AIDS had difficulty getting into the conversation. For example, few of the people in the health care sector were able to raise their questions. A number of participants simply gave up and left the workshop.

I've attended many conferences on social justice issues that have followed precisely the same course. One that stands out in my mind was a United Nations-sponsored conference against apartheid and in support of the African National Congress. The people who came needed to issue their own statement because at that time few people agreed with them or knew what they were talking about. The declaration issued at the end of that conference was remarkably similar to the one issued by this stream of the AIDS Consultation. In each case, the declaration served the needs of the participants to belong to a group—however transitory its life—that could make a statement contrary to the kind of public opinion that makes their lives and work difficult. That's what people in the early stages of movements do.

The statement approved by the group emphasized the need for churches to foster explicit education as a means of prevention plus dialogue with those most affected by AIDS. The specific social consequences of AIDS addressed in the statement were primarily in four areas:

1. possible denial of civil liberties of those who have AIDS;
2. the need for adequate government funding for education, health care, and research (both domestically and internationally);

3. the need for HIV antibody testing to be voluntary and confidential;
4. opposition to quarantining as a means of preventing the spread of AIDS.

It was clear to me at the end of the Consultation that the conversation on the social implications of AIDS had not advanced during the course of the weekend. The workshop may well have served as a catalyst, but the work of dealing with the issue still lies ahead.

Those of us who made the declaration now face the task of building a minimum consensus in our institutions and professional organizations. Neither the difficulty nor the value of that task ought to be underestimated. Statements from conference participants can help focus a debate and strengthen the hands of those who share the views but work alone in their local communities. Declarations take on real power as the behavior of communities across the continent begins to reflect the beliefs we declare. Those who attended the Consultation have an important role to play in helping build a broad consensus of behavior as well as words.

There still remains the task that we chose not to do during the course of the weekend: pressing the ecumenical community to deal with the issues on which we have not yet achieved consensus. During the coffee breaks the dilemmas individuals faced in their work places became clearer. Would churches advocate the distribution of condoms in prisons? What position should denominational chaplains take? What about administrators of homes for the mentally handicapped? Should mission boards require the testing of personnel returning from long stays in countries with a known AIDS problem?

What is the most appropriate way to restrain those who are infected but choose to engage in behavior that infects others without their knowledge? What obligations do counselors, chaplains, health care workers in our institutions have when they encounter such individuals?

Dr. Sommerville's paper cast the public health issues regarding AIDS in the war imagery of states appealing to national security in dealing with an enemy. It was an apt image, given the stage of the public debate on AIDS. The most useful debate on global security is being recast from the pursuit of national security to the pursuit of common security. It is a difficult, tedious, and critical debate that involves detailed agreements on the kinds of behavior all parties to a security agreement will adhere to in the interests of protecting even the most vulnerable members of the community. In foreign policy, there is no such thing as blind faith. There is only trust built on dialogue, on reducing enemy images, and on a commitment by states to acting only in ways that don't threaten those who might be cast in the role of "enemy" in tense times. In the foreign policy jargon, we speak of such steps as "confidence-building measures."

The next step in the dialogue on AIDS will be working out "confidence-building measures." The conversation will have to shift from protecting the public from persons with AIDS and vice versa. That conversation is still within the framework of "national security." The people who attended this Consultation have a major job ahead in shifting the conversation to a search for common security for all, including those who are vulnerable: persons with AIDS, health care workers, unwitting sexual partners of people who test positive for the HIV antibody, people with compromised immune systems, sexually active young adults, prisoners and others in institutions, and so on. In my view, that's the next item on the agenda.

Bringing Our Faith to Bear

The Rev. Adele M. Resmer

It is difficult to know where to begin with thoughts on a conference that still seems overwhelming a week later. There were so many things going on at the same time. Perhaps that's the place to start—with the different groups and agendas.

There seemed to be two major groups of people in our section. First, there were those who were considered to be professional theologians and ethicists. This group saw the mandate in the program outline, which was to produce a document in response to the question "What ought the churches be doing?" and geared their activity to that end.

Second, there were those who work firsthand with persons with AIDS, such as social workers and health care providers. A number of these expressed a need to talk about their experiences. They wanted to share the pain and hurt and even the joy that comes with working in such an emotionally intense setting. These people were less concerned about producing a formal document than one grounded in their personal experiences of working with persons with AIDS.

Many times these two groups were at odds with each other; sometimes the tension in the room was palpable and tempers were barely kept in check. It was difficult for those who wanted to produce a structured document to allow the time and space for people who wanted to focus on experiences. In the same vein, it was difficult for those who wanted to share experiences to acknowledge the validity of producing a document with a mandate for action directed to the participating church bodies.

It is indicative of the tenacity and commitment of the people in our group that despite different agendas and needs, we learned some new things about AIDS. This knowledge, derived from firsthand experience as well as from recent medical information, helped in establishing guidelines for our document.

Although a number of points were raised in our large-group discussion, there were two that were repeatedly stressed. First, AIDS is not an isolated issue. Reactions to AIDS are also reactions to other realities, such as racism and sexism; we cannot deal with one without dealing with the others. Yet, while we acknowledged the complexity of the situation in which AIDS exists, as a group we had difficulty integrating the number of different issues associated with AIDS into a fuller picture of reality. As a result, we often faced the issue as though it was isolated from other problems in society.

Second, not only does AIDS reveal other problems in North America, but it exists with unique complexities on other continents. There was an attempt in the group to say something about the global context, recognizing our tendency to behave as though the only reality exists in our two countries. However, we had difficulty actually visualizing ourselves as part of a broader global context; again, we struggled with our inability to integrate our sense of reality with a larger picture of the world.

It was interesting to me that there was one point our group had difficulty discussing. We had difficulty speaking about God. I don't think it was simply because the name and character of God have been used against persons with AIDS. Rather, it seemed to be part of the larger struggle of our group to integrate different pieces of the reality in which AIDS and persons with AIDS exists. We had difficulty talking about what our faith had to say to this situation, and we dealt with faith as if it were a separate piece to be added or removed as needed. My sense is that because we were afraid to say anything too easily about God, we then said too little; again, we struggled for integration rather than separation.

Although we had difficulty as a group bringing the different aspects of this concern together, it was persons with AIDS themselves who, in the final plenary session, helped us to view the situation as a whole. They encouraged us to continue working in the awkward way we do for those who have AIDS. I remember most clearly two men who spoke in the closing session. The first man, from Vancouver, spoke of his fear of death and his need for us, as people of the church, to witness to our beliefs so that he will be able to face what is ahead in his life. He acknowledged and thanked many who, although from different traditions and with different approaches, had already shared themselves and their faith with him. He urged us both to continue our work fighting AIDS and to care for people with AIDS.

A second man came to the microphone. He did not look as well as the first; his voice cracked as he spoke. He encouraged us to continue our work and to challenge our churches to respond more fully and with a stronger commitment. He also reminded us that although our work might help others in the future, it would not help him because he was dying. That simple statement brought a deeper level of intensity to the people gathered. For many, that statement brought together the intellectual concerns and the experiential reality of AIDS—at least it did that for me. He talked about those who, while we were speaking, would die. He spoke of not wanting to die without God and how he needed us to speak about God and bring the experience of a caring God to him. I still feel the weight of that request.

This conference, like many others, was helpful in bringing us a great deal of information in a brief period. It involved conflicts over different agendas, all of which seemed of utmost importance to their owners. This gathering, however, was also unique. Although we could not easily find a way to bring together the intellectual and the experiential information about AIDS, the two men with AIDS were able to give us the permission we could not give ourselves: to commit ourselves to challenge our churches to new action and to bring the message of God's mercy to those who now fight this fatal disease.

Part 3

Illness and Health

8

A World Suffering with AIDS: Community or Ideology? Reflections on Illness and Health

Dr. A. Gene Copello

The rise of acquired immune deficiency syndrome (AIDS) and the prevalence of its causal agent, human immunodeficiency virus (HIV), cannot be viewed as isolated medical or scientific phenomena. Social and even political discomfort attends the epidemics of AIDS and HIV infection. The current worldwide health emergency has caused us to reflect on the meaning we attach to such concepts as illness and health. This reflection has been both secular and religious, rational and irrational, helpful and destructive. People of faith as well as people without faith can be found reacting both rationally and irrationally to the scientific, clinical, social, and political aspects of the emergency. Likewise, those with faith claims have been both helpful and destructive as the emergency has widened and deepened.

This paper is concerned with raising serious concerns about the impact our social and political reactions to AIDS may have on our understanding of community. The discussion will be grounded in Christian faith with the broader experience of the Judeo-Christian tradition as a background. Five assumptions need to be expressed and clarified before proceeding.

First, AIDS and HIV infection are primarily biological events without theological or social significance apart from the social context in which they exist. AIDS itself has no religious or sociopolitical meaning. The social context of AIDS (e.g., the manner in which persons with AIDS are treated in society) creates opportunities and challenges for theological, social, and political change or reaction.

Second, the modes of transmission and modes of prevention regarding HIV are known. HIV is a blood-borne and sexually transmitted virus that behaves in much the same way a hepatitis B virus behaves. Because no vaccine or curative therapy is currently available for HIV infection, society's major tool in preventing further spread of the virus is education and counseling.

Third, although AIDS and HIV infection are primarily biological events, their prevention and control currently rely on behavioral techniques of education, counseling, and behavior modification. In these senses, AIDS is a behavioral problem.

Fourth, the modification of behavior raises ethical issues. Behavior, attitudes, and values are closely related. For example, changing sexual behavior to prevent HIV transmission will necessitate value and attitudinal changes if the behavioral change is to become sustained over time. Changing social values inherently raises ethical questions. Who has the right to change another's values? How will criteria be established in assessing "positive" versus "negative" values? These are important, and for many of us theological, issues. For people of faith a critical question may become, what values should be encouraged from a Christian perspective? What behaviors should be encouraged from such a perspective?

And fifth, the health emergency before us raises significant concerns over the notion of "community." AIDS is not an isolated epidemic impacting neatly defined "risk groups." The data is clear that any person who engages in behaviors that place him or her at risk for contracting HIV may become infected with the virus and ultimately become a person with AIDS. The riskiest of these behaviors are now well defined: the sharing of contaminated needles during drug use and unprotected vaginal or anal intercourse. Viewing AIDS as an epidemic of the human community will lead one to interpretations of the sociopolitical

112

and perhaps even theological changes and reactions to AIDS different from viewing the situation in terms of isolates (i.e., "AIDS is a gay disease" or "AIDS only impacts minorities" or "AIDS strikes the immoral").

These five assumptions and the general perspective of Christianity will inform the remainder of the paper. The thesis is this: the social context of AIDS permits either opportunities and challenges for human community or the disorientation and reaction of society owing to ideological separation. Much of this choice before us will be defined in terms of how we interpret "illness" and "health" during the current emergency. The use of the term choice is quite intentional. Just as the prevention of HIV transmission is within our control, so, too, is the control of the disorientation of society because of the epidemic.

We will first look at the rise of ideology. It has become increasingly clear that an opposition movement has developed in reaction to such orthodox institutions as public health, academic medicine, and education. A recent publication by Gene Antonio, *The AIDS Cover-Up*,[1] demonstrates the growing influence of this countermovement. Two examples will suffice. Orthodox medicine has been able to evidence that HIV is a blood-borne and sexually transmitted virus, the transmission of which can be prevented behaviorally. Antonio raises concerns about the airborne transmission of HIV in the context that the orthodox view is a "cover-up" of the truth. Likewise, the orthodox view would hold that all people are at risk of HIV infection if certain types of behavior occur. While generally agreeing with this, Antonio also sets up two communities in his book—the wicked world of the infected and the pure world of the uninfected. Health resides with the uninfected community, whereas illness resides with the infected community. And his major concern is keeping the boundary intact in part by exposing the so-called cover-up. Writing about the recommendations for safer sex he claims, "The promotion of 'safe' techniques of homosexual perversion by homosexual leaders and their bedfellows in the media, medical, and educational establishments is a fradulent myth."[2]

When we compare Antonio's writing with the increase in violence against persons with AIDS and AIDS professionals, his comments seem mild. In Arcadia, Florida, the home of three

HIV-infected hemophiliac children was burned; in Lake City, Tennessee, a family with an infected child received death threats; and so on. The rise of violence in the AIDS epidemic is certainly related to ignorance about the disease, but it is also related to the rise of ideologies. Prejudice plays on ignorance. What are these ideologies of reaction? They share the common belief that the uninfected world is well and healthy and that the infected world is dysfunctional and ill. The boundary between these two worlds or communities must be absolute.

Of the many possible ideological variations on this general theme, three appear to dominate the countermovement. The first would claim Christian roots. These are individuals who see in the AIDS epidemic a historical, cosmological event. This interpretation tends to be independent of the social context of the epidemic. The emergence of HIV and AIDS as biological events is viewed as a "sign" of the end of the world. A variety of biblical understandings (primarily interpretations of the book of Revelation) ground this thinking. Through some "evil act" persons become infected with HIV and the presence of a worldwide epidemic itself becomes the sign of the end of the world. The people of God (i.e., the "good" people) do not become infected with the virus.

The second dominant ideology is similar to the first but is more fixated on sexuality. Here, homosexuality is stigmatized. For example, during the early 1980s the Rev. Jerry Falwell claimed that AIDS was God's punishment for homosexuals. More recently those holding to this sexual ideology have enlarged the damnation by God to include prostitutes and promiscuous heterosexuals. But homosexuality is usually the main target by these types of Christians. Human community is divided by this point of view into those who practice abstinence before and monogomy after heterosexual marriage and those who do not conform to this package. The conformers do not get AIDS because God blesses them with health; nonconformers get AIDS because God punishes them with illness.

Another ideological variant is perhaps more political than religious; however, it appears to complement the first two well. In some ways this is Gene Antonio's grounding. The argument is simple: we must protect the uninfected from the infected or

114

potentially infected (i.e., the "high-risk groups"). There are usually cries from this group to "protect society" and to "protect our community." The assumption in such statements is that persons infected with HIV are not members of society or of any respective community. Such statements also ignore the fact that one contracts HIV infection through specific behaviors that are within the control of individuals. An individual becomes infected with HIV by engaging in these behaviors, not by going to school with, or eating near, or working with a person infected with HIV. The basic direction of this perspective is that the "health" of the uninfected community must be protected from the "illness" of the infected community. Demonstrations against the construction of an AIDS hospice and the many protests we have seen by parents opposing the inclusion of infected children in various school systems are examples of this perspective. Unlike the other two variants, this third ideological perspective has been involved in classic political activities (e.g., protests). Although religious belief is not required for membership in this ideology, there is an obvious alliance between it and the other two.

The common theme for these reactive ideologies concerns the separation of human community on the basis of infection with HIV (or potential infection, e.g., homosexual men). "Health" resides with the uninfected community because of God's blessings or a vaguer sense of "good living." "Illness" resides with the infected community as an expression of God's wrath, a sign of the end of time, and/or because of "sin" or a vague sense of "bad living." In addition, there appears to be a general distrust in all these ideologies for the "establishment," as Antonio calls it. I refer to these perspectives as "ideology" because they encourage reactions based on absolutistic or doctrinal ideas and are aimed at facilitating sociopolitical (even theocratic) domination of one group (the uninfected) over another (the infected) as a historical (if not metaphysical) event.

Ideological reaction is only one response to the social, political, and theological challenges of the AIDS epidemic. The other general response is that of community. This approach has been characterized by attempts to reduce HIV transmission through education and counseling, research into vaccine development and therapeutics, the care of HIV-infected individuals, and the protection of the public health through the dissemination of information on risk-reduction strategies (e.g., safer sex). The advocates of this approach belong to the orthodox establishment: public health officials, academicians, researchers, medical ethicists, social service workers, and health professionals. These advocates generally claim "expertise" and "knowledge" based on epidemiology, scientific research, and ethical analysis as well as a historically understood duty to protect the rights of individual patients and the rights of society. The underlying philosophy of this response is grounded in an interpretation of health and illness that draws together the currently infected and the currently uninfected into community. Although religious belief is not necessary for membership in this "establishment," several who identify with it (including myself) view this response as grounded in the Judeo-Christian tradition.

The orthodox view is this: AIDS is a problem of the whole community. All people need to be educated and counseled about the modes of transmission and prevention of HIV. This education must be culture-sensitive, age-specific, and demonstrate an understanding of human values and attitudes if resulting behavioral changes are to be long term. In addition, this view holds the responsibility for caring for AIDS patients and persons infected with HIV to be that of the whole community. An excellent summary of the orthodox position is found in *Confronting AIDS: Directions for Public Health, Health Care, and Research.*[3]

As we have witnessed over 42,000 reported cases of AIDS in the United States and 100,000 globally with tens of thousands of deaths, it is clear that the human community has been infected as a whole. As children with AIDS or viral infection enter our schools there is a sense that our educational system has become infected; as persons with AIDS worship with us in our church buildings, there is a sense that HIV has come knocking on our doors; as we as parents become concerned about the sexual behaviors of our adolescents, there is a sense that everyone is potentially at risk for acquiring AIDS; as our hospitals and clinics come to treat more and more persons with AIDS or other forms of symptomatic HIV infection, there is a sense that our health care systems are overburdened; and as our political leaders speak more directly about the epidemic, it has become clear that AIDS is an issue for the entire society.

We are citizens of a world suffering with AIDS. Since the early days of the epidemic the sense of "emergency" has become more personal, closer to home. During 1985 Nashville, Tennessee, had twenty-five cases of AIDS; today over 100 cases have been reported. In Nashville, in Toronto, in Bonn, in São Paulo, and in Kampala the face of the epidemic is coming to reflect the many faces of humanity: gay and heterosexual, color and white, male and female, young and old, poor and rich.

Given the enormous diversity of cases in the worldwide epidemics of AIDS and HIV infection and the potential for so many more cases in the future, the boundary between health and illness becomes increasingly artificial. The human community is ill and suffering; this community needs love, hope, and healing.

To respond as a whole community to the epidemic is not an easy task. Was Jesus Christ not criticized for his work with the lepers of his day? His attempts to draw the prostitute into community with his followers was seen as heresy. Yet we are told throughout the Gospels of his attempts to bring diverse, even hostile, groups into community with one another. The Judeo-Christian tradition views the world as fundamentally flawed. Each of us is a sinner in need of redemption. Whether one carries HIV or not is a moot point in terms of symbolic meanings of "health" and "illness." There is only one community—one that is ill and in need of healing. The AIDS epidemic has come to amplify the nature of illness. The human community is suffering with AIDS, but this community has always been suffering. Healing and redemption were sought in ancient times as they are today.

In religious terms this second approach to AIDS is best said this way: AIDS calls the people of God as a community to healing and redemption as do all forms of suffering. Rather than "protecting" "us" from "them," we are called to help and heal the human community. Jonathan Mann, director of the World Health Organization's Global Programme on AIDS, has recently said that no one nation will be safe from AIDS until all nations are safe from AIDS.[4] Likewise, no person and no com-

117

munity will be safe from AIDS until all people and communities are cared for and healed. And I am not only referring to the physical healing of those impacted by HIV (unfortunately this may not be possible for several years). We need to interpret "healing" and "health" globally, wholistically. Our communities and each person—infected or uninfected—need to be healed of the emotional, social, and spiritual illnesses that attend the epidemic. In this sense, the whole community is "infected" with HIV and "dying" of AIDS. This flawed community must turn to itself and to its faith to be healed.

Across the world glimpses of reconciliation and healing are occurring. In San Francisco, community groups help care for persons living with AIDS and their loved ones; infants abandoned because of HIV infection are given a home and love in a northern California monastery; Mother Teresa and her congregation provide hospice care for hundreds of AIDS patients around the world; children in Lake City, Tennessee, cry out, "But he is a human being," as angry parents threaten the life of a boy with hemophilia and HIV infection they want removed from the local school; AIDS service organizations around the world are serving the social and spiritual needs of people impacted by the epidemic; thousands of health care workers daily minister to the needs of their patients; and this list could continue.

These glimpses of community need to be nourished. Community happens during this epidemic where AIDS education and counseling are provided across diverse populations with a sensitivity for issues of culture, age, and value systems. Municipalities that provide quality health care for AIDS patients through hospitals and home health care demonstrate community. When social organizations include persons living with AIDS on their rosters, community is happening. Whenever humanity is drawn together to heal itself, educate itself, and care for itself, community is happening in the midst of this epidemic. As we empower ourselves to prevent the further spread of HIV, to care for those already impacted by the virus, and to manifest love and hope, we come closer to becoming a healthy community.

The Christian churches need to be among the leadership in

this epidemic. As stated earlier, Christians can be found in both camps: ideological reaction and community. Many of the churches have released community-oriented statements at the national level. These statements generally call on Christians to provide care to the infected, welcome the infected into the congregations, provide education, and other characteristics of the orthodox response to the epidemic. While I affirm these statements, I also understand the problems that attend them. First, there is no identifiable leadership within the churches. There may be committees and councils, but most Christians and citizens probably could not identify them. This leadership gap also exists at many local levels. Second, although the statements establish goals (e.g., congregational education), they do not assist in how a local congregation would manifest these goals. In other words, the practical element is missing. At the local level the manifestation of national goals is uneven. It is here where greater collaboration between churches and the public health, academic, and professional communities would be helpful. And third, the statements do not generally discuss the need for ecumenism. The epidemic calls for enlarging networks of community at local, national, and global levels.

The question then for the churches is how to respond to the social, political, and theological challenges of the epidemic. The Christian establishment may respond reactively and ideologically—some segments of Christianity have already done so—or may respond in terms of community. Regardless of whether one's Christian foundation is biblical or theological (or both) it seems clear that those who call themselves Christians are called to serve. Historically the church has interpreted this servant role to include care of the sick. In addition, the Christian faith is essentially a faith of a community (i.e., the church). The time has come for this community of faith to minister to itself and the wider community. We who are Christians must provide healing to a world suffering with AIDS. The whole community—infected and uninfected—is suffering the social and political illnesses of this epidemic. Healing will occur whenever and wherever the church provides education, counseling, care, and community.

AIDS is a tragic chapter in human history. Immunologists will often say that one positive aspect of the epidemic (if we can speak in such terms) is the amount of information we will learn about the human immune system. I would add that another "positive" aspect is the opportunity provided for human community. As the people of God move through this period of history my hope is that we will respond as Christ responded to the physical, social, and political illnesses of his day. If the church fails in this calling, its relevance to modern society will be challenged. More important, however, some may ask whether or not it has become an empty institution, void of Spirit.

Notes

1. Gene Antonio, *The AIDS Cover-Up* (San Francisco: Ignatius Press, 1986).
2. Ibid., pp. 192–93.
3. *Confronting AIDS: Directions for Public Health, Health Care, and Research* (Washington, DC: Institute for Medicine of the National Academy of Sciences, 1986).
4. Third International Conference on AIDS, June 1987, Washington, DC.

9

AIDS-Related Suffering: Therapy, Healing, or ?

Dr. Abbyann Lynch

"To suffer" is "to experience severe distress associated with events that threaten the intactness of the person. . . . Suffering occurs when an impending destruction of the person is perceived; it continues until the threat of disintegration has passed, or until the integrity of the person can be restored in some other manner."[1]

Those who have contracted AIDS may suffer on that account; those of significance to the AIDS patient may suffer as well. Human services practitioners called on to treat the AIDS victim may experience suffering in such a role; their colleagues may suffer in terms of the response such practitioners give when that request for treatment is made. Society as a whole suffers with AIDS in its midst; there is concern lest the pressures created by the disease fracture the community in which it is found.

According to Cassel, suffering can occur in relation to any aspect of the person, whether it is in the realm of social roles; group identification; the relation with self, body, or family; or the relation with the transpersonal, transcendent source of meaning. All the aspects of personhood—the lived past, the family's lived past, culture and society, the instrumental dimension, associations and relationships, the body, the unconscious mind, the political being, the secret life, the perceived future, and the transcendent dimension—are susceptible to damage and loss. If the damage or injury is sufficient to cause concern that disintegration of the whole person (personal wholeness) might ensue (not disintegration of body or mind or spirit only), then the *person* suffers.

Given this definition of suffering and this description of its "mechanics," how is AIDS suffering made manifest? How do affected individuals actually experience the threat to personal intactness in the AIDS situation, and how do they respond to it? To answer the last question first, in general terms, those who suffer injury to the integrity of person may express sadness, anger, loneliness, depression, grief, unhappiness, melancholy, rage, withdrawal, or yearning.

In more precise terms, the AIDS victim may experience anxiety with regard to the physical and mental pain associated with the disease; there may be dread concerning the progressive deterioration associated with this malady and fear concerning the certainty of proximate death it brings. As well, the AIDS-affected person may experience the alienation common to many who are "ill": "I" am controlled by "it," with "it" in this case as more personally and socially repugnant than many other illnesses. Socially, the AIDS victim may experience isolation as a result of rejection or abandonment by family, friends, colleagues, lover(s); many AIDS victims must endure stigmatization because of their life-style. There is still further anguish for those afflicted with AIDS: concern about employment, financial status, access to care, living accommodation. Diagnostic and hospital activity may appear depersonalizing to the AIDS patient; so much depends on the results of sophisticated technology; the elaborate infection control procedure may intimidate. In anger, many of those "ill" with AIDS may attempt "to take others with them; infect as many as possible." In despair, many victims of the disease try to hide their disease with deception; some attempt suicide; others seek early euthanasia.

The human services practitioner may experience AIDS suffering first in fear about contracting the disease personally and then in terms of being a carrier of infection for family; there may be concern here for fulfillment of family responsibilities if the disease should actually be "caught." Such fear may extend to concern about being the carrier of such disease to others now

122

unaffected by the disease (e.g., other patients, colleagues, friends, lover[s]). The fears are those of "future perceived" and, in this case, are commonly shared with the AIDS victim as just described. Given the scientific evidence regarding the modes of AIDS infection, these fears may be judged unrealistic by others, but fears to the one concerned are very real. Additionally, "I may be the exception," and "Were there not three health care workers who tested HIV positive recently after being splattered with the blood of AIDS patients?" These practitioners may experience frustration with the lack of real scientific progress regarding treatment and cure of AIDS. They may be wearied by the demands made on those who care for dying patients on a regular basis; they may grieve for many of their patients personally in their painful and early death. Revulsion concerning association with AIDS patients is not uncommon; the practitioner may be angry that the victims have "caused their own disease," that they have infected others, that some of them have "sinned," and that some are "innocent" victims, suffering miserably. Some practitioners who care for AIDS patients may be isolated by peers and friends who are concerned that they may become physically or morally contaminated through association with such practitioners; some such practitioners have actually been prohibited by spouse or lover from undertaking the care of these patients. Because some practitioners "opt out" of caring for these patients, those who continue their care must often do the work of several others—a serious threat to staff relations and a cause of low staff morale. Whether practitioners "stay or go," they will all be faced with anxiety concerning possible loss of self-esteem or esteem for the profession if they should decide to leave this work to others; in terms of their professional promise, they will be concerned about the effect of their "opting out" on patients, their professional groups, and the public.

Society suffers from AIDS collectively as well as in the individual anguish of its members. In fear of physical contact with AIDS victims, as well as in repudiation of the life-styles of some of these persons, group anger and hatred are becoming more common in the confrontations regarding the presence of AIDS-infected persons in the work place, schools, housing accommodation, neighborhoods. On the same grounds, nations are now suspicious of immigrants and travelers from other parts of the world. There are charges that AIDS patients are further victimized in their search for health and life insurance by those who fear a financial loss in terms of those transactions. Misrepresentation and covert practice are increasing within the scientific community as individuals and laboratory groups fear they will be left behind in the race to find the cure for the disease. More abstractly, and fueled by some of these same concerns, a new sense of "we" (who do not have AIDS) and "they" (who do) is developing. Many are concerned lest it lead to an even greater impersonalization and depersonalization in society than is now evident; in many groups there is the growing preoccupation with "me" rather than "neighbor." In attempting to escape the reality of these various kinds of social suffering, some have taken refuge in even further estrangement: a morbid interest in the "natural order" of the disease, and intellectualization of the misery it brings by way of reducing it all to "statistics." Carried far enough, society (and those within it) can persuade itself that it is at the mercy of atomic movements, anonymous forces, biological processes, about which individuals can do nothing. AIDS is seen then as proliferating by chance; no one is secure; there is little hope and little incentive to act against this impersonal force. Deriddean *difference,* the absurd, the irrational prevails; in the words of Thucydides, describing the characteristics of a plague-ridden society, the people become "indifferent to every rule of religion or law."

The focus of concern in this paper is the suffering of the AIDS victim. There have been many attempts to respond to that suffering, some of which appear to engender or exacerbate it. Members of this Consultation are invited to consider two such medically related responses with a view to reform(ul)ation of them in a wider context. Such consideration may stimulate a more general concern with this aspect of AIDS even as it may further reflection on the general mystery of suffering and appropriate attitudes toward it.

1. *Ought physicians treat persons diseased with AIDS?* One cause of suffering for the AIDS patient will be the rejection, stigmatization, and isolation experienced when physicians[2] refuse to treat

them. Conversely, treatment of such a patient may result not only in alleviation of some symptoms of the disease, but also in alleviation of some of the suffering caused through experience of those symptoms; additionally, the physician's treatment of the AIDS victim may prevent the suffering for the AIDS patient that might be occasioned by refusal to treat. Relative to the focus of suffering and the AIDS patient, the question asked here is related, but not directly on target. Nonetheless, it should be asked, not only because it has bearing on the point, but also because it seems unreasonable to speak about responses to the suffering of such patients if the topic of treatment is not even addressed.

As the beginning of a response to the question asked, there is a more general question: ought physicians treat persons with disease? The answer here can only be affirmative. Presumably, the physician's choice of life work is to treat those who are sick; otherwise, why be a physician? True, many other "reasons" could be proffered: desire for income or status, for example. These achievements rest on the primary work, however; one achieves the income or status of physician as one performs the work of a physician. Overall, in the ordinary use of the language, one expects that physicians treat patients; the treatment role defines "physician."

This view has further foundation on consideration of the implicit contract in force between the medical profession and society. In those terms, only physicians have the "right to treat" (diagnose, prescribe, admit to hospital, etc.); as exercising that "right," physicians are self-regulating. In return for those privileges, society expects the medical profession to commit itself to provision of the medical treatment society needs. The profession as such cannot treat individual patients; the expectation is that individual physicians will treat individual patients.

Those who accept the license to practice are recognized as competent and expected to practice; that is the purpose of the license. Acceptance of the status "doctor" connotes the intention of the person accepting it that the work associated with the status will be undertaken. That work is to treat people who are diseased.

Professionally and legally, it is recognized that the individual physician has the "right to refuse" to accept any person as patient (except in an emergency); if a person is accepted as a patient, the physician is not required to recommend (or provide) treatment contrary to conscience (except in an emergency). Further, it is professionally and legally recognized that once the physician commences treatment of a patient, the physician may not abandon that patient (provision must be made for continuity of treatment); treatment rendered is to be provided without reference to "color, religion, or political belief." The widely recognized need to state these refinements and exceptions merely strengthens the general case made here: as a rule, physicians are expected to treat people who are diseased. If the general understanding were not the rule, what sense is there in speaking of the "right to refuse"?[3]

Overall, then, it seems that physicians are to treat those who have disease. Although there is no requirement that the individual physician justify a refusal to treat, the sense is that such refusal somehow requires justification (i.e., the norm here is "nonrefusal to treat").

If the foregoing is correct, why ask the first, more specific question: ought physicians treat persons diseased with AIDS? Aside from particular situations that might arise with reference to any physician and a person with any disease, why ask particularly about persons diseased with AIDS?

Several concerns of physicians in this regard have already been mentioned: fear of physical contagion, dislike of some AIDS patients' life-style, revulsion in "cooperating with one who has sinned." There is also a sense among physicians that those who cause their own illness should suffer for it, coupled with a concern that valuable resources are wasted in the treatment of such people. A case adapted from material provided by Steinbrook illustrates some physicians' concerns (as well as the source of some of AIDS patients' suffering).

A 43-year-old homosexual male musician was hospitalized for evaluation of weight loss, diarrhea, and lymphadenopathy.

Several nurses refused to care for the patient. Physicians were anxious about contaminating themselves while examining the patient because of his frequent fecal incontinence; some delayed treatment of him because they were uncomfortable

126

with his lifestyle and image; others refused to care for him for "private reasons" (he caused his own grief).

Sigmoidoscopy was done in the operating room after everything was removed from the room except the operating table. Housekeepers would not clean the patient's room or empty the trash. Food workers left meal trays in the hallway. A crisis developed when the patient's toilet became clogged. The employees who fixed the toilet were convinced that they had acquired AIDS. After two weeks, the patient transferred to another hospital.[4]

Speaking only to the physician's uneasiness here, serious conflict arises as between a professional duty to care for patients (who are diseased with AIDS) on the one hand and the dual responsibility for personal well-being (physical, social, self-respect) and prevention of harm to others (family, peers, patients) on the other—in the event the physician contracts AIDS. There is conflict as well between the professional duty to care for patients (with AIDS) and the perceived civic responsibility of the physician-gatekeeper to prevent waste of health care resources.[5] There is further conflict as between the threat to self-integrity if the (general) professional promise is broken and the threat to personal integrity if the physician "cooperates with those who have sinned."[6]

The medical profession has responded to these concerns of physicians by reminding its membership that physicians have a responsibility to "care for their patients with the disease" in virtue of the profession's general contract with society and in view of the individual physician's acceptance of that general commitment on entering the profession. In the light of this reminder, as well as in light of similar statements by the leadership of the profession, it is clear that the fact that a patient is "diseased with AIDS" is not ipso facto justification for a physician's refusal to treat such persons.

There are several other points to be made here in arguing that physicians ought to treat AIDS-diseased persons. First: the "promise to treat" made on joining the profession was not made unilaterally by the individual physician. It was an implicit agreement with society ("I will do what physicians do"); in consideration of it, "license to practice" was given. If the contract is to be

127

abrogated by one party (the physician), due notice should be given to the other party (society), so that there may be consultation as to whether the agreement should remain in place. Second: if physicians are to refuse to treat those diseased with AIDS, what alternatives are there for such victims? If there is general social agreement that such individuals should receive treatment, should physicians perhaps be forced to provide that service? Should special "Pest Doctors" be appointed to care for these patients, as was the case in earlier eras of plague? Should significant others be given "medical license"? Consideration of any of these alternatives will reveal grave consequences for the well-being of patients, for social harmony, and for the general progress of medicine, if they should be adopted.

In the end, resolution of this question will turn on the reasoned priority to be assigned to "professional responsibility to treat" as compared with "personal responsibility to protect self and others" or as compared with "individual pursuit of social justice." Although there may be exceptions in individual cases, the norm for physicians is that those diseased with AIDS should be treated. The various lines of reasoning that converge on this conclusion have been made often and well elsewhere;[7] they will not be repeated here.

All this being said, there is the matter of implementing the reasoned conclusion. On the plane of practice, how can the "fearful physician," for example, carry out the professional responsibility? Such a physician may be convinced that treatment should be given, yet afraid to provide it (possibility of contagion), while also afraid not to provide it (possible loss of peer and self-esteem, possible loss of respect for the profession on the part of the public). Such concern with "doing what one knows to be right" has engendered a growing discussion of courage as applied to physicians' life work. This "excellence" enables the physician to suit action to thought when such action is difficult.

In responding to the question "Ought physicians treat persons diseased with AIDS?" the practice of the affirmative response given here may well lessen the suffering of the AIDS patients who receive such treatment. It will not alleviate all the suffering they experience on account of AIDS; further, in providing such treatment, the physician may suffer. More must be said relative to both matters.

2. *Ought physicians treat those who suffer on account of AIDS?* To ask this question is to query the scope of medical practice; is treatment of those who suffer within the medical mandate? If it is, does that mandate include treatment not only of those who suffer in terms of their disease-based illness, but also those who suffer "on account of AIDS" absent the infection?

Some general comments first about disease/nondisease and about health/illness. Relative to the traditional understanding of medical practice, disease/the disease process is synonymous with pathology in the physical and chemical ordering of the body; such disordering produces bodily change evident to the trained observer. A person is said to have a particular disease on the basis of such bodily evidence as matches an agreed-on physical paradigm for identification of that disease. The person whose body is affected by such a disease may sense no inner or outer dysfunction resulting from the disease; the person may, however, feel bodily or mental discomfort (i.e., pain). When the diseased person does experience such pathology, when the person "connects" the pathology and the symptoms, the person is said to be "ill." Remove consciousness; pain will vanish, as will the more general intellectual experience of illness. By combining the person's report of sensed dysfunction, the person's account of pain or discomfort, and such outwardly observable signs of pathology as may exist (laboratory results, respiratory function, behavior, etc.), the physician makes a clinical diagnosis: the patient is diseased with "X." Depending on the criteria used, a diseased person can thus be "diseased only" or "diseased and ill."

Can one be ill without demonstrable pathology? This raises the difficult question of psychiatric (functional) disturbance as contrasted with the illness that is organically based; that question requires longer discussion best left to another occasion. That being said, certain epiphenomena not associated with identifiable bodily pathology and not recognized as psychiatric disturbance are cited by patients as experienced dysfunction (e.g., the successful businessman still complains of angina after a bypass has greatly improved his coronary circulation; a busy woman experiences occasional incapacitating tension headaches). These might be identified as illnesses on the basis of experience, but such illness is different from that which is pathology-based. Many people seek medical treatment for such illness. By reason of the fact that such health is sought from and given by those medical practitioners requested to provide it, these epiphenomena are seen as within the scope of medical practice.

Differently from disease, differently from a disease, and differently from illness (pathological in origin or existential) there are maladies created by social forces (e.g., the sickness of the terrorist, the disease of the gambler). In many cases the physician is expected to treat those "afflicted" with such malady. By virtue of the physician's agreement to do so, and by virtue of the social expectation that the physician should do so, these, too, are often placed within the scope of medical practice.

To summarize here: disease and disease-based illness may be seen to be within the parameter of medical practice, given a definition of such practice that restricts it to bodily disease and the experience of one who is so diseased. If the definition of medical practice turns on what people do (e.g., seek help for this "problem of living" or assign this "problem of living" to the category of "medicine") or on what physicians do ("treat" illness or malady that is not pathology-based), then, as adding to the current concern for disease and disease-based illness that now defines the limit of medical practice, the scope of medical practice will be quite enlarged (as will the area of competence expected in the practitioner).[8]

What is the place of suffering in such a taxonomy?

Suffering is not disease or illness; it more closely resembles pain, with which it is often confused. Pain is symptomatic of disease or disorder; absent reflection, it arises as direct response to pathological change.[9] Like suffering and illness, pain is present only with consciousness; unlike them, it does not require a self-reflective subject for its existence. Pain may be part of the illness-experience; if it is, and if it is seen as a threat to the integrity of the person, suffering ensues. Pain may be given a meaning quite foreign to the injury that produces suffering, of course; it might be seen as rewarding (e.g., as in the case of childbirth). Pain and suffering are both experienced individually. The former is somewhat predictable, since all people afflicted with the same disease will have similar symptomatic pain. But although all people suffer in the face of an injury that threatens personal integrity, and although some situations seem more injurious in those terms than others, the prediction of suffering is not so accurate as prediction of pain. People's perception of which injury might lead to personal disintegration differs. As related to disease and illness, suffering is more akin to the latter. Its scope exceeds that of illness, since suffering may arise in the absence of illness (disease-based or experiential) and since suffering is experienced more fundamentally than illness. To compare pain, illness, suffering, pain arises because of disease; it may be part of illness (the type that is induced by disease) but need not be (not all pathology causes pain); pain will not characterize the illness that is nonpathology based. As part of pathology-based illness, pain may also be part of the suffering experienced as arising from that illness, but need not be; pain will not be part of the suffering that arises in connection with non-disease-based illness. Pain, suffering, and illness may coexist; they are not identical; they differ in degree and kind.[10]

As noted earlier, medicine's raison d'être is treatment of people with disease; in fulfilling that role, physicians treat not only the underlying disease insofar as that is possible, but also the symptoms of that disease (e.g., pain). They do this in virtue of their educated competence, developed according to a certain view of what medicine is, as well as by reason of their acceptance of the responsibility associated with achievement of that competence. In treating people with disease, physicians often "treat" illness as well as disease and symptoms. They do this indirectly inasmuch as their treatment of the person's diseased body then affects the person's experience (or illness). Some physicians also attempt to treat such disease-based illness directly, out of a conviction that there is unity of person here—as between the one whose body is treated and the one who experiences the bodily disease being treated. In an earlier time a question frequently asked was whether the physician treated the disease or the person (a question asked today by some on the view that medicine's increasing reliance on specialization and technology is depersonalizing medical practice!). The earlier question reflected a mind-set now largely displaced. Instead, the question being asked is, does the physician treat the diseased person or the person who is ill? Most physicians seem to accept responsibility for both: they see the unity of person underlying disease and disease-based illness in the presenting patient; even without acknowledging such unity, they may practice in a way that recognizes this unity implicitly. The issue is whether the physician is competent to provide treatment of that kind. Is the concept of medicine, which accommodates treatment of the ill person within the context of treating that same person as diseased, well accepted by the profession? Is competence in this dual area taught and expected of those who graduate from medical school? There is doubt expressed in the literature on all three counts. At the same time, there are those who argue that ill people *should* be treated by physicians, that the concept of medicine *should* accommodate this kind of treatment as well as treatment of those who are diseased, that this area *should* be one included in the medical curriculum.

If the debate continues with reference to "medical illness," then so much more so with nonmedical illness. In considering whether the physician should treat this type of illness, there is concern for competence again, as well as concern for the greatly widened scope of medical practice this would entail. Should all "illness" be medicalized so that health, not only disease and disease-based illness, will be the responsibility of medical practitioners? In this light, consider the WHO definition of health: "a state of complete physical, mental and social well-being and not merely the absence of disease and infirmity." What will the practice of medicine embrace in those terms; how limit it; what is the work of the nonmedical human services practitioner?

Similar difficulties arise on consideration of treatment of suffering, including AIDS-related suffering. Such suffering may accompany the disease/illness of AIDS; it may accompany existential illness; it may exist quite apart from them. Is the physician able to treat all suffering, AIDS-related and other, some, none? Indirectly, directly? By virtue of education based on a defined scope of medicine? By virtue of public request and physician acquiescence? There are those who argue that the physician should treat those who suffer, those who are ill and those who are diseased. As in the case of illness-treatment, a change in the biomedical model will be required if treatment of suffering is to be included in the scope of medical practice. Even the biological psychological/social model that might enable treat-

132

ment of illness would require alteration if suffering is to be part of the medical mandate. If the physician is to treat any kind of illness or suffering, some argue that the contemporary guiding model for medical practice would require total transformation; others believe that addition only to the prevailing "medical model" is necessary. As Cassel remarks in this context:

> Attempts to understand all the known dimensions of person-hood and their relation to illness and suffering present problems of staggering complexity. The problems are no greater, however, than those initially posed by the question of how the body works—a question we have managed to answer in extraordinary detail.

One might not agree with the comparison made (presuming there is a difference in kind as between disease on the one hand, and illness and suffering on the other), and one might not accept the scale of similarity of difficulty posed. The point, however, is well taken: the education and competence required to treat illness and suffering differ from the education and competence required to treat disease. The model on which education and competence to treat illness and suffering should be based is not firmly in place, although there are advocates for it, and some are trying to practice now according to such a model.

How will this discussion resolve the question: ought physicians treat those who suffer on account of AIDS? There is concern that all those who suffer should somehow be treated. There is pressure to see the medical practitioner as apt to provide such treatment. This pressure exists, since many of those who suffer on account of AIDS suffer in terms of their AIDS disease/illness; if physicians have the mandate to deal with disease generally and with AIDS disease in particular, and if they also (perhaps) have the mandate to deal with illness in general and with AIDS illness in particular, then by "transfer of expertise," why should they not treat the suffering that arises in disease generally and in the case of AIDS particularly? In exerting such pressure it should be noted that the scope of medical practice is widened beyond that now considered acceptable by the profession. The individual practitioner may be convinced that attempted treatment according to the view of underlying patient unity will compensate for lack of competence here or for the gap as between this type of attempted practice and the practice approved according to the profession's model. The question is whether such conviction and its practice will so compensate and whether the profession will see such practice as within its professional mandate. The difficulty is even greater when considering the treatment of those who suffer on account of AIDS, but not because that suffering arises from the AIDS disease/illness.

Ought the physician, then, not attempt to treat the person suffering in terms of having the AIDS disease/illness? Physicians must do what they believe should be done. If they attempt such treatment, however, given lack of professional support and no certain guide for competence, their patients may suffer further. However, the mere effort of the physician to provide treatment may prevent some suffering, as already noted. Should the physician attempt to treat those suffering because of AIDS, but not by reason of being infected with it? Again, the physician should do what the physician believes should be done, but the question of competence and definition of scope of practice remains, even more pressingly.

What, then, is the resolution of this second question? The answer is mixed. Clearly, if suffering is to be the focus of medical treatment (including that suffering "on account of AIDS"), the scope of medical practice must be revised and competence in this area ensured, according to a definition of medical practice that includes specific relation to suffering. Such a definition should make clear whether all suffering or only that suffering which is disease-based is to be the goal of such practice. The current practice in medicine (i.e., attempted treatment of suffering people without standards of definition and competence) may be temporarily acceptable, but it is neither intellectually nor professionally satisfactory. But perhaps treatment of suffering (AIDS-related and other) should be left to nonmedical "specialists in suffering" whose particular work is just that—the prevention and alleviation of such severe distress. This seems to be the view of those who would restrict medical practice to biomedicine: leave non-scientifically based work to those not scientifically trained; "consolation" is not a work for physicians. Again, there may be some other solution, some other approach to suffering that will accommodate a medical expertise with an expertise in ameliorating suffering.

Anwser to the second query: agreed temporarily, but with reservations.

3. *Is the Christian philosophy of suffering a useful paradigm in further development of the medical profession's response to those who suffer on account of AIDS?* The preceding discussion makes clear that physicians can and should treat patients diseased with AIDS. The validity of this view can be established within the context of the medical and social practices now in place. The discussion makes clear as well that medicine (now) lacks the ability to "treat" those suffering on account of AIDS. In terms of the focus of this paper: medical practice can now be of indirect assistance regarding such suffering as it offers treatment for disease; medical practice is not (now) coextensive with ameliora- tion of such suffering (or other suffering) so far as the usual medical modalities are concerned.

Debate as to whether such coextensiveness can or should be established will not likely be concluded for some little time. In the interim some practitioners will continue in their attempt to work with such suffering people. As important to the debate mentioned, and as conceptual grounding for such attempted amelioration of the AIDS-diseased person's suffering, some con- sideration must be given to a foundational philosophy of suffer- ing. The need here is philosophic, not medical; it will involve discussion of the essential meaning and place of suffering in all human living, a subject beyond the purview of disciplinary medi- cine. Once such a philosophy of suffering is in place, medicine can draw from it whatever is appropriate to medical practice as regards any "treatment" of suffering patients, whether they are suffering as AIDS-diseased, or by reason of some other cause.

One such philosophy of suffering is that developed within the Christian tradition. The parameters for this "philosophy" are given by theologians; development of that "philosophy" is a matter for theologians and philosophers together.

In this particular context, all human living is seen as God- related; each person is equal before God and each person is loved by God. Disease and suffering take on a dimension beyond

135

time and matter here; their cause is seen to be alienation from God by way of sin ("If you will diligently hearken to the voice of the Lord your God . . . I will put none of the diseases upon you which I put upon the Egyptians [Exod. 15:26]"; "There is no health in my bones because of my sin [Ps. 38:3]"). This alienation is common to all human beings, and all, including the "innocent," suffer on its account (Job was "blameless, upright, fearing God and turning away from evil"). Jesus who was "without sin" took suffering on himself when he could have done otherwise, and wanted to do otherwise; who shall escape it? Theologians view suffering as central in this tradition, for without it there is no salvation. Human living parallels the human living of Jesus in this respect. Like Jesus, those who suffer are to have faith and trust in God's love; with Jesus, they will overcome suffering and death (the consequences of sin's alienation) in resurrection ("the light shines in the darkness, and the darkness has not overcome it [John 1:1–5])". The tradition's response to those who suffer is one of compassion (Job's companions stayed with him a long time; the good Samaritan took pity on the stranger; "if one member suffers, all together suffer [1 Cor. 12:26]"); in attempting to alleviate the suffering of another, one finds Christ ("Whatever you did for them, you did for me" [see Matthew 25:31–46]). True relief of suffering comes not by way of physical or mental attention only, but in terms of spiritual healing ("I acknowledged my sin to thee, and I did not hide my iniquity . . . then thou didst forgive the guilt of my sin [Ps. 32:3–5]"; Jesus first forgave his sin and then [thereby?] cured the man with paralysis [see Matthew 2:1–12]).

Reflecting on this approach, those within and those outside the tradition might ask, why has God allowed suffering? Surely, it could have been avoided in the divine plan? With J.S. Mill, the nineteenth-century philosopher, one might observe: "If God is able to prevent evil and does not, He is not good; if He would prevent evil and cannot, He is not almighty." For many, suffering has been a stumbling block by reason of which God is rejected; others see it as an opening to faith in God and trust in God's love. Christians do not profess to understand suffering; they are not required to seek it out. For them suffering is essentially a mystery. At the same time, their reflection on it in the context described enables them to give meaning to suffering, and helps them to develop some capability of response to it.

How might this paradigm be useful to those who work with suffering people? One troubling aspect of suffering is its apparent lack of meaning. As noted, the Christian tradition accommodates that concern, if not in ultimate explanation of why suffering exists, at least in its teaching as to its value. Further, the tradition gives special recognition to the encounter between practitioner and the one who suffers: this is an opportunity to meet Christ.[11] Respect is to be shown to all who suffer, as is compassion; all share in suffering and all are equal in their need for comfort in enduring it. Because suffering is a consequence of general and particular alienation from God, its "treatment" must be more than materially and temporarily directed. These are helpful, but unless "healing" is part of any therapeutic maneuver, relief of suffering cannot be achieved.[12] Given the supernatural dimension in which this tradition views human living and suffering, it follows that genuine relief of suffering is a matter beyond human capability and experience. Human intervention may be of assistance, and human competence is certainly required in helping to relieve suffering, but true healing is within the scope of divine activity only. Those who respond to victims of suffering cannot thus sustain their activity by way of their natural resources only; a continually renewed vision of the supernatural dimension is required, as is continuing recourse to God for the grace and courage to persevere in this work.

With specific reference to those who suffer on account of AIDS, what is the Christian response to be? First, and most generally, it must come in three areas: that of church, that of the medical profession, and that of the individual. Churches must give public institutional witness to their Christian heritage in terms of their statements and their activity vis-à-vis AIDS-related suffering. In this connection, the United Church of Canada has prepared a useful document, "Statement on AIDS." It calls specific attention to the respect to be shown to those with AIDS; it speaks more generally to the need to develop social policy and planned institutional capability in regard of care for these persons.[13] The Roman Catholic group has also shown leadership in providing fiscal resources to meet the needs of AIDS patients

137

(i.e., in building and staffing hospices for their care). Those within the medical profession must reflect their Christian outlook in the respect they demonstrate when attending these patients. If the encounter with the AIDS patient is an encounter with Christ, the practitioner will not retreat from it, but bring to it a high level of skill and compassion. Recognizing that relief of such suffering is beyond medical competence, the practitioner will still do what can be humanly done to the limit of ability. Persons who suffer on account of AIDS may draw some comfort from this philosophy of suffering. It provides a context for it as well as some hope for relief from it when borne prayerfully in faith and trust. Those not suffering from AIDS but assisting those who do will find steady direction in this approach: AIDS sufferers are to be respected, encouraged, and assisted as fellow creatures of God and coheirs of Jesus' triumph over suffering.

All this being said in the philosophical vein, there are many very real problems encountered as an attempt is made to put this philosophy of suffering into practice. Four are mentioned here for purposes of discussion and reflection, not resolution.

The first is the obvious and general one: of what use is this paradigm with colleagues and patients who do not accept its inspiration or find its elaboration meaningful (e.g., non-Christians)? Can the paradigm minus its "Christianity" be effective? How would it be defended; how would it work? Would the fact of its Christian derivation render it suspect were that generally known? Or is the basis for cooperation here to be found in some implications of the philosophy, set aside its foundation?

Second, what practical effect will this philosophy have for the AIDS victim or the others who suffer "on account of AIDS"? Can it actually make suffering bearable? Can it prevent despair? Will it change the attitudes of those working well with diseased patients, but not with those who are AIDS-diseased? If it be agreed that it will be effective as it is adopted, how is it to be known, and how motivate toward adoption of it? Or perhaps it is sufficient that the view has been articulated?

The third query concerns healing and its relation to medical practice, both with reference to those patients who suffer the disease of AIDS and those who suffer on other accounts. Healing is evidently central to suffering here; its "scope of practice" is "spiritual life." Healing of the spirit may be an activity more akin to the work of the minister of religion than to that of the physician, but it is certainly not limited to ministers so far as practice goes. Beyond medical practice and in society more generally, for example, people assist in healing when they work for justice regarding housing for AIDS victims or when they attempt to foster community tolerance of the neighborhood AIDS hospice. Within the scope of medical practice more particularly, however, how is the physician to assist in healing? If healing is more fundamental to the well-being of the patient than medical practice, will there be competition betweeen them?[14] If God will do all the healing, why bother with medical practice?

A fourth query concerns the assumed unity of person within the tradition discussed. Presumably, all aspects of the one person should be in harmony if true relief from suffering is to take place. This is a point made long ago by Plato in *Charmides;* it is a point made in contemporary theological discussion by Tillich (who speaks of "unhealthy health" if one aspect of person is "made better" and the others not).[15] Currently, many see patients as "fractured": noncoordinated specialization in services offered is responsible for that. If assistance toward healing is required for each facet of the patient's personality, will some overall "audit" ensure that it is done? Will each specialist within medicine and each of the other health care practitioners concerned with a patient be required to assist in healing, or will there be some further specialist named in this area? How prepare for this activity; is "healing" a subject to be learned? Is there a "healing" specific to medicine and another to nursing, or is this a personal competence extended by the person concerned with each of these areas? Overall, as the physician is ultimately responsible for patient "treatment," is the physician "one among many" healers, or "captain of the team" of healers?

The challenge of AIDS-related suffering arises not only among patients and those of significance to them, not only among practitioners and public generally, but in setting the paradigms for thinking about such suffering. In the end, thought is reflected in action. The reflection of this Consultation on this subject will thus be of inestimable value in helping all those who suffer "on account of" AIDS.

Notes

1. Generally, see E.J. Cassel, "The Nature of Suffering and the Goals of Medicine," *New England Journal of Medicine* 306: 639–45, 1982.
2. Other health care practitioners could be mentioned here; discussion is confined to physicians for reasons of brevity.
3. Compare the physician's "right to refuse" with the disciplinary sanction in force for those other health care workers who "refuse to treat."
4. R. Steinbrook et al., "Ethical Dilemmas in Caring for Patients with the Acquired Immunodeficiency Syndrome," *Annals of Internal Medicine* 103: 787–90, 1985.
5. A quote from the medical columnist Gifford-Jones: "Will the public question cost of AIDS? . . . Perhaps there are some who might suggest it would be helpful if we didn't work so hard to pay for care of those many homosexuals with AIDS who simply refuse to change their sexual habits. Their attitude is to live it up until they die. Drug addicts continue to shoot themselves full of dope using contaminated needles and syringes. Then, when they develop AIDS, they expect taxpayers to spend millions of dollars for their sympathetic medical care. I predict that society will soon rebel at financing a medical problem that is largely a self-inflicted disease."

   Further questions for consideration: In a publicly financed health services delivery system, is it the role of the individual physician to determine the public's priority in this matter. How is self-caused disease to be defined and identified? What constitutes "waste" as contrasted with "good use" and how ensure that monies "not wasted" are really attached to "good projects"?
6. In this connection, consider that comment of a physician concerning treatment of a patient with venereal disease some years ago: "You have had the disease one year and I hope it may plague you many more to punish you for your sins, for I would not think of treating you."
7. Cf. E. Shelp, "Courage: A Neglected Virtue in the Patient-Physician Relationship," *Social Science and Medicine* 18: 351–61, 1984. See also E. Loewy, "Duties, Fears and Physicians," *Social Science and Medicine* 22: 1363–66, 1986.
8. Generally, see P. Morgan, "Diseases and the Scope of Medical Practice," *Canadian Medical Association Journal* 135: 835–55, 1986; Dr. Jennings, "The Confusion Between Disease and Illness in Clinical Medicine," ibid., pp. 865–70; D. Stalker and C. Glymour, ed., *Examining Holistic Medicine* (Buffalo, NY: Prometheus Books,

1985); especially C. Glymour and D. Stalker, "Engineers, Cranks, Physicians, Magicians," pp. 21–28.

9. Leave aside the question of "psychiatric pain."

10. Generally, see Cassel. See also I. McWhinney, "Are We on the Brink of a Major Transformation of Clinical Method?" *Canadian Medical Association Journal* 35: 873–78, 1986.

11. R.A. McCormick, "Theology and Bioethics: Christian foundations," *Theology and Bioethics,* ed. Earl Shelp (Dordrecht: D. Reidel Pub. Co., 1985), pp. 95–114.

12. P. Tillich, "The Meaning of Health," *The Meaning of Health,* ed. Perry LeFevre (Chicago: Exploration Press, 1984), pp. 100–15.

13. Of particular interest in this statement is the comment "We affirm that the Christian conviction that God loves and cares for all people includes persons with AIDS and we reject the argument made by some that AIDS is God's punishment for homosexuals." The distinction between what some perceive as wrongdoing here, and the wrongdoer, might be worthy of further discussion in the group.

14. Generally, cf. S. Hauerwas, "Salvation and Health: Why Medicine Needs the Church," *Theology and Bioethics,* pp. 205–24.

15. Cf. note 12.

10

AIDS: Ethics and Theology at the Bedside

Dr. David J. Roy

We were just gay—and now we're human.
—Quoted in the CBC program
AIDS and the Arts

We are all passengers together on the spaceship earth.
—Dr. Halfdan Mahler, WHO

Love resurrected them; the heart of one contained
infinite sources of life for the other.
—F. Dostoyevsky, *Crime and Punishment*

An old Spanish proverb has God saying: "Take what you want—but pay for it." AIDS and death equal the wages of sin and sexual disorder? So would some interpret the meaning and reality of our late twentieth century epidemic: the collapse of the body's defenses and the ensuing loss of health and life are consequences of immoral behavior. One could pyramid quotations that carry this interpretation—expressed succinctly by Cardinal Basil Hume, the archbishop of Westminster.

AIDS is but one of the many disastrous consequences of promiscuous sexual behaviour. Promiscuity is the root cause of the present epidemic. It has always been sinful; it is rapidly becoming suicidal. We are, then, dealing with an intrinsically moral issue and not simply one of public health. No campaign against Aids can ignore or trivialize the moral question.[1]

The prescription following on this cause-effect observation is conversion! An immediate transformation of attitudes and behavior in sexual relations offers, according to the cardinal, a third way, an alternative to a binary fixation on condoms or contagion. Conversion means a refusal to enter sexual relations outside marriage. The self-discipline this requires is demanding, although not impossible.

Although this position cuts across the three streams of discussion set up to divide the labor of our Consultation, I take it as a starting point for my mandate: *focus* on illness and health; *begin* with clinical reality to *identify* ethical issues; *lead* from ethical issues to relevant theological considerations; *design* the paper to launch discussion; *do not attempt* a comprehensive ethical analysis, but *select* the ethical issues that most clearly reveal a theological problem.

My Initial and Unresolved Malaise

I am uneasy with the organizer's insistence that I lead from a clinical-ethical discussion of AIDS to a discussion of theological issues. I should not be uneasy because there is a link between *ethos, morality,* and *ethics* in the analysis and resolution of any conflict or uncertainty centering on values and responsibilities.

An *ethos* comprises our governing perceptions, beliefs, and assumptions—often incompletely conceptualized and incompetently articulated—about the status, destiny, and meanings of life and various human experiences, or about the purposes and roles of society's various institutions in maintaining human community. An ethos is a foundation of moral life. It partially determines a hierarchy of values. We often do differ quite sharply about what is of greater or lesser importance, even if we are not always to say clearly why we differ. The conflict then is on the level of *morality,* a conflict about which values may be sacrificed, which not, when all cannot be respected or achieved. *Ethics* works out the judgments and compromises that have to be made when individuals or communities in a pluralistic society clash on the levels of ethos and morality. Such judgments are required, even within a morally homogeneous community, when a moral tradition confronts new and unforeseen constraints on the real possibilities available to people.

My malaise centers on the fact that effective safeguards of public health require a sympathetic accommodation with homosexuals and drug addicts. An editorial in *Nature* took this reality as the basis for a plea to "keep politics out of AIDS." I take it as a reason to ask about "keeping religion out of AIDS," *if* religion means moralizing resistance to the minimal effective means currently available to reduce the spread of HIV infection.

There is another dimension to my malaise. Effective care of persons with AIDS demands much more than a simple sympathetic accommodation with persons engaged in activities many find morally degenerate. It requires the capacity to transcend these behaviors, to grasp that an AIDS person's identity and dignity are so much greater than any behavioral preference or activity we or others may morally reject. This care for persons, who frequently are stripped of all defenses and all outward symbols of dignity, requires the ability—in a sense to be described below—to mediate the experience of God. My malaise is that religious moralizing and a perfervid commitment to principles blinds one to persons and sets up a static so violent as to swamp all frequencies for sensitive and suffering presence to, and effective communication with, AIDS patients.

I am uneasy with the mandate to raise theological considerations because I sense, initially at least, that theologizing is as counterproductive as moralizing when we face three central challenges of HIV infection and AIDS:

1. how to reduce the spread of HIV infection effectively;
2. how to counsel and support those who must now live as HIV carriers;
3. how to achieve solidarity with those who must die bereft of the normal buttresses of hope.

To burrow the first step in the Thomistic analysis of a Quaestio, I face a *videtur quod non*: it seems that theological considerations have little effective to offer in meeting the basic challenges of HIV infection and AIDS. Let's see if I, in this presentation, and we, in this consultation, can develop the lines of a *sed contra*.

At the Bedside: Clinical Ethics

Some of the most sensitive and poignant ethical dilemmas occur at the bedside of those entering the final stages of HIV disease. These are challenges to *clinical ethics*. Protecting others from being infected unknowingly may require that a clinician break the confidentiality of relationship to a patient who is sexually irresponsible. The code of *professional ethics* may clash with the concerns of *social ethics*. The physician may clash with the clinical investigator and researcher—and this conflict may be within the one and same person—when the strategy for mastering the disease conflicts with the commitment to do everything possible for an individual patient. The values to be achieved, and those to be protected, in research with human beings brings AIDS to the center of *research ethics*. Preventing or reducing the spread of HIV infection is a goal of public health. Proposals to institute screening programs, and policies on reporting, raise issues of *epidemiological ethics* and in the *ethics of public health*. Three modes of HIV transmission—sexual behavior, IV drug use, and maternal transmission to fetus or child—offer foci for controversy in *moral theology or religious ethics*.

To respect the constraints of my mandate. I shall restrict my attention to certain issues of clinical ethics that have theological implications.

First, a word on the method of clinical ethics. Value conflicts at the bedside frequently arise from uncertainty about how best to care for the gravely ill and dying when available treatments affect patients' clinical needs and total life interests in quite different ways. The key question of clinical ethics is, how can we help *this person* live or die in a way that honors his or her dignity, and ours as well?

Utilization of the patient as a battlefield for contending moral persuasions and traditions totally undermines the method of clinical ethics. This method centers on the patient as the primary norm for the resolution of uncertainties and differences of view about treatment options. The patient's biography—his or her

145

clinical course, relationships, beliefs, life plans, and total-life interests—constitute this primary norm. The skillful use of it requires the most accurate possible description of the patient. The results of laboratory tests and diagnostic imaging show only part of the whole patient. The maxim of clinical ethics is, each case contains its own resolution. Understand the patient as comprehensively as possible, and the balance of elements required to resolve the ethical dilemma or conflict will emerge.

The ethical uncertainties, issues, and dilemmas of modern medicine are inextricably bound up with the unique circumstances of particular cases. Although general propositions and principles define moral perimeters, they do not of themselves decide concrete cases. The specific norms required for such cases are not prefabricated and available for deductive application; they have to be constructed slowly and inductively from discriminating judgments about individual patients and the unique problems of specific clinical trials. Without such norms, general principles remain mute about what they command, prohibit, or permit.

This, then, is the situation of ethics in clinical practice and research. General principles need the resolving power of specific norms to focus on the detail of individual cases. The norms are designed inductively from ethical judgments constructed to fit these cases as equitably as possible. The construction of practical judgments, rather than arguments, is essentially interdisciplinary work. Case reasoning, which constitutes a return to a method of moral thinking favored by leading minds in ancient Greece and in medieval times, has helped medicine to extricate ethics from the deadlock of interminable discourse about matters on which people are likely never to agree.

Each clinical case, particularly those involving life-death decisions, brings thousands of years of cultural and moral tradition to bear on this particular human crisis. The principles of the great philosophers, the moral traditions of medicine and the world's religions, and the moral common sense of preceding generations pass more or less clearly through the prism of a small circle of minds gathered around this patient to illuminate the one governing question of the moment: how can we help *this person* live or die in a way that honors his or her dignity and ours as well?

146

Issues of Clinical Ethics

Autonomy. If confusion, the brainwashing influence of other people, and pathologic depression can be excluded, many would hold to Dr. Ned Cassem's principle that "the will of the patient, not the health of the patient, should be the supreme law" governing decisions about initiating or discontinuing life-prolongation measures.[2]

This clear and reasonable principle may conflict sharply with strongly held clinical perceptions and certain dominant values in our culture. We increasingly give public support to patient autonomy and the value of self-determination against the potential abuse of medical technology. However, we do not always find it easy to live according to the same categories in which we think. People can generally agree on the justification of abandoning life-prolonging procedures when a patient's loss of consciousness is irreversible. Many, however, experience a strong visceral opposition to discontinuing or withholding life-prolongation treatment—whether this be respiratory support, chemotherapy, or total parenteral nutrition—from an intelligent, conscious, and lucid patient.

This spontaneous opposition may be reinforced by bonds to the patient forged during the earlier fight for life. Decisive and distressed family members may intensify the difficulty of respecting a patient's refusal of life support. Moreover, one may wonder if a patient's refusal of life support is not tantamount to suicide. And if it is, should such a refusal always be opposed? Of course, we have come to define death in terms of neurological criteria. How difficult it can be to withhold or stop life-prolonging treatment when this is seen as equivalent to destroying a perfectly functioning brain. Is a professional ever justified in collaborating with a request to do that?

In other situations, perhaps particularly in the case of AIDS patients entering the irreversibly terminal phase of their illnesses, one may be tempted to oppose insistent patient requests for aggressive treatment. Decisions about initiating or continuing aggressive life-sustaining procedures may be difficult when patients are anxious and have unrealistic expectations about the power of these procedures. When physicians judge aggressive life-sustaining treatment to be futile, decisions may be difficult if a patient's persistent demands for treatment are not properly interpreted.

An AIDS patient requesting that "everything possible be done" may mean just that. We may then ask if a physician is ethically justified in unilaterally refusing to administer treatment he or she judges to be futile. However, the AIDS patient may be using these words to express a fear of being abandoned rather than to really insist on the use of a particular intensive care procedure or medical device. The question then is, how can we be effectively present to such patients when the medical instrumentarium has reached the limits of its usefulness? To this question we return below.

Proportionality. The proportionality principle, expressed and strongly supported in the Canadian Law Reform Commission's recommendation that the criminal code not bind physicians to administer therapeutically useless treatments or treatments in conflict with a patient's best interests,[3] is widely known and theoretically uncontroversial. The Vatican Declaration on Euthanasia supports both the principle of self-determination and proportionality ethics with its observation that

> One cannot impose on anyone the obligation to have recourse to a technique which is already in use but carries a risk or is burdensome. Such a refusal is not the equivalent of suicide; on the contrary, it should be considered as an acceptance of the human condition, or a wish to void the application of a medical procedure disproportionate to the results that can be expected, or a desire not to impose excessive expenses on the family or the community.[4]

Some who have little difficulty in accepting proportionality ethics as a basis for stopping respirators or chemotherapy balk at discontinuing such a basic support as nutrition. Although many would accept that the ultimate aim of total parenteral nutrition "is to prolong meaningful life, and not to prolong the process of an inevitable death,"[5] others hold to the conviction that "for willful starvation there can be no excuse."[6]

Feeding is surely a powerful symbolic expression of human solidarity. Nevertheless, appellate courts in three states of the

148

United States have recently agreed that there is no legal difference between artificial feeding and any other medical treatment.[7] Proportionality ethics should work for artificial feeding as well as it does for respirators and chemotherapy. Yet, if stopping treatment, in clinically similar conditions, is *ethically* no different from never starting it,[8] this may not easily be reconciled with feelings and perceptions. They may differ regarding initiation and discontinuance of treatment from the principle described. The "executioner perception" should not be simply brushed aside. Physicians, and others as well, may experience an intolerable discord between a principled justification for discontinuing life-prolonging treatment and the personal perception that one has become a killer in so doing.

Dominion. The film *Breaker Morant* demonstrated the thesis that, in war, situations arise that fall outside all existing rules. Similar situations seem to arise from time to time in caring for the terminally ill. If decisions to stop all life-prolonging treatment and to allow "nature to take its course" are morally and legally justifiable, should not society, as Dr. John Freeman asked more than ten years ago, allow physicians to help nature take its course—quickly?[9]

How is such a question to be answered? By measuring the proportion of benefits to damages? The focus then would be on the patient. If the patient is bound to die, given the irreversibility of a lethal disease and the rightness of a decision not to intervene to prolong life, of what good to the patient, family or anyone is an interim period of slow decline into death? Why should patients, families, and care-givers be bound passively to await death?

Do we answer the question by considering long-term consequences? Here the focus would be on the medical profession and society. Should a society give such power to doctors, or to any profession? There are many kinds of suffering, and there are sufferers of all ages. If we justify active euthanasia for some patients on the grounds of mercy, is it possible to establish generally acceptable and nonarbitrary limits to the putative medical mandate to shorten "useless dying curves" by direct termination of life? Do we try this as an experiment, and closely

149

monitor what happens? Or do we, in the fear that "things might get out of hand," arbitrarily decree that no one, doctors included, is ever morally justified in terminating a patient's life?

Some, many perhaps, would argue that such a decree is not arbitrary. It is simply the expression of the most basic of all principles: that no human being has dominion over the life of another. Dominion claimed and dominion exercised over the life of another human being is not dominion justified. Judges, philosophers, and religious leaders have reiterated their principle in various ways over the ages.

That fact, however, does not silence the questions. How do we know that this principle should hold, and should hold without exception? How can the constraint of the dominion principle be justified, when the act it prohibits, active euthanasia, appears, in some circumstances, desirable from every empirical point of view, and is, in fact, desired by everyone involved in a particular case? Is the authority of reason able to resolve this most important of our ethical questions, or does the dominion principle and its prohibition of active euthanasia rest rather on a belief?

Some AIDS patients have taken their own lives. The general rule regarding suicide attempts is, don't aid and abet such attempts and attempt resuscitation of those who have tried to kill themselves. However, should attempts always be made to resuscitate persons with AIDS who have tried to take their own lives? Does it make clinical or ethical sense to resuscitate AIDS patients who have attempted suicide out of deep depression and existential emptiness, patients who are destined to die in a short time? Does the act of resuscitation not entail a correlative duty to follow up with a personal presence that counters the isolation and emptiness that motivated the suicide attempt? And if we cannot offer that presence? Do we resuscitate these patients only to leave them suffer through several more weeks or months of anguish? Is suicide sometimes a rational act, the expression of a liberty and dominion over one's self that others should respect?

Mastering the disease. Many other ethical issues arise in the care and treatment of seropositive persons and persons with AIDS.

Physicians who are also clinical investigators face an ethical challenge in selecting patients for admission to research protocols that offer access to potentially life-prolonging innovative therapies. How does one ethically select patients when many request such admission, when only certain patients can be selected, given the needs of the research protocol, and when refusal may mean death earlier than might have been necessary?

Indiscriminate admission of patients to unproved therapies is not ethically more acceptable than selective acceptance of patients into controlled studies that will produce reliable knowledge about the true power of a new therapy. The common good requires that we expend every effort to master a lethal and epidemic disease. However, this conviction does not dissolve the apprehension physician-clinical investigators may have that perhaps less than the "best possible" has been done for a number of particular patients.

Trust and confidentiality. There are few acceptable exceptions to a physician's duty to keep confidential the information she or he has received about a person's body, life, and secrets in the course of diagnosis and treatment. Fidelity, along with lucidity, autonomy, and humanity, is a moral foundation of a physician's relations with patients. Patient trust in physician confidentiality is essential for treatment and healing and, given the stigma and discrimination associated with seropositivity and AIDS, is equally important for effective surveillance of this epidemic and the prevention of the spread of HIV infection.

However, when a physician's patient is sexually irresponsible or blinded by psychological denial and places the health and lives of others in danger, is a physician justified in disclosing confidential information? Surely not always! But when the physician is the only one, other than the recalcitrant patient, who possesses the knowledge needed to protect others from an unsuspected danger of an almost certain personal disaster?

AIDS: A Matter of Theology?

I take up the *videtur quod non* sketched in the opening pages of this paper. It would seem to me that most of the clinical-ethical issues arising at the bedside can be most effectively resolved without explicit appeal to theological considerations. People of widely disparate philosophical and religious backgrounds can generally come to agree on what is best for a particular patient, if the patient, as described above, is taken as the norm. Dissension and controversy become most acute when these same people articulate too explicitly the deep reasons for an ethical consensus. Fundamental assumptions, perceptions, and beliefs set the ground for a conceptual and linguistic Babel and invite interminable controversy.

Ethics and anamnesis. One identifiable challenge to theology, and one of its functions, emerges in the face of what Bernard Lonergan has called the problem of liberation. The problem of liberation arises from an incapacity for sustained development. Sustaining development is a process of transcendence. Transcendence occurs with the recurrence of the dynamic structure expressed in the transcendental imperatives: be attentive, be intelligent, be reflective, be responsible, be consistent, be loving.

The problem of liberation occurs when this structure fails to recur. On one level the problem appears as a "succession of ever less comprehensive viewpoints." On this level the solution "has to be the attainment of a higher viewpoint." On another level the problem appears as a breakdown of communication. How could it be otherwise? On the level of the mind, transcendence occurs when an unconditioned is grasped. On the level of human living transcendence occurs when an unconditioned is realized, made real. Human communication reaches its full scope in such an achievement, the achievement of unconditioned acceptance and unconditioned gift. However, when one can or will no longer grasp the unconditional in the level of the mind, how can one achieve the unconditional in human living? So on this level the solution to the problem of liberation "has to be a still higher integration of human living."

The decisive insight, however, defines the order governing higher viewpoint and higher integration within the solution to the problem of liberation: "The needed higher viewpoint is a concrete possibility only as a consequence of an actual higher integration."[10]

If such an integration has occurred as a historical event, then appeal to that event and the elaboration of codes, guidelines, and policies in the light of that event is as much a function of ethics as is the interpretation and application of ancient and recent documents on principles, values, and responsibilities. Christians believe that the life, death, and resurrection of Jesus Christ is the historical communication that all human beings are unconditionally affirmed and accepted by the Unconditioned. The appropriation of this historical communication of unconditioned acceptance is anamnesis. The *challenge to theology* is to articulate this anamnesis in ways that promote the emergence of higher viewpoints as the framework for ethical decisions, choices, and policies. The *challenge to the religions* is to create and realize events of community and presence that exemplify the higher integration of human beings as a fact in society and history.

Theology and suffering. I cannot recall the name of the author of the cry, this is pain! To think, to speak, to love, and yet—to have to die! The words capture the truth that the time of dying is a time for questions that shake the foundation of one's existence and threaten to expose the emptiness of one's most encompassing dreams. These questions may be only sensed, vaguely and anxiously, or they may be lucidly faced in all their starkness. They are the expression, whatever the form they take, of the profound suffering human beings experience in the face of impending disintegration or destruction. These are the questions of broken experience and the experience of being broken.

Of the many elements in the *phenomenology of suffering*, I shall highlight guilt. *Guilt* involves many things, but among all these it expresses a gap between what I am and what I could have been. We usually think of guilt in terms of something we have done. We have harmed this particular person, broken this particular commandment. We have *done* something or *failed to do* something and this, traditionally, is where guilt enters our consciousness. That is "everyday guilt." Another dimension of guilt, *existential guilt*, finds its locus of expression at the end of things, when I have no time left. It is the most profound guilt, really, because it deals not just with a limited domain of something we have done, but with the whole-person domain of what we have failed to become. This is the crushing experience, the realization: "I could have been . . ."—but I have no more time, no more opportunities.

This experience is always unique. Each person is distinctive, individuated, profoundly different from everyone else. So also is each person's suffering. Memories, lost opportunities, guilts, dated moments of hurt or betrayal, the fragility of one's most unforgettable loves and joys, and unfulfilled dreams all are as unique as the days, times, places, and people to which they are bound. Suffering is the message between the unwritten lines of a singular personal biography.

Grasping the individual form and content of each person's suffering can be attained, if at all, only within the subject-to-subject frame of reference. We cannot enter the inner sanctum of a personal history with a white coat, a mantle of professional authority, or a mask of dispassionate scientific objectivity. One enters with one's personal self, or not at all.

A knowledge of the nature of suffering will help us to be compassionate, but we need to suffer with another person to attain that unique kind of individual knowledge of a suffering person that permits us to join hands with another human being at the crossroads of our greatest vulnerability.

John Donne was right. Entering into the suffering of another reveals to me the plight I share with everyone facing the threat of disintegration. The trust and identification required for the individualized knowledge of another person's suffering also open windows onto the communication of hope. The challenge is to touch, awaken, and release the saving power of another's latent beliefs. Then perhaps each suffering person may find the strength to carry his vulnerability like "a pine in solitude cradling a dove."[11]

However, can one really carry existential guilt as a pine in *solitude* cradles a dove? Terminal illness intensified existential guilt with its threat of disintegration, a threat the poet G.M. Hopkins described as the untwisting of "these last strands of man in me." Compassion does bring its own special knowledge and may reveal the solitude of suffering to be an illusion. Yet how can anyone help a dying person, a young dying person with AIDS whose life is untwisting before his or her very eyes, to hold so together as to say with the poet: "I'll not despair, . . . not untwist, slack they may be, these last strands of man in me"?[12]

Suffering of the profound sort we are talking about here cannot be borne by me or by anyone alone. One can be drugged or distracted, but to face consciously the threat of impending disintegration and the eternity of the gap between what I am and what I could or even should have become? How can I or anyone do that alone?

Recall at this point that the revelation of God in Jesus Christ was never, and could never have been, directed to one human being alone. That revelation, that the Unconditioned accepts and affirms every person, unconditionally, needs a community, generations and generations of communities of human beings, to attain its full historical realization. Only such a community can carry God's revelation, and only such a community can carry the threat of impending disintegration and the internal personal split of existential guilt. What will such a community answer to the question, can existential guilt be forgiven?

So, the challenge, if that is the word, we face in the presence of those who suffer so deeply is in the poet Matthew Arnold's reminder: "Such a price/The Gods exact for song—/That we become what we sing." Only people who "become the song"— and there are many versions of the song—can activate in another the tremendous forces of the human spirit required to counter the emptying echo of the cry, This is pain! To think, to speak, to love, and yet—to have to die!

In André Gide's *Symphonie Pastorale,* a pastor is trying to bring a blind girl to some kind of understanding of color. He attempts to do this by correlating differences in sound. He uses the girl's experience of sound to mediate for her some kind of experience of color. After the pastor's efforts during the concert at Neuchatel, Gertrude had no more of a sensation of color and light than before the concert. But the *sounds had changed.* The same sounds acquired a totally new meaning. They were no longer the same sounds.

Mediating the experience of God to those who are experiencing an untwisting of the last strands of life in themselves demands effective communication of the experience of unbounded presence. It means mobilizing in another the forces of the spirit required to do the most difficult of human acts: to hope. Theology alone cannot do that. Only a person or a community of people can do that—if and only if their hearts contain infinite sources of life for others. When that communication is achieved, suffering people still suffer and they still die. But they are not the same people any more. They die ahead of themselves, "yonder, yonder," as G.M. Hopkins has said, not "under" the crushing suppression of utter aloneness and the finality of incompletion.

If people who claim to believe in God's self-communication in Jesus Christ cannot help persons with AIDS, and others who must face death, to die in this way, then I really see little place for theology and religion in AIDS. It would be better then to keep religion out of AIDS.

Notes

1. Basil Hume "AIDS: Time for a Moral Renaissance," *The Times*, January 7, 1987, p. 10.
2. N. Cassem, "When Illness Is Judged Irreversible: Imperative and Elective Treatments," *Man and Medicine* 5:154, 1980.
3. Law Reform Commission of Canada, *Euthanasia, Aiding Suicide, and Cessation of Treatment* (Ottawa, Minister of Supply and Services Canada, 1983): p. 32.
4. Vatican Congregation for the Doctrine of the Faith, *Declaration on Euthanasia*, Rome, 1980:9–10.
5. G.S. Cowan and W. Scheetz, *Intravenous Hyperalimentation* (Philadelphia: Lea & Febiger, 1972), p. 112.
6. G.E.M. Anscombe, "Ethical Problems in the Management of Some Severely Handicapped Children: Commentary," *Journal of Medical Ethics* 7:122, 1981.
7. G. Annas, "Fashion and Freedom: When Artificial Feeding Should Be Withdrawn," *American Journal of Public Health* 75:685–688, 1985.
8. Cassem, p. 154.
9. J. Freeman, "Is There a Right to Die Quickly?" *Journal of Pediatrics* 80:905, 1972.
10. All statements in quotation marks in the two paragraphs ending with this reference number are from B. Lonergan, *Insight. A Study of Human Understanding* (New York: Longman, 1958), pp. 231, 234, 632, 633.
11. E. Thomas, *Collected Poems* (London: Faber & Faber Ltd., 1969), p. 187.
12. W.H. Gardner, and N.H. MacKenzie, eds., *The Poems of Gerard Manley Hopkins*, 4th ed. (Oxford: Oxford University Press, 1970), p. 99.

11

Report from "Illness and Health" Stream

We have begun grappling with the theological and ethical issues related to the meaning of illness and health in the AIDS crisis. As a diverse group including clergy, laity, and health and social workers, we believe that our discussions brought increased clarity and direction to these issues. The persons living with AIDS who were among us spoke with authority and taught us much. At the same time, we recognize that we have only begun the lengthy process of dialogue and action so necessary in the midst of AIDS. The insights that follow come from a North American perspective. Acknowledging AIDS as a global problem yet lacking the insights of other continents, we cannot make specific global recommendations, but charge the church with responsibility for pressing the questions of equitable worldwide active and preventive health care.

The questions surrounding AIDS are often ambiguous and the answers often inadequate; nonetheless, each individual and each church must struggle with this uncertainty. To do nothing is to make a profound statement about the nature of illness and health in our society. Silence can be deadly.

Persons with AIDS and those with HIV infection are among us, and not separate from us; the crisis of AIDS is our crisis, it is not a we/they issue. The church must share in this experience, changing and being changed so as to enable society to provide a supporting presence for those who are grieving and suffering. The church must become part of the AIDS pilgrimage to deeper understanding; it must join the journey toward human wholeness.

Faced with the urgency of AIDS, we as a global community recognize our brokenness and common need for healing and reconciliation. Special attention here must be given to deepening our understanding of healing. This comprises inner reconciliation and physical restoration: healing of persons with AIDS, partners, care-givers, family, friends, and the community. One can be cured without being healed, one can be healed without being cured.

We as a community must continue to struggle toward genuine acceptance of and respect for each individual person; to do this we must overcome prejudice and discrimination. We are not called to be judgmental; we are called to be a healing church.

We believe that the church and health care institutions, in cooperation with community organizations, can influence change of attitudes and of ongoing education. These three bodies must, in particular, reexamine their understanding of spiritual need, acceptance of and respect for all people, death, patient advocacy, justice, health promotion and disease prevention, and holistic health care. In effecting such change of attitudes and education, the church must network with and support those who are involved in dealing with the AIDS crisis.

Because we believe that all people have a just claim to care, the church, institutions, and health care providers are obliged to be dynamic and visionary in meeting the needs of people who are ill and of those who care for them in a holistic fashion.

We uphold and respect the historical role and tradition of the churches in responding to the health care needs of people. We affirm those who continue to carry on this tradition in a variety of settings. We affirm and support those in the health care and research community who are struggling to develop effective therapies and treatments for AIDS. However, we strongly oppose unjust discrimination in research, treatment, and admission to and provision of care.

We believe that all people are equal before God. In view of their professional commitments, even in situations of perceived personal risk, we are affirming that the role of health care providers is to care for the sick, regardless of illness, race, gender, sexual orientation, color, life-style, economic status, or creed.

AIDS is a disease that highlights the fragmented nature of our world. It frightens many into a response of isolation, injustice, and abandonment of those in need. These responses are contrary to the scriptural mandate of reconcilation.

AIDS challenges us all into a new level of introspection and communication that releases the energy of human hope, courage, and love. Such energy is required to respond through a radical and profound realization of living the core principles of our faiths. The supreme challenge of AIDS is for the church truly to be God's agent of love and reconciliation in the world.

12

Reflections on "Illness and Health" Stream

A Pastoral-Care Perspective

The Rev. Douglas Graydon

Why did we come together? It seemed apparent that we gathered to discuss, to learn, to share our experiences of dealing with AIDS. We were persons with AIDS, chaplains, doctors, administrators, social workers, professionals, interested people. We were all Christian, trying to live our faith in an environment of fear, courage, disease, death, life.

We had an impossible task: to discuss the theological and ethical implications of AIDS as it related to our North American understanding of illness and health. We accomplished, to a degree, that task. And the document that was the result of that discussion is important. I hope people will read and hear the message we are sending out, the message that a new sense of healing and wholeness must be understood if we are to survive this crisis; that we, as a global and North American community, must heal the pain of a fragmented society, and that through such reconciliation, heal the divisions of morality, sexuality, humanity, and faith that lie within ourselves.

AIDS is the catalyst disease that opens the wounds of our divisions. A cure for AIDS will not cure our brokenness as a human family, but our suffering because of AIDS may cause us finally to address the illness of a world that alienates, oppresses, and denies who we are as the people of God.

However, the document was almost secondary to the feeling and emotion of the Consultation members. I was moved and excited by the level of intimacy and honesty that was so quickly achieved in a group of relative strangers. I could feel the common struggle, pain, and frustration of dealing with AIDS trying to express itself in the testimony of others.

AIDS is a plague. It is horrific in its magnitude and manifestation as a disease. It causes deep pain on so many levels of our being, for AIDS strikes to the very core of my soul. It reaches down to those primitive fears of disease, death, and sexuality. And it challenges the very essense of my faith and how I try to live and order my life. AIDS has compelled me to journey to that deepest, most intimate level of who and what I am, as a man, a Christian, and a chaplain. Confusion and pain are integral parts of that journey. And I am only beginning. I saw others begin that journey as well. I saw those around me caught in that same struggle, yearning to listen, to open themselves to hear the words of others. I saw people who were trying to build bridges between themselves and the reality of AIDS, people who were trying to make the AIDS experience their experience.

To understand AIDS is to understand yourself. Confronting AIDS is personally confronting those issues of mortality, sexuality, and morality now so intertwined with the disease. AIDS may be the ultimate mirror, in that looking at AIDS is to see a stark reflection of oneself.

We gathered not simply to intellectualize or objectify the crisis. We did not produce any new insight or gain any profound theological or ethical understanding. We began simply to share, to listen, to attempt to grow from our collected experience. And in that realization lies the value of this Consultation.

David Roy, presenter within our Stream, challenges the church and, therefore, all Christians to act as mediators between God and he or she who suffers from AIDS. And yet to achieve that goal requires that we who profess the Christ crucified transcend our own conditioned morals and beliefs. If we believe that the life, death, and resurrection of Jesus Christ is that historical event which communicates the unconditional affirmation and acceptance of all human beings by God, then we must act out that conviction and create a community that accepts those with AIDS with joy and celebration, for we shall not be complete as a people of God until we do so. That challenge cannot be answered without pain, pain that signals growth, for it draws out of each one of us a reply so personal, so intimate that the result is nothing less than individual transformation.

That transformation was witnessed to in this event. I stood in fearful awe of the horror of AIDS, but I also stood in awe of the beauty of the human spirit, of our capacity to love, and our yearning to see God in the midst of us. I heard the anger and urgency of persons with AIDS who rejected the church because of its silence. And then I felt love and understanding flow from these same persons toward those still fighting battles against personal and institutional fears and beliefs.

I saw a love and compassion grow and develop among us, that compassionate love that is, I believe, a true testimony of the loving grace of God. We were being challenged and pulled by that love from the common, socially acceptable Christian witness, with all its attendant dogma and doctrine, to a deeper level of discipleship, that which releases the energy of Christian hope, courage, and love in its purest form, that transformation that will allow us to be true agents of God's love and reconciliation.

The long-range impact of this Consultation does not rest on the value of these collected documents. For they only catch a glimpse of the emotion and passion of the event. The true impact lies within the people themselves and the witness they will continue to give wherever they travel.

I left the Consultation exhausted from the intensity and scope of people's experience. And yet I felt renewed and empowered in my struggle to see God within this AIDS crisis. I am now assured that God is with me, with us, with all who face this disease. The future is uncertain. We left with sadness, knowing the suffering that lies ahead. Yet we left with hope—true, living, faith-filled hope. And so this suffering has meaning. It is not clear yet, but it might just be the beginning of a new age of sisterhood and brotherhood. We are all, in our own way, calling out to God. And the Consultation proved that although the church may not be hearing our call of pain, God is. So therefore, regardless of our human state or condition, we are valued and revered by God. We will not suffer alone or without purpose. We will overcome.

A Community Perspective

The Rev. Janet Pierce

Dr. Cécile De Sweemer told a story on the first night of the Consultation that kept resurfacing as a theme in the Illness and Health Stream. She told of her first visit, as a young woman, to a missionary outpost in Africa. When she arrived the missionaries told her that the natives weren't friendly and that it probably wasn't safe for her, as a young woman, to go out to the village alone. Later Cécile decided to take a walk and came to a small clearing near the village. As she stood at the edge of the clearing, she noticed women watching her in the surrounding brush. Not knowing what to do, and feeling somewhat fearful, she stood still. The women began to come closer, eventually arriving at the edge of the clearing, still watching her closely. Noticing that some of the women were swaying, Cécile began to hum and sway with them. Slowly the women came out of the brush and entered the clearing. As Cécile watched the movements of the women and answered with movements of her own, they began to dance. Soon they were all dancing together in the clearing. Then, one by one, each of the women came up to Cécile and offered her baby for Cécile to hold and dance with and hand back. After all the younger women had come up, the oldest woman in the village danced up to Cécile and began to dance in front of her. As they danced together, their steps grew faster and faster until they both collapsed in each other's arms.

At the first meeting of the Illness and Health Stream, thirty-six of us came together—uncertain of one another, some of us distrustful of the church and some of us in pain from our experiences of AIDS. We came together much like the women at the edge of the clearing, uncertain about venturing in. We met together and told of our experiences of AIDS and of our expectations of the Consultation.

Throughout the weekend we were given many gifts. The men with AIDS in our Stream offered us the gifts of courage and wisdom. We came away with a profound awareness of their place among us as rabbis, as healers and teachers of faith. Dr. David Roy gave us the gift of radical challenge, pushing us to go beyond words to action and challenging us to question our actions, the actions of the church. Others gave the gifts of sharing stories, expressing doubts, and being open about concerns. Each of these were gifts of trust like the women offering their babies one by one to Cécile De Sweemer.

As we broke into smaller groups to do the practical work of writing a paper, a variety of issues of importance surfaced. The first was an incredible sense of urgency that was portrayed, perhaps most strongly, by those with AIDS who were feeling the immediacy of death. This was reflected in the urgency felt by the group to be involved and to involve more of the church.

The second issue that continued to resurface was the question of who was the church. It first surfaced as distrust of the church—at least the institutional church—distrust of its willingness or ability to be involved with AIDS without moralizing or being judgmental. As we explored our distrust, it became clearer to us that we were the church and as such could be prophetic and pastoral, but did that from within the community of faith.

Equally strong were the feelings that not only did we, as the church, have to become involved, but also that we had the resources and abilities to offer a unique perspective. The church has traditionally been a reservoir of insight and support, of courage in the face of pain or death. The church has, at times, had an awareness of (and ability to bring) holistic healing of body and spirit. And the church has vast reservoirs of people who could minister and funds that could house, feed, and clothe.

And I believe that the church has the ability, perhaps more than any other institution, to reduce or remove the fear surrounding AIDS. Much of the strategy for combating AIDS is based on the belief that, in the absence of a cure, education is the only hope. There is a belief that if people could just get the facts, they wouldn't be afraid, or they'd stop putting themselves at risk. We know from experience that this simply isn't so. I have rarely seen facts alone change behavior. Both mind and emotion must be involved in lasting behavioral change. The church has had years of experience in dealing with people's emotions. To reduce fear of AIDS, to change risky behavior, or to get people involved in AIDS ministry takes more of an experience of conversion than of education. And the church has been in the business of conversion for years.

As we neared the end of the Consultation, and the pressure grew to produce a document that would share the insights gained, a growing discomfort and grief was felt about the product that could come out of this short period. We were aware that it had taken time to grow to trust one another; aware that it was in wrestling with the issues that we had grown; aware that our experience together had changed each of us and involved us more deeply, more faithfully in AIDS ministry; and aware that no paper we could produce would have the same effect as our experience together. In coming together from many walks of life we were learning to trust and love one another, experiencing courage and growing in faith.

Those of us in the Illness and Health Stream came away from the Consultation with a profound awareness that, in this time, we are all living with AIDS. We can choose to live and learn together in community as one body, or die separately, isolated, and alone. Our deepest hope is that as we go back to our separate communities others might join us in this dance of life.

Part 4

Sexuality

Sexuality

13

The Sexual Bankruptcy of the Christian Traditions: A Perspective of Radical Suspicion and of Fundamental Trust

Mr. Kevin Gordon

This Consultation, intended in part as a regional follow-up to the International Consultation on AIDS held by the World Council of Churches (WCC) in June 1986 in Geneva, challenges us to tackle the theological and ethical issues posed by the emergence of AIDS, issues most religious groups have not been as ready to tackle as they have educational, pastoral, and public policy issues, possibly for such reasons as the daunting complexity of the issues involved, and the association of the disease in Canada and the United States primarily with marginalized groups.

As chairperson of the drafting committee of the June 1986 Geneva Consultation that produced the WCC statement "AIDS and the Church as a Healing Community" (included in this book as Appendix A), and having had the opportunity in January 1987 to address the Central Committee of WCC in plenary session as it prepared to vote on that statement, I enthusiastically embrace this Canadian challenge to do theology and ethics regarding sexuality and AIDS, both as geographical locus to extend the conversations begun in Geneva and as Aristotelian *topoi:* those places where insight, reflection, and argument may be found; places of living conversation where we might discern those commonplaces *(topoi)* that constitute the right places for discussing differences, the commonplaces on what constitutes argument itself.

Although AIDS statistics get dated even as we cite them, I want to begin with them because they provide the first ethical issue I want to signal and serve to illustrate my own sense of what consititutes an ethical issue; they also directly connect us back to an earlier conversation in Geneva, January 1987. Canada is reported by the World Health Organization (WHO), as of July 30, 1987, as being one of the seven countries with more than 1,000 AIDS cases. The United States accounted for 70 percent, Brazil was second with 1,695 cases, France third with 1,632 cases; the four other countries who reported more than 1,000 cases were Canada (1,000), West Germany (1,089), Tanzania (1,130), and Uganda (1,138). WHO also provided the following geographical statistics: Africa (4,082 cases in 34 countries), Americas (43,798 cases in 40 countries), Asia (160 cases in 18 countries), Europe (6,067 cases in 27 countries) and Oceania (569 cases in 3 countries). The number of reported cases of AIDS worldwide is 55,396. WHO spokespersons emphasized that only about half of all cases are reported, indicating that the more accurate total to date would be 100,000 diagnosed cases, with more than 50 percent already dead.

When I addressed WCC's Central Committee in plenary session, January 24, 1987, I was responding to queries from the floor as to the statistical picture of AIDS at that time and to an unfriendly characterization of the proposed AIDS statement to be voted on as being at best a pastoral statement that avoided the real moral and theological issues. I cite this intervention now to connect us back to an earlier *topos:*

> The statistics are from the World Health Organization, and what we can be absolutely sure of is that they are conservative figures. WHO publically admits to vastly conservative initial estimations, and now terms the world situation "pandemic," not withstanding the fact that some countries are grossly under-reporting their cases because of fear of stigma, national pride, and fears of publicity that threaten loss of tourism and valued foreign exchange. . . .

I want to speak to the characterization that this statement is one that is basically pastoral, and that it avoids addressing the moral issues. I speak to that characterization as a Roman Catholic, and as a systematic theologian associated with Union Theological Seminary, New York City. As a theologian, I am vitally interested in theology and morality, and not only with pastoral issues, as important as they are. This AIDS statement is not only a pastoral statement. Unfortunately, when we think of morality, we too often think of the sexual activities and behavior of people. I cannot stress too much that the statement's call for "free exchange of medical and educational information about the disease within countries and across borders . . . the freedom to pursue research . . . the free flow of information"— these are *the* moral issues in view of under-reporting that enormously impedes the information we desperately need for seeing the full picture, for research, and for finding a cure.

Our statement's call, not only for "responsible forms of behavior by all," for "altered behavior patterns," but also "for the improvement of physical and socio-economic conditions in many parts of the world"—this too is a moral issue.

The need that we be sexually explicit in our education for prevention, so that "the different modes of transmission prevalent regionally be clearly described and understood"—that is a moral issue. Our conscious decision as a Consultation not to moralize in the statement, was a moral stance, as was our refusal to give any theological support to a rigid and narrow "tit-for-tat" God who sends AIDS as an act of divine retribution. Such an assertion is shocking to unbeliever and believer alike. Surely with Job we have learned in the face of profound incomprehensibility to put our finger to our lips. We "affirm that God deals with us in love and mercy and that we are therefore freed from simplistic moralizing about those who are attacked by the virus."

AIDS, then, is on the ecumenical agenda because of the alarming rate at which the disease is increasing, and also because much of the discrimination against people with AIDS, shockingly, claims religious foundation. This statement on "AIDS and the Church as a Healing Community" is important for what it does not say, as for what it does say. We must be part of the answer—Good News—and not part of the problem. Some may think that this disease provides a natural occasion for the churches to judge AIDS; ironically, and in the long run, it will be AIDS that judges the churches.[1]

Subduing the Cyclops

I also enthusiastically embrace this Canadian Consultation's challenge to do theology and ethics regarding sexuality because it connects back to yet another challenging *topos,* a memorable essay in 1971, "Subduing the Cyclops: A Giant Step Toward Ethics," by W. Dwight Oberholtzer, in an otherwise forgettable volume *Is Gay Good? Ethics, Theology and Homosexuality.*[2] Oberholtzer's arresting metaphor of the ethical analyses of lesbian/gay sexuality coming from a "one-eyed cyclops" was a challenge to fill the current ethical vacuum of studies on lesbian/gay sexuality that originate without serious methodological commitment to both the intricate processes, and to the striking variety of the "lebenswelt," the "lived world" of lesbian/gay people. Without such methodological commitment, resultant analyses are without appropriate texturing of the underlying variety and complexity of what it purports to investigate. Poor investigators and subsequent intelligence reports squint through a single eye, unaware of depth and breadth. The reports of these one-eyed cyclopes are simplistic, fictitious, simple-minded, static, stereotypical, and ideological.

I propose to accept that challenge to fill, in part, what is still an ethical vacuum some sixteen years later, and move toward what must be eventually a true interdisciplinary discussion—one of the rarest of occurrences in the churches. Let me be explicit about my own "squinting," my *topoi,* my own geographical and social locations from the outset, since no one writes the full, complete theology or ethics of anything. Each effort is its own scandal of particularity. Mine is that of a white, middle-class, well-educated gay male from the United States, largely from New York City, and San Francisco from 1972 to 1985, vibrant and vital years in the heart of that city's lesbian/gay community. My perspective is that of a Roman Catholic lay theologian, a feminist perspective, a perspective that strives to retrieve and reappropriate in the Christian traditions no more than can be creditably supported, rather than what the traditions have proclaimed.

As such, I find it impossible as a contemporary Christian theologian to support my own tradition's unambiguous certitude about reality, its canonical assertions of the androcentric as normative, and the heterocentric as normal. Nevertheless, I can support, and propose as *topoi*, as commonplaces for our discussion and possible agreement, three traditional places to revisit in the service of retrieval and reappropriation of a viable sexual theology and ethics: (1) the incarnational principle grounded in human embodiedness, (2) the sacramental principle that God's grace involves exterior manifestation as well as interior disposition, (3) the classic recovery of a sense of truth as the revelatory emergence of authentic being-in-the-world as an embodied person. These three *topoi* constitute three central touchstones of my hermeneutics of fundamental trust in the Christian traditions; however, I signal traditional unambiguous approaches to religion and sexuality as two *topoi* for a hermeneutics of radical suspicion of the Christian tradition's credibility and reliability.

This Consultation's organizing committee suggested a few seemingly disparate examples of some of the issues this stream of papers on sexuality and AIDS could address. Among them were (1) uncertainty and anxiety about sexual mores in contemporary society, and (2) individual responsibility and consequences. I will focus on the first, uncertainty and anxiety, and show the second, individual responsibility and consequences, to be organically related to the first, indeed, its corollary. I will proceed by way of my own kind of metaphorical theologizing because good metaphors shock, bring unalikes together, upset conventions, involve tensions, and are implicitly revolutionary. I will move through the "bankruptcy" of our theological traditions and their wooden gods; through sexuality imaged as "dams bursting," "rudderless boats," and "wild horses without reins"; and urge that we attend to and trust "moral geography," most especially the necessity for gay men to confront "the hairy man lying at the bottom of the pond."

Uncertainty and Anxiety About Sexual Mores in Contemporary Society

That contemporary society suffers from uncertainty and anxiety about sexual mores should come as no surprise. This is as it must be. It simply follows from the fact that our Christian sexual traditions are bankrupt. It is an open secret, not only among professional theologians, but also among the public at large, that Roman Catholic sexual morality, as a case in point, is in a crisis of credibility, and has been for some time. The *Los Angeles Times* in August 1987 polled 2,040 American adults, of whom 957 were Roman Catholics. Artificial birth control was considered sinful by fewer than one in four Catholics, with the ratio dipping to fewer than one in six for Catholics age forty and younger. A majority of all religious groups—except for white fundamentalists—said divorce was not a sin. Catholics took this view by a ratio of two to one. Only one-third of Catholics sampled said masturbation was a sin—the same percentage as Protestants. Although a majority of the Protestant and other Christian respondents said they thought sexual relations between unmarried people was a sin, Catholics were nearly evenly divided on the issue. However, nearly two-thirds of the younger Catholics said such sexual activity was not a sin. Only 14% of Catholics and 10% of all polled thought it sinful to use condoms for safer sex as a protection against AIDS.

On the question of women priests, 60% of Catholics said it is wrong to bar women from the clergy. Engaging in homosexual behavior was considered sinful in the Catholic sample by a ratio of more than two to one; Protestants took the same view by a ratio of four to one. Nearly 70% of all Americans think homosexual behavior is sinful. However, 50% of Catholics are apt to favor legalizing homosexual acts between consenting adults, as compared with 40% of Protestants. No more than 20% of members of all religious groups, Catholics included, agreed with the recent Vatican document declaring that most forms of human artificial insemination are morally wrong. Only 35% of Catholics said they would favor a law prohibiting federally funded abortions. Nearly half of both Protestants and Catholics said they would oppose such a law. On sexual morals, 41% of Catholics said they thought the Church's position should remain the same. But more than twice as many want more liberal policies as those who want these teachings to become more conservative. One in five older Catholics said they would like to see the Church move in that direction. The inference is that unless U.S. Catholics change their views as they grow older, the Catholic population

174

will become increasingly liberal and thus in greater conflict with their own Church.

Of course the first response of Church officials is always to disregard polls as irrelevant to theological methodology—the Christian traditions "are not democracies." But the experience of so many millions of believers cannot be so easily dismissed. For millions of people it is not that the churches need a new and individual theology of divorce and remarriage, or theology of pre-marital sexuality, or theology of contraception, or theology of homosexuality, but rather, the real question is whether the churches really have a viable and embodied sexual theology to begin with when they disenfranchise so many millions of people on one sexual basis or another. Homosexuality is hardly the one problematic in the otherwise widely accepted and vibrant, embodied sexual theology.

The particulars of Roman Catholic sexual theology are useful examples to cite because their inner logic is so thoroughgoing. However, non-Roman denominations have no reason to feel superior or off the hook about the issues of a lack of viable sexual theology, and the role that plays in the uncertainty and anxiety about sexual mores in contemporary society. As in most ecumenical issues, there is more that unites us than divides us. Differences in sexual ethics among Roman Catholicism and most denominations are differences only of degree, not kind.

If the Roman Catholic Church, as a dramatic case in point, is ever to regain credibility in matters sexual, it will need to develop an appropriately sophisticated sexual ethic beyond what it currently has. Its current positive ethical guidance is essentially fashioned for sacramentally married heterosexual couples in procreative unions, and for absolute celibates. For all the others, for instance, the 50 million single people in the United States over eighteen, sexual options are few, if any. There is to be no directly willed "venereal pleasure" for anyone outside of marriage, neither intercourse nor masturbation; married couples who use contraceptives "manipulate and degrade human sexuality"; Catholics married in civil ceremonies cannot be admitted to the sacraments, and divorced Catholics who remarry without a previous annulment cannot receive the sacraments unless they live as brother and sister "in complete continence, that is, by abstinence from acts proper to married couples." All homosexual women and men are functionally to be lifelong celibates. There can be no married priests, and no woman priests because "their anatomy is symbolically inadequate."

Whatever change is proposed is largely at the level of pastoral practice, internal forum solutions of benign neglect, leaving basic theological positions untouched. Thus artificial contraception remains theoretically banned, while couples conscientiously make their own decisions and cease to discuss it, or to be asked about it, in the confessional. Divorce continues to be a theoretical impossibility, while Church annulments become more available on the grounds of a broader understanding of characterological disorders; couples in second marriages without an annulment and homosexual people are not permitted any genital expression. They are meant to be sustained by the charism of celibacy, presumed as given, and should that fail, the ministrations of understanding clergy who will administer penance and eucharist, given a firm purpose of amendment, and a fresh resolve to venereal abstinence. Without that amendment and resolve, these sacraments will be withheld. Rather than go to the very root of the problems, pastoral ministries are then set up, to and for the very problems that the theories first created and continue to maintain. It is no wonder that there is a crisis of credibility, causing "uncertainty and anxiety about sexual mores in contemporary society," and throwing people back to "individual responsibility and consequences" in matters sexual. Brushing off, and holding up our traditional sexual ethics, whether in a time of AIDS or otherwise, can hardly be the answer, when they are themselves the problem.

Most recently and strikingly, the "bankruptcy" of the Roman Catholic sexual tradition can be seen in the October 1986 "Letter to the Bishops of the Catholic Church on the Pastoral Care of Homosexual Persons." Commentators have already noted the document's unconscionable sliding together of AIDS and homosexuality, "Even when the practice of homosexuality may seriously threaten the lives and well-being of a large number of people, its advocates remain undeterred and refuse to consider the magnitude of the risks involved," and the document's own collusion in violence by asserting that "when civil legislation is introduced to protect behavior to which no one has any conceivable right, neither the Church nor society at large should be surprised when other distorted notions and practices gain ground, and irrational and violent reactions increase."

The document defines the homosexual "condition," "tendencies," "inclinations" as "ordered toward an intrinsic moral evil," and so the homosexual condition itself must be seen as "an objective disorder." This negative reading backward from homosexual behavior, to the homosexual condition itself, as an objective disorder tending toward intrinsic evil, is a severe retrenchment of an already severe position. What commentators have not yet noted is that the document studiously avoids the very use of the word orientation, except in three places, and there to discredit it as a useful concept and distinction vis-à-vis sexual behavior. This distinction has been used by Catholic moral theology, and the denominations, with a certain sense of self-congratulation for at least a quarter century. It reached something of a high point in the American bishop's pastoral letter "To Live in Christ Jesus" in 1976, a document and distinction reaffirmed by John Paul II during his 1979 U.S. visit.

Substituting a vocabulary of "condition," "tendency," and "inclination" for "orientation" is a sleight of hand that is not linguistically innocent. In so doing, Roman Catholic theology is attempting to shift the grounds of the discussion with psychology over the past 100 years, removing itself from the discussion in the modern period, and taking a majestic leap backward into a medieval world of philosophical language and distinctions. This strategic move renders an already unconscionable and violent document literally incredible, and this incredible situation is more than an invitation, or even a challenge—it creates a moral imperative for lesbian/gay people "in uncertainty and anxiety about sexual mores in contemporary society" to do their own sexual theology and ethics about "individual responsibility and consequences," whether about sexuality in general or AIDS in particular.

Of Bankrupt Traditions and Wooden Gods

As the lesbian/gay community and others take up this moral imperative to do theology and ethics, it is well to do so with great sensitivity to language because this rightfully serious theological and ethical enterprise has unfortunately turned grim all too often in the history of theology, constructing with architectonic sobriety, and without a trace of serious doubt, a seemingly full and fully adequate account of the moral life. Theology is an "artful" science, and not a science as such, however much that has been the prevalent view. While in no way devaluing or underestimating the enormous theological-ethical contribution of bringing to bear a sense of coherence, cohesion, systematization, conceptual lucidity and linguistic clarity to the messy stuff of human living, the moral traditions too often conceptually pressed the poetry of truthful lives into flat prose, forgetful that caught between the necessity and impossibility of speaking and writing adequately of God and the things of God, we would best go about our immensely serious work with a wry smile.

If ours is to craft lives of truth, goodness, and beauty, then we might better image such crafting and its emerging revelation, not as finalities and intentionalities being inexorably directed to their intrinsic ends and goals, but rather to image the human vocation to truth, goodness, and beauty more in an aesthetic mode. Not the unpacking of a teleological design, but the artistic shaping and reshaping of one's life-forms within the relatively narrow margins of freedom that is the hallmark of all things human.

Our sexual theological traditions are bankrupt in a very precise sense.[3] Bankruptcy does not mean that you have no inheritance, that you are without resources. It means, more precisely, that your resources have been badly managed, poorly used, or possibly even neglected. One now has an opportunity to regroup, to fundamentally restructure, to revisit, revise, and revision. In mismanaging one's own heritage and inheritance, one has neglected one's own best genius and become one's own worst enemy. It is now time to cut one's losses, to retrieve and reappropriate whatever is, indeed, retrievable and reappropriative within a hermeneutics of suspicion, as well as a hermeneutics of trust.

Bringing a critique of radical suspicion to bear on our traditional sexual ethics is the critical task done in the service of retrieval and reappropriation. Bringing to bear a fundamental trust in the tradition opens up the constructive task, that beneath the malpractice of our own conceptual strengths we hope lie some treasures worth holding on to—that the rightfully serious enterprise unfortunately turned grim with architectonic sobriety; the lively poetry flattened into deadly prose; the transcendental jest turned back into the joke's on you—that the traditions, nevertheless, and nonetheless, often enough had their finger on something or another that we throw out only at our own peril.

The uses and abuses of our "God-talk," our traditional images of God and God's ways have certainly returned to haunt us in the AIDS epidemic. The point is not to throw out God, but to do radical and sustained surgery on our theological images and metaphors precisely aware of them as images and metaphors. When 42% of Gallup respondents, six years into the AIDS epidemic, can still agree with the statement "I sometimes think that AIDS is a punishment from God for the decline in moral standards," then we have either failed abysmally as religious educators, or, more likely, we have been only too successful, and the transcendental joke is tragically on us. Forty-two percent cannot be an accident, but an index of a job only too well done.

The Western world has grown up with an image of God as an all-wise, all-powerful parent figure who will treat us as our earthly parents have, or even better. If we are obedient and deserving, he will reward us. If we get out of line, he will punish us, reluctantly, but firmly. He will protect us from being hurt, or from hurting ourselves, and will see to it that we get what we deserve in this life. Logically enough, when things go badly in this "theology," one moves into blaming, blaming either ourselves or blaming God. What most popular theology/conventional wisdom works out of, then, and despite the theological watershed that is the book of God, is a trite, infantile, parental model of a tit-for-tat God of divine retribution.

Nathan Fain, an AIDS reporter who himself has died of AIDS, wrote:

> We stand at a high moment in our history, actually in all of history. We have been stricken by a renegade germ at our most vulnerable point, our newly freed sexuality. It's a bad Dorothy Lamour movie: The volcano went off at the height of our

fertility rites, so naturally the gods must be angry, . . . but we are not savages, not unless we choose to be.[4]

The choice and the challenge to the lesiban/gay community is to do better theology in a bankrupt tradition. Tolstoy said:

> If the thought comes to you that everything that you have thought about God is mistaken and that there is no God, do not be dismayed. It happens to many people. But do not think that the source of your unbelief is that there is no God. If you no longer believe in the God in whom you believed before, this comes from the fact that there is something wrong with your belief, and you must strive to grasp better that which you call God. When a savage ceases to believe in his wooden God, this does not mean that there is no God, but only that the true God is not made of wood.

Suspicious Religion

Two *topoi*, two commonplaces to revisit as places where suspicious insight, reflection, and argument might be fruitful, are our traditions' uncritical approaches to religion and to sexuality. Critical hermeneutics is helpful here. Hermeneutics most simply means a science of interpretation, not just interpretation as in exegeting classical texts, but interpretation as a methodology for reaching understanding, and for appreciating, as we do in the modern period, the ideological basis of understandings, and the social construction of knowledge and reality.

As the Enlightenment had a second phase characterized by critique, a post-critical Enlightenment, so also theology needs to, and in some quarters, is becoming post-critical, self-critical about how it is done, especially about sources and procedures. This is a move from historical criticism to socio-critical method. Karl Rahner himself acknowledged that in the past we took the *loci theologici* of fundamental theology for granted. What is new in the theological world, however, is that these sources themselves have been put into question, together with the material they have produced. Thus it is fundamental theology itself that is in trouble and needs support.[5]

Ideology is not necessarily bad, but it is inevitable and, like all things human, ambiguous. Ideology is a cluster of ideas and values that provides a class or a nation or some human group with a picture of the world that can guide and inspire corporate action. It interprets and defends the perceived life interests, the power and privilege of an identifiable social group. Ideology becomes dangerous when it goes unrecognized.

Paul Ricoeur focuses attention on the service of hermeneutics as a tool for suspicion of the ideological pre-understandings, historical and cultural biases that every interpreter and each of us, of necessity, brings to everything we seek to understand. This is true of religion trying to interpret and understand itself, let alone sexuality. It is true of sexuality trying to interpret and understand itself, let alone religion. It is true of all of us trying to analyze and understand ourselves as such, and as religious and sexual people and communities. As multidimensional realities, religion and sexuality never wholly leave behind their ambiguous character, but always stand in need of transformation. The corruption of the best is the worst. A hermeneutics of suspicion is a critique of false consciousness focused on inherited traditions, as well as turned back on one's own research and reflection.

Ricoeur speaks appreciatively of the three great hermeneutes of suspicion—Marx, Nietzsche, and Freud—as "these three masters of suspicion" exposing false consciousness.[6] Their critiques are a call to all disciplines, not excluding theology, especially that done in ecclesiastical settings in the service of the institution, to examine their uncritiqued ideological origins. If human subjectivity is rooted, of necessity, in concrete, historical, economic society, then *no* theology is transcendent of the social-political-economic realities of its own historical epoch. Post-critical theology recognizes how the pervasive ideology of the dominant class in any society influences the theology it produces. Most theology is freighted with an overload of the dominant ideological perspective. No theology that claims to be critical can ignore the ideological-critical dimension. It should be noted that the notion that class automatically "determines" ideas is not defended here. What is being investigated is the relation among class, ideology, and ideas.[7]

All theology is ideo-theology, of necessity, and some is blatantly so, the accounts of the "historical winners." If the critiquing process not only demythologizes and demystifies, but even de-divinizes at some points, then so be it. All traditions, including religious traditions, and despite their disclaimers, share in a radical ambiguity that invites us to approach them with a radical suspicion in one sense, as well as a more fundamental trust and consent in another.

Paul Tillich understood this very well and, as such, serves as both an appreciative and a suspicious hermeneute of religion. Insistent that life is multidimensional, there is, consequently, hardly a page in Volume III of his systematic theology that doesn't have the word ambiguity. Ambiguity is in our language because it is first in our lives. "Life transcends itself ambiguously. Although this ambiguity is most conspicuous in the religious realm, it is manifest under all dimensions."

> The real object of honest attacks on organized religion is the ambiguity of religion in the context of its institutionalized form. Instead of transcending the finite in the direction of the infinite, institutionalized religion actually becomes a fine reality itself—a set of prescribed activities to be performed, a set of stated doctrines to be accepted, a social pressure group along with others, a political power with all the implications of power politics. . . . The pettiness of average daily-life religion is no argument against its greatness, and the way in which it is drawn down to the level of undignified mechanization is no argument against its dignity. Life, transcending itself, at the same time remains within itself, and the first ambiguity of religion follows from this tension.
>
> The basic ambiguity of religion has a deeper root than any of the other ambiguities of life. . . . No examples need be given for this ambiguity of religion, for they fill the pages of world history. It is enough to show why the quest for unambiguous life must transcend religion, even though the answer is given in religion.[8]

Without a healthy initial methodological hermeneutics of suspicion in the service of retrieval and reappropriation, we condemn ourselves to ambiguous religious institutions uncritically regulating ambiguous religion and ambiguous sexuality unambiguously.

The insistence of religious institutions like the Roman Catholic Church on unquestionable certitudes is germane to lesbian/gay ministries that are often dismantled precisely because they are said to be "ambiguous about the Church's clear and constant teaching." Charles Davis has noted the temptations of religion as the lust for certitude, cosmic vanity, the pride of history, and the anger of morality.[9] Certitude corrupts religion and has the same relation to genuine faith as lust has to love. Cosmic vanity is the constant temptation to suppose one is somehow privy to the secrets of the cosmos and able to give, not just a scheme devised from a human viewpoint, but an objective picture of the order of the universe. The pride of history is a refusal to accept the precariousness of finite and temporal existence, but rather to accept the pretentious offering of some humanly conceived plan of total history as saving gnosis or knowledge.

The anger of morality is the insistence on an established pattern of behavior and thought for its own sake, a hostile reaction that chokes love, a bitter rejection of what does not conform, the sharp repulsion of anything that disturbs or threatens an enclosed self. In view of this lust for certitude, cosmic vanity, pride of history, and anger of morality, religions and their theologies might, especially in matters sexual, want to make more modest proposals about compulsory reality. This is especially true of homosexuality where much institutional "court-theology" systemically resists uncongenial data from the natural and social sciences, as well as dismisses personal testimony as merely that. The resultant silence and invisibility of the closet trivializes, marginalizes, and renders invisible lesbian women and gay men, as is not accidentally also true of the trivialization, marginalization, and invisibility of women generally.

It is at this point that citing some of the inner connections between lesbian/gay issues and liberation hermeneutics, especially a critical feminist liberation hermeneutic, moves our question methodologically further along. John McNeill, in *The Church and the Homosexual,* concluded "that it is the same age-old tradition of male control, domination, and oppression of women which underlies the oppression of the homosexual."[10] Whatever is not male, preferably white, hierarchical and patriarchal, is other than and less than—that is, women, women not wanting men, and men perceived as acting otherwise than within the prerogatives of their privileged gender.

Radical questioning and challenges that come from feminist theologians and ethicists working not from the established center, but from the jagged edge, the peripheries, the margins, the "underside of history," go right to the root of theological and ethical methodology. What can and what cannot be considered normative or canonical within theologies written by "the historical winners," mostly heterosexual white males who were largely celibate priests and monks whose theologies established and maintain patriarchy and hierarchy? What would the genius of Christianity look like written from the perspective of "the historical losers," the oppressed, the dispossessed, and disenfranchised?

If we are to retrieve and reappropriate whatever is most authentic in our religious traditions, we must have the courage to begin by suspiciously critiquing sexist, racist, classist ideologies whether called theologies or not. We must be willing to demythologize, demystify, even de-divinize, if necessary, pre-suppositions of the androcentric, that is, the male-centered as normative, and pre-suppositions of the heterocentric as normal. That androcentrism and heterocentrism prevailed in their own time is understandable historically and culturally. That it is understandable does not make it acceptable any longer, let alone normative. We must systematically suspect patriarchy's unambiguous accounts of compulsory reality, the suspicious normativeness of compulsory androcentrism, and the suspcious normality of compulsory heterosexism.

I propose that lesbian/gay theological and ethical methodology come in on a slant, so to speak, and methodologically appropriate many emphases of a feminist liberation hermeneutic. Elizabeth Schussler Fiorenza maintains that a feminist critical theology of liberation must reject all texts that contribute to women's unfreedom. In a public feminist critical discourse, this theology seeks to evaluate all biblical texts, interpretations, and contemporary uses of the Bible for their contribution to the religious legitimation of patriarchy, as well as for their stand toward patriarchal oppression. A feminist critical theology of liberation, therefore, develops a hermeneutics of critical evaluation, rather than one of correlation. It does not focus on text as revelatory word, but on the story of women as the people of

God. Its canonical hermeneutics insists that the people of God are not restricted to Israel and the Christian church, but include all of humanity. Texts that are not in the service of liberation from oppressive patriarchy are biblical texts, but not scripture.[11]

So also is all of this true for lesbian/gay theology and ethics. We have not been called to spend our lives on endless revisions of revisionist exegeses, or on one more guided tour through the flora and fauna of Sodom and Gomorrah. When push comes to shove between the liberation of lesbian/gay persons already given in Jesus Christ and the so-called canonical and normative tradition, then so much the worse for the canon and normative tradition. For instance, lesbian/gay theological and ethical methodology should share with feminist liberation methodology the following:

1. Its basic methodological assumption that theology begins with daily lived experience, and especially with a preferential focus on the experience of one's own oppression
2. Its focus on doing theology from the perspective of the "historical losers," "the underside of history," from the viewpoint of suspicious women and other marginals at the jagged edge, rather than at the establishment center
3. Its focus on consciousness—what we think, why we think, where we think from, how we think, and for whom it makes a difference
4. Its epistomological and hermeneutical principles that all consciousness is rooted in human experience, and that human always includes female as well as male experience, indeed, more than one kind of male experience, that is, patriarchal
5. Its stress on the importance of the advocacy stance as a refusal to enter into the false objectivity claimed by exegesis that systematically refuses to see elements of the text that call into question prevailing societal contexts
6. Its investigation and reassessment of the singular, fundamental, and normative status of scripture
7. Its interest in the social setting out of which scripture and traditions arose, the importance of the sociological factors in the formation of perspectives within the traditions, in the first place, and also in the receptivity to various perspectives on the part of the interpreter, and implications for the claims of scriptural and traditional authority

8. Its critique of premature closure on accounts of reality (compulsory certitude); of premature closure on accounts of the normative (compulsory androcentrism); as precedent for a parallel critique of premature closure on accounts of the normal (compulsory heterocentrism)[12]

Suspicious Sexuality—of Bursting Dams, Rudderless Boats, Wild Horses

A second *topos* to revisit as a place where suspicious insight, reflection, and argument might be fruitful is our religious traditions' approaches to sexuality. Sexuality, like religion, indeed, as in all things human, never wholly leaves behind its ambiguous character. It transcends itself ambiguously. From its origins, the infant participates in a drama of overpowering dimensions, often overwhelmed, then and later, by issues of attachment, dependency, competition, and hostility—early linkages that tend to get transferred and repeated in one's life and relations.[13]

Sexuality's ambiguities are rooted in its own multidimensionalities, often conflicting and interpenetrating. This necessary ambiguity is lost on those religious traditions that reduce and collapse these multiple meanings, polyvalences, multidimensionalities, into one teleological purpose, most often, procreation. Historically, the meaning of sexuality has been monovalent—sexuality is essentially for procreation. Moving from "primary/secondary ends" language to "co-equal ends," however late and begrudgingly, represented some attempt to honor the other valences of sexuality. What needs to be more fully exposed with the assistance of other disciplines is the polyvalent nature of sexuality, the pluralistic modes of sexuality, its relative plasticity and malleability, its range of sexual triggers, the multidimensional variety and variability of sexuality's functions, which are not equally present and operative at every stage of life, whether conceived of as broadly generative or more narrowly procreative.

Sexuality is clearly reproductive and other than reproductive—to give pleasure and to receive it; to give and receive comfort, affection, warmth; to escape the confines of the ego; to repair and contain earlier traumas and defeats, whether remembered or repressed; to exercise oneself in ritual and theatrics, in dramaturgical reconstruction; to relax, to relieve tension, to enjoy oneself.[14] It need not always have the permanence, the duration, the exclusivity that reproductive sexuality leading to parenting most often requires. People and the services into which they unconsciously press sexuality are infinitely interesting, and we need to be infinitely interested. More interesting than sexual behavior as such is the manner in which it relates to and is in the service of one's sense of identity, one's sense of continuity, coherence, and cohesion. This calls for a hermeneutics of the various meanings our sexual conducts carry for us out of our own idiosyncratic and personal histories.

Another ambiguity of sexuality is the extent to which it is a social construction, formed by the requirements of social organization. What would the shape of sexual issues, sexual ethics look like if shaped by different social determinations than those of the needs of patriarchy and androcentrism, with its resultant host of current sexual issues shaped by uncritiqued sexist ideology collapsed into merely "women's issues," peripheral, trivial, trouble-making concerns of a small minority of women threatening the family because they do not know their place?

Much of the attraction to the family as a sociological unit needs to be suspiciously revisited. The question arises whether a person kept in such prolonged dependence on a parental group (unlike any other animal) does not become a hyperfamilial animal, incapable of conceiving of any other social tie save as a dim projection of the parental bond: a need to be on familiar terms with others, a need to find in spouse, patron, monarch, president, or leader another father or mother. Much of the rhetoric of the family is precisely rhetoric—a politics of resentment, sex-negativity under the rhetoric of family—the last battle in the wrong ditch, with lesbian/gay people as the scapegoats. The debate that pits pro-family against anti-family, with lesbian/gay people lumped with the latter, is unresolvable because it is a misplaced debate and the terms of the debate are wrong. The "family" whose "sanctity" is being maintained is in actuality the patriarchal, male-dominated family.

That the Christian traditions have been deeply suspicious of sexuality is no secret. They have never really known what to do with sex because they have never really known what to do with pleasure and, at a deeper level, what to do with passion. On what grounds can we turn a hermeneutics of suspicion as a critique of false consciousness back on itself and suspect the suspectors? The grounds have been so well picked over and the recital so commonplace, whether through Greek and Gnostic dualisms hostile to the body, delayed eschatology and consequent adulation of martyrdom and virginity, the impact of Platonism on the third- and fourth-century "fathers" of the church, Augustine influenced by the Manichaeans, and on and on, that the only wonder is that the churches continue to reiterate and attempt to refurbish superstructures whose foundations are in such incredible disarray.[15] Mindful of ambiguous religious institutions uncritically regulating ambiguous religion and ambiguous sexuality unambiguously, and in view of religion's lust for certitude, cosmic vanity, pride of history, and anger of morality, they might want to make more modest proposals about sexuality, as well as about religions and their theologies.

Sexual paradigms, exemplars, models, fictions, metaphors, images are final areas for suspicious revisiting in order to analyze and imaginatively test the appropriateness and adequacy of the language we use to score our lives. Many contemporary theorists view sexuality as a motivational system that is derivative, not from drive, but from the psychological record of sensual experience integrated through a series of object relations. While the object-relations theory of sexuality does not preclude adherence to a drive theory of sexuality, it renders it superfluous. A rightful demythologizing of the metaphor of drive-discharge as a model of sexuality would release us from our ascetical bondage to posing sex as basically a problem of abstinence and control. Those inexperienced in sexual matters, particularly celibates, tend to think of the sexual act as mysterious, passionate, and immediate. They tend to think that the sexual impulse once stimulated is simple and strong. Images of water held in check by a dam, the dangers of boats without rudders, or horses needing to be reined in by a driver, do not jar their sensibilities. For those more sexually experienced, sex is more often calm and ordinary, even boring and in need of conscious efforts at re-stimulating interest and desire.

George S. Klein argues convincingly that Freud had two theories of sexuality, the one a clinical theory centered on the properties peculiar to sexuality, on the values and meanings associated with sensual experiences in the motivational history of a person from birth to adulthood, on how nonsexual motives and activities are altered when they acquire a sensual aspect, and vice versa. The second version, the drive-discharge theory, translates this psychological conception into the quasi-physiological terms of a model of energetic force that "seeks" discharge. This energetic conception was part of a metapsychology designed to create interfaces with other disciplines, particularly with physiology.[16]

Klein argues that these two theories have been conflated and confounded, that they are on different logical planes, not reducible to each other, requiring different data for confirmation, and, in critical ways, inconsistent with each other. It is the clinical theory, not drive-discharge, that is the revolutionary contribution. Drive-discharge blurs the distinction between drive and motive. The clinical theory emphasizes the cognitive matrix, the meaning of sexuality.

> An essential point of the clinical theory is that sensual pleasure is not an autonomous experience sought after simply for its own sake. Sensual mobilization is an organismic event whose motivational importance arises from the requirements of a developing self that seeks always to perpetuate and preserve its unity, integrity and coherence. Encounters that have linked sensual activity to self-conception and self-esteem are retained as part of the cognitive record of sensual pleasure and are therefore very much part of the stimulation of sexual activity. Consequently, the stimulations and gratifications in every sensual experience reverberate to affect self-conception, self-identity, and self-esteem. Conversely, crisis in these very respects affects the search for, the choices of, and the circumstances of sensual pleasure. In such instances, anxiety is not necessarily associated with erotic wishes per se, but rather, the erotic wishes are responses to the state of anxiety.[17]

Whereas the drive-discharge model invites Newtonian metaphors of the motion of particles, the clinical theory implies a system lending itself to description in value meanings to self. The language of drive is about compelling holds, cravings, engrossing, implacable, peremptory alien pressures that implode from without oneself.

> The clinical theory makes less dramatic assumptions about the unobservable, dammed-up impulsions. The organized appearance of a sensual appetite lends itself to metaphoric description as the reflection of an implacable force, but it is misleading to take the experience of forcefulness as the process of sexual arousal per se. In the clinical theory, sexuality is viewed as appetitive activity within a reticulum of motivational meanings rather than the manifestation of a linear force impelling itself against a barrier.[18]

One cannot provide a full-scale conception and account of sexuality here. My purpose is at least to give some small sense of what an account might be like that is beyond wooden gods and one-eyed cyclopes.

Three *Topoi* of Trust

Bringing to bear a fundamental trust in our traditions opens up the constructive task that beneath the malpractice of our own conceptual strengths lies some treasures worth holding on to, some *topoi* as to where to start to revisit, revise, and revision a viable sexual ethic and embodied sexual theology. I will signal three: (1) a recovery of the incarnational emphasis grounded in human embodiedness as basis for a truly embodied sexual theology, (2) a restoration of the authentic Catholic sacramental sense that God's grace involves exterior manifestation as well as interior disposition—sacraments as outward signs of inner reality, and (3) a rehabilitation of the classical understanding of truth as the revelatory emergence of authenticity as an embodied person, the unfolding of genuine being-in-the-world. Let me say just a few words about each.

1. It only shows how far we moved away from our own best genius that in working toward an embodied sexual theology we have to remind ourselves that ours is an incarnational religion wherein the Word became *flesh*. This is more than a necessary reminder for Roman Catholic theology. Johann Baptist Metz

190

calls for a second Reformation that eats as it were a second time from the tree of Reformation knowledge. The original Reformation question was, How can we attain to grace? Metz calls for a second Protestant Reformation that would overcome the Protestant constitutional suspicion of the senses, of the visible and representational dimension of grace—in brief, that restores the incarnational principle and allows grace to penetrate the senses; he calls for a Second Catholic Reformation that would overcome Catholicism's constitutional suspicion of grace as freedom; and he calls for a world-political Second Reformation that goes beyond the privatization of religion to invoke grace in the polis, a Second Reformation as grace returning to the senses, grace returning to freedom, and grace returning to politics.[19]

All great religions are grounded in sweat, sperm, a woman's cry, soil, grapes, tears, blood. Around the edges of all religious worship have been orgies, feasting, fertility rites, purpled feet pressing grapes, the joys of a sweaty harvest time. When religions' tie with earth is cut, they die. If churches were really to listen to the embodied testimony of the lived sexual experience of their people, they would hear more often than not that people do not simply testify to what they do. They testify that they have found their active sexuality to be good. They do not experience their active sexual lives as evil, but as good, worthy of human beings, and often beautiful. Like all things human, they are imperfect, with ambiguous and demonic aspects, selfishness, dishonesty, etc. But on balance, their active sexual lives and loves stand out in their experience as essentially good and spirit-filled. If we followed our own best incarnational genius, and were not our own worst enemies, we would never have come up with a theology of marriage that saw the procreative "end" of marriage as primary, and the mutual love and support of the couple expresssed physically as clearly secondary, indeed as "a remedy for concupiscence." The belated and begrudging elevation of both "ends" as coequal still sits uneasy with many sexual fundamentalists.

2. In the authentic Catholic tradition, the interior needs exterior manifestation, and the exterior affects the interior. This is part of the Catholic Church's sacramental view of the universe.

Grace is truly embodied so the physical is not merely expression or consequence. The sacramental principle affirms the goodness of earthly, bodily, communal, institutional, and cosmic patterns. If God creates an inner movement, its outward expression is necessary and good. If we followed our own best sacramental genius, and were not our own worst enemies, we would never come up with the uses and abuses we made of a distinction between sexual orientation and sexual behavior. To distinguish is not to separate, and that is precisely the point. What could be a useful distinction between a person's way-of-being-in-the-world and that person's sexual expressions of that existential reality is most often abused by Church officials, and turned into a separation of the two.

The orientation/behavior distinction as proposed by Roman Catholic Church officials for homosexual Catholics is that the natural, expected expression of their homosexual orientation in responsbile homosexual behavior is forbidden them throughout their lifetimes, rendering them lifelong celibates as with monks and nuns. The Catholic Church's concern with the integrity of nature—its sacramental view of the universe—is not easily reconciled with positing a total split here. The Church is in some conflict with its own sacramental belief; what is central to a person and yet has no legitimate expression seems to be "unnatural" in that it has nowhere to go.[20]

3. A rehabilitation of the classic understanding of truth as the revelatory emergence of authenticity as an embodied person, the unfolding of genuine being-in-the-world, is a final *topos* that would allow us to transcend homophobia's closet and extend sacramentality discussed above to an appreciation of "the sacrament of coming out." Some beginnings can be made in considering John 8:32: "And the truth will make you free." It needs to be said straight out that truth as understood and presented by the writer of John's Gospel is nothing other than Jesus Christ. Unlike religions and philosophies that claim freedom through truth, as such, deliverance from sin by truth, as such, is not found in the scriptures. Ultimately the truth that makes free is Jesus Christ as the revelation, disclosure, manifestation of God. At another level, how we psychologically come to personal truth

of ourselves, a sense of our personal identity, integrity, and authenticity is an important question.

In a real sense, identity is never a finished product. We come to know truth of ourselves that, we hope, frees us into authenticity and integrity, and we do that mainly through our being-in-the-world-with-others. We are unfinished poems, engaged in a lifelong process of becoming, of letting being emerge and unfold within us, and of shaping that raw material of life into a truly human form. Some etymology is helpful here—that of the word for being and that of the word for truth. Martin Heidegger notes that the Greek word *phusis* normally translated into English as nature—it is here that we get the arguments about what is unnatural, against natural law, contrary to the orders of creation, etc.—is really the same as "Being." *Phusis* is basically "emerging," the rising of the sun, the growth of plants, the coming forth from the womb. *Phusis* means the power that emerges.

In Greek thought, the most fundamental meaning of truth is "unconcealedness," unhiddenness. Human beings are like a clearing in being, the locus, the place where being emerges, comes forth, comes out, is lit up, and becomes unconcealed, uncovered, revealed, disclosed, manifest, brought to light, and shows itself without distortion or denial. In early Greek thought, revelation, or unconcealedness, was the very name of truth. The very existence of Jesus was the revelation of the being of God, disclosed, made manifest, lit up, the light of life, the truth of being. Being gives itself, and in so doing confers its truth. The process of emergence, of coming out from hiddenness into light, is also the process of establishing the truth of being. This is how truth makes free. It is the organic unfolding of our deepest being.[21] And conversely, slavery is bondage to our own untruth; it is the fundamental, rock bottom, violent, internal, twisted, unnatural, distorted destruction of one's own innermost personal being, life and truth, one's onetime stake in personal authenticity and integrity—often advised against under the metaphor of "staying in the closet." It should be noted here that my development of being does not require that one understand sexual orientation totally as a given, as a facticity, as a *res*. A social constructionist nominalist understanding of homosexuality can still allow for a developed sense of one's sexuality that becomes functionally pivotal. Neither the realist nor the nominalist position is usually held absolutely, so one can hope for some dialogue among "moderate realists" and "moderate nominalists."

Resistence to paying the personal and political dues of "the sacrament of coming out" is exceedingly high. Resignation to a shadow life of deception and duplicity, the denial of one's self to one's self, or to others, is a betrayal of one's own existence, being, and truth, as well as a collusion in the denial of the very existence, being, and truth of lesbian/gay people; the active repression and suppression of information of one's own people's history, struggles, and contributions on this planet. It is collusion in an effort of cosmic erasure and "disinformation" that feeds into homophobia which is not more ignorance, but the systematic distortion of language, socially approved compulsory mis-education. If we followed our own best genius and were not our own worst enemies, we could understand the lesbian/gay community not as a ghetto, but as a sacrament, a demonstration community of shared goals and discourse, a self-generated hermeneutic of the meaning, possibilities, and public face of homosexuality, a sign of a profound deeper reality. "Avowed," if it must be used at all, would refer not to the "avowed homosexual," but to this sacrament of public witness, the word becoming flesh, the incarnational witness of a human face of God, shattering the quiet and dark closet, unmasking anonymity and hypocrisy. Here public would mean "out in the light", the realm in which human life is sustained and fully exercised, as contrasted with "in the shadow", the realm of necessity, restriction, and isolation, "privation." What is hidden and concealed is revealed and made manifest. It discloses itself.

In a hermeneutics of fundamental trust in our traditions, these are three *topoi*, or to introduce an inorganic metaphor, three pieces of track already laid by the religious traditions that might lead us exactly where we need to go. Pure and applied mathematicians are often in tension, with the pure mathematicians having little interest in immediate applicability, trustful that what they explore is valuable as such, and can eventually be seen to be a practical treasure. If the mathematicians were inclined toward parable and metaphor, they might describe a vast wilderness, and in it a small society of men and women whose business it is to lay railroad track. This has become an art, and they have become artists—artists of track, lovers of track, connoisseurs of track.

Almost perversely they ignore the landscape around them. A network of track may head to the northeast for many years and then be abandoned. An old, nearly forgotten line to the south may sprout new branches heading toward a horizon that the tracklayers seem unable or unwilling to see. As long as each new piece of track is carefully joined to the old, so that the progression is not broken, an odd thing happens. People come along hoping to explore this forest or that desert, and they find that a certain stretch of track takes them exactly where they need to go. The tracklayers, for their part, may have long since abandoned that place. But the track remains, and track of course is the stuff on which the engines roll forward. A hermeneutics of trust searches out continuities where only radical disjunctions initially seemed possible.

Individual Responsibility and Consequences

While the "uncertainty and anxiety" generated by literally incredible sexual ethics and theologies have as their corrolary "individual responsibility and consequences," that is not as individualistic an enterprise as it seems posed to be. The responsibilities emerge and are discerned in a community context. "Where is wisdom to be found?" It is to be found in a lesbian/gay ethical methodology that is inclusive of the many voices of the lesbian/gay community, including the aging and the very young, the healthy and the physically challenged, the worried and persons with AIDS and AIDS-related complexes in particular; the coupled, the single, those in and those outside traditional families, the racial and ethnic experience within the larger culture; those in and those outside of ordained ministry, religious congregations, and orders. Its inclusive methodology must embrace not only lesbian/gay people, but also those millions of others who are sexually disenfranchised by an inadequate sexual ethic: single people, the separated, divorced and remarried without annulments, the widowed, those who practice artificial birth control, priests unable to marry and remain in ministry, and women who are refused ordination because "their anatomy is symbolically inadequate."

In comparing and contrasting the sixteenth-century Reformation, various theologies of liberation today, and the different kinds of base communities from which they are issuing, Harvey Cox describes these base communities as "young," "noisy," and "assertive." Their theologizing crops up on the "margin," coming from what is viewed as the periphery of cultural and intellectual life. The establishment Vatican theologians, like the sixteenth-century curial loyalists, continue to hope the whole thing will die out. Whether in the Netherlands, Switzerland, Brazil, or the United States, the threat of bulls of excommunication are revived and raw ecclesiastical power reactivated. Like *sole fide* of the sixteenth century, the twentieth-century recovery of God's preferential option for the poor and oppressed as being the locus of revelation is a dangerous recovery.[22]

So also has the relatively brief history of lesbian/gay liberation been "young," "noisy," and "assertive." It is grassroots analyses and political activity for liberation from below, generated by communities of the "historical losers" from "the underside of history," from the jagged edge rather than from the establishment center; ethical issues passionately erupting at the peripheries by lesbian/gay people who have been marginalized, trivialized, and rendered invisible. AIDS and its ethical issues are a striking example of the politization of a health crisis and the medicalization of homophobia, made possible precisely because AIDS first broke out in the United States on the jagged edges of American life, in some of society's most despised and stigmatized parts. "No More Lies," the rallying cry of GLAAD, the Gay and Lesbian Alliance Against Defamation, is the contemporary cry of the Peasant's Revolt.

Like the sixteenth-century Reformation, the questions being raised by lesbian/gay theologians and ethicists are both similar and similarly radical: there is dissent from papal authority that is authoritative but not infallible; there is a radical revisiting of scripture and canonical normativeness; there are challenges to

196

distinctions between clergy and laity; there are questions that reach into convents, monasteries, and rectories themselves, challenging who can be admitted and excluded on the basis of sexual orientation; who can be admitted to or refused ordination, and whether celibacy need be a condition for formal church ministry.

Is Theology Possible After AIDS?

Even more radical than the Reformation questions is the contemporary question of whether faith and theology are possible after AIDS. All of us these days do our theologizing "between the times" in one way or other, whether those times be marked by the bomb that fell on Hiroshima cutting history in two like a knife, leaving the before and after of two different worlds; or whether the very possibility of ever doing theology again is bracketed between the Jewish holocaust of yesterday and the very real possibility of nuclear holocaust tomorrow.[23] Even after six years of immersion in the AIDS epidemic, the boundary marking the time before AIDS and after AIDS is not clear because there is no light yet at the end of the tunnel. But when there is, so also will emerge the questions of the possibilities of faith and of ever doing theology again within the lesbian/gay community after AIDS.

Will AIDS mark the unbroachable chasm between the time that faith and theology was possible and is now no longer possible, or will AIDS mark the boundary situation for the creative analysis, criticism, and imaginative construction beyond wooden gods that is the theological task? What are the religious options, if any, After Hiroshima, After Auschwitz, After AIDS? It is too early to say about AIDS. The question is literally premature, but I signal it here as inevitable and inescapable agenda. For the time being, the immediate, consuming tasks of comforting the sick and burying the dead preclude us from systematically raising as a community the larger religious questions of ultimate meaning and meaninglessness, but the time will come.

Every religious lesbian/gay person somewhere along the line has, like Jacob, had to contest with God, grappling with God until sunrise to receive blessing, wounded in the thigh, yet, one hopes, able to say in the end: "I have seen God face to face, and

197

yet my life is preserved [Gen. 32:30]." Now with Job, we have been challenged a second time to "gird up your loins," "brace yourself as a fighter." It is too early to say whether lesbian/gay people will, like Job, find a language to speak of God in the midst of unjust suffering: "I had heard of thee by the hearing of the ear, but now my eye sees you [Job 42:5]"; "I lay my hand on my mouth [Job 40:4]," or whether Satan's wager will prove true: "Put forth thy hand now, and touch his bone and his flesh, and he will curse thee to thy face [Job 2:5]." The question of "speaking ill" and "speaking well" of God is central in the book of Job. How that question ultimately fares in the lesbian/gay community is not easy to predict. Lesbian/gay people, like Job, are not patient in the usual sense of the word. They are rebellious believers at best, rebelling against unjust suffering, against a theology that justifies it, and against the depiction of a wooden God that such a theology conveys.[24]

Discernment of Emerging Ethical Wisdom

"Where shall wisdom be found? [Job 28:12]." While the question of a grand theological scheme may be on hold, the necessity of practical wisdom for the time between the times cannot be avoided. It is crucial that the question of wisdom comes in the Job chapter 28, at the decisive turn from the first twenty-seven chapters, in which Job and his friends argue about the conventional theology of retribution. Job 28 provides the daring move from a conventional quarrel to a confrontation that reduces all conventions to irrelevance. Job asks the hard question about the source of wisdom.[25]

The question comes to be answered that wisdom is found in the experience of the world, in the experience of the specific, concrete experiences that individuals and communities discern for themselves. That is where wisdom shall be found—in the stuff of human living, in the world, in our experience. The ethical task, then, is discernment, to attend to what is given in experience. True discernment or genuine wisdom is to move in and out on the giving that lets us understand and on the taking away that places us always in new perspective. God's speeches in the book of Job did not so much answer the question of suffering as put the question in a broader and changed perspective. No simple answer was provided, but complexity was honored, and several aspects of the human condition brilliantly illuminated.

Out of our ongoing human and sexual lives we eventually get data, facts about sexual living. That is sexology, the study of sexuality, its logos, its data. That is not yet sexosophy, wisdom about sexuality, its sophia. That wisdom eventually comes out of a combination of a number of related sources, religious texts, church traditions, empirical evidence, sound reasonings; but a major and indispensable focus is the lived experience of the community itself. Sex and sexuality need examination, but the text that needs most attention is the fabric of people's lives. Before any book, however holy, are people's communal experiences, later attested to in the book within the historical and cultural world of its time.

Contrary to popular opinion, Christianity does not in the first place propose a set of moral principles, a code of conduct, although eventually some principles are not out of place in indicating what the notion of love might include and exclude, if it is not to collapse into vagueness and meaninglessness. But what Christianity does propose in the first place is a way of discovering about the depths of life, out of which decisions about our behavior will emerge. The way to make an accurate assessment of a problem is for the community so involved to be sufficiently immersed in the problematic over a sufficient time. Out of the *immersion* will *emerge* the dictates of wisdom on that issue. That wisdom needs to maintain dialogue with other sources of ethical wisdom and with the larger community, but the primary community of lived experience cannot be short-circuited.

The lesbian/gay community has clearly been immersed in the problematic of AIDS long enough that emerging ethical wisdom is already in process. Some of it will prove to be long-standing wisdom; much of it is "an interim ethic" of safer-sex practices necessitated by troubled and difficult times. Such is the way of wisdom literature. Some of it is concerned with inculcating the governing values of the community in the next generation, the positive, embodiment of "the way" of what we do in our com-

199

munity. It helps people to discern the shape, boundaries, and limits of conduct in the community. Much of it has specificity, while much substance remains to be decided on the basis of pragmatic and experiential grounds. The immoral is what diminishes life and disrupts community. The moral supports and sustains. It is not always known in advance what in detail constitutes the one and the other.

The other type of wisdom instruction is even more ad hoc. It is about how to get around in the world, how to cope, to survive, to be street-smart. It claims no authority beyond the weight and persuasion of insight, on the appeal to good sense made by the statement itself. Precisely because we are reflecting on sex, the true, the good, and the beautiful against the traumatic reality of AIDS, it is important to say a clear word in support of sex, as such, at a time when a virus is being transmitted by sexual activity.

Because sex provides fluid contact between physical organisms, diseases can be transmitted sexually. This fact says more about the dynamics of microbe evolution than about the morality of the vectors by which microorganisms are spread. To drink water is not morally questioned because it can spread typhoid, nor to transfuse blood because it can spread hepatitis. Coughing is not condemned because it can spread flu. Coal mining is not called an abomination to God because miners can develop black lung disease. But coughing in another's face is considered unacceptable behavior, and the failure to protect miners from particle inhalation is thought to be unfair labor practice, not because these are inherently sinful, but because they violate the human responsibility we bear for one another. The moral issue in a time of AIDS is not sex, but the tangential problem that sexual contact can be exploited by microorganisms that take the opportunity to proliferate through the contact of mucous membranes and body fluids.

To be even more precise, at the most pragmatic level, the issue is not who you are, whether you are in a so-called high-risk group, but what you do. It is largely an issue of certain kinds of behavior. People who do not do certain things (exchange semen, share drug apparatus, etc., or get sexually involved with those who do) very likely will not get AIDS. People who do do certain

200

things risk getting it. The point is that an infectious agent has been introduced into various communities around the world and is showing up in various places, at various rates, and in various ways because it is spread in ways that now have to be considered unsafe. To be precise, even multiple partners is not really the health issue if one engages only in safer sex practices. However, a person may meet and become monogamous with one unknowingly infected person and, by engaging in unsafe sex practices with that one person, become infected oneself. To discern, beyond being street-smart some governing wisdom for the lesbian/gay community, that community would do well to attend to its own "moral geography."

Three topoi *of moral geography.* Travelers in the seventeenth-century Netherlands reported that the Dutch had adapted their penology to their landscape. The "drowning cell" was an enclosed room slowly filling with water in which prisoners were forced to pump for their lives, faced with a stark choice: drown or be Dutch. The drowning cell, both as metaphor and as an exercise in regulated terror, drew its psychological force from the watery depths of Dutch culture. It was, in effect, an exercise in that sort of pedagogy around which Dutch identity had itself crystallized: moral geography. The frightening experience inflicted *in extremis* was designed to be an intensive rehearsal of the primal Dutch experience: the struggle to survive rising waters. *Luctor et Emergo*—""I fight to emerge." The ordeal, or its threat, was a trauma meant to shake down to the elemental essentials. Arguably, even the most vicious and abandoned person wanted to respond with the effort and perseverance that would, at last, proclaim him a member of the Dutch community.[26]

The incredibly vigorous and sustained creative response of the lesbian/gay community to AIDS in its generating of national, state, citywide, and individual support systems and services—a tremendous burden that the lesbian/gay tax-paying community has borne to make up for an inadequate federal response to education, social service, patient care, general health, and prevention programs—is not an ordinary effort. The primal lesbian/gay experience of the world through the centuries, the moral geography around which lesbian/gay identity has itself

201

crystalized, is that of knowing themselves to be a "throw-away" people, dispensable and disposable to both church and state. Collusion by benign neglect in the genocide of one's own by both church and state was not unthinkable to the lesbian/gay community in this time of AIDS because it was in no way novel. In that sense, the lesbian/gay response to AIDS is an ordinary effort drawn from centuries of community wisdom—"Do for yourselves, before you are done in for."

Thrown back, as usual, on its own resources to discern ethical wisdom emerging from the communal experience of its own moral geography, this community, I suggest, has three *topoi* of moral geography, three places to look for the possibilities of emerging ethical wisdom—through a richer and deeper understanding of consent, autonomy, and friendships. The consent in sexual activity needs to be informed, and the autonomy relative, that is, related to friendship that is genuinely fraternal.

Informed consent and AIDS means becoming knowledgeable about AIDS, informed about the risk factors involved in various sexual activities and their personal implications. This focus on informed consent in this health crisis is not original, but what I would like to add is a more positive philosophical grounding of informed consent within an appreciation for related autonomy. The notion of informed consent comes out of contemporary medical ethics as an ethical-legal way to protect the patient's right to self-determination and as the articulation of a negative right—the right of noninterference. Useful as it is in providing an important protection for the preferences of patients, the informed consent rule is deceptively simple and has a number of shortcomings. It tends, understandably as a legal concept, to be minimalistic—informed consent requires adequate disclosure of relevant facts (data, logos, sexology) without any serious reflection on what values may be involved (wisdom, sophia, sexosophy). It tends also to be individualistic and isolationist—the person makes decisions for himself or herself, seldom with any explicit awareness of communal connections, of social solidarity. Of course, in raising the question of relevant values, the danger of value imposition is immediately present, as well as the possibilities of a field day of moralizing. However, to suggest that value considerations are an ingredient in the issues at stake does not determine what value options a person will determine as relevant, but at least it introduces a search for wisdom into the search "for an adequate disclosure of relevant facts," which the more minimalistic notion of informed consent does not.

One walks on shaky ground in even suggesting, not imposing, one or another value to ground one's informed consent. I suggest related autonomy. The noun autonomy suggests that my decision is authentic and free because *I* have made it *mine* and my *own*. The adjective related is meant to carry a sense of relationship—my own decisions, authentic and free, are made in the awareness and appreciation that my existence is tied up with that of everyone else—brothers and sisters, known and unknown, near and far. It is like the awareness generated by nuclear issues: we are all in this together. Related to AIDS and a sexual ethic emerging from within the community, it means that as a person decides what health risks, if any, he is going to take in sexual activity as a person who is worried, but well, he does so in solidarity with the best interests of the community at large, himself, his partner. As he makes decisions as a person with AIDS, whether about activity or types of medical treatment, he does so with this same sense of autonomous decisions of informed consent made *in relation to* more than himself. In this way, the individualistic isolationist's minimal sense of informed consent is broadened and balanced. I would suggest that possibilities for responsible autonomy and adulthood get literally fleshed out in fraternal friendship.

The noun is friendship. The suggested adjective is fraternal. It is only a sketch because a full picture of what conscious fraternal friendship within the male gay community would look like will have to be filled out as time goes on and as it emerges from within the community. I have maintained the noninclusive pronoun he, and now, a focus on fraternal, as particularly applicable to the gay male community, not unmindful that leaving out at least 50% of the human race is no small flaw in one's language; not unmindful that women and children get AIDS; and not unmindful of the enormous contributions of many of our lesbian sisters to their gay brothers during these tragic deaths in the family. I am regrettably mindful that fraternity carries connotations of beer-sopped "jocks" and their related antics, and of "male-bonding" in its most clubbish forms. Nonetheless, I remain convinced that the word is worth fighting for because of the lived reality it represents at its best.

For some time now, women have discovered that sisterhood is powerful. This is not as true for men discovering that brotherhood is powerful. Friendship is hardly new to gay men, even deep friendships within groups over many years. Without insisting that this friendship among men manifest itself exactly as friendship does among women or heterosexual couples, much less use those as criteria for authenticity, I am proposing that friendship, fraternity, become our central lens for watching for ethical wisdom to emerge from our ongoing life together; that friendship, fraternity, be the grounding for our sense of autonomy in relatedness, for informed decisions in solidarity, decisions both sexual and otherwise.

A concerted focus on fraternal friendship by the gay male community, especially at this time of AIDS, might provide a relational context creatively to see what we can come up with that is not necessarily monogamy on the one hand nor genital anonymity on the other. "Attitude" is not about friendship. Ironically, many have paid great personal prices to be with other men, but then help to create a community climate in which we systemically cruise by one another. The response of gay men to one another, especially in creating organizations like the Gay Men's Health Crisis in New York City, or the San Francisco Shanti project General Hospital, or Hospice, San Francisco, and similar institutions across the country, makes it clear that something new, exciting, and moving has come alive within the gay community and its friends across the country.

This remarkable generation of individual, citywide, statewide, and national support systems and services has demonstrated that the prior conditions of fraternal friendship were there all along, which comes as no surprise whatever to gay men. It is explicable as merely clubhouse bonds only to the outsider. Nevertheless, gay men themselves in search of emerging ethical wisdom would do well to attend further to one final *topos* of their own moral geography, the necessity and legitimacy of gay men confronting the "hairy man lying at the bottom of the pond."

The hairy man lying at the bottom of the pond. Something strange has been happening in a remote area of the forest near the king's castle; the hunters go into this area, disappear, and never come back. One day a young man goes into the forest alone, taking only his dog. He does not ask a group to go with him. As he and his dog wander about in the forest, they come across a pond. Suddenly a hand reaches up from the pond, grabs the dog, and drags it down. The young man's response is neither to become hysterical, nor to abandon his dog. Instead, he does something sensible; he goes back to the castle, rounds up some men with buckets, and then they bucket out the pond. Lying at the bottom of the pond is a large man covered with hair all the way down to his feet. He's kind of reddish—he looks a little like rusty iron. So they capture him and bring him back to the castle, where the king puts him in an iron cage in the courtyard.

One day the king's eight-year-old son is playing in the courtyard and he loses his beloved golden ball. It rolls into the cage, and the wildman grabs it. If the prince wants the ball back, he is going to have to go to this rusty, hairy man who has been lying at the bottom of the pond for a very long time and ask for it. A deal is made. The wildman agrees to give the golden ball back if the boy opens the cage. At first the boy is frightened and runs off.

Finally, the third time the wildman offers the same deal, the boy says, "I couldn't open it even if I wanted to because I don't know where the key is." The wildman says, "The key is under your mother's pillow."

The mother and father are away on the day that the boy finally obeys the wildman. The wildman comes out of the cage and starts toward the forest and the boy shouts after him, "Don't run away! My parents are going to be very angry when they get back." And the wildman says, "I guess you're right; you'd better come with me." He hoists the boy on his shoulders and off they go. As they go off together, the wildman says, "You'll never see your mother and father again."

This tale is told and commented on by Robert Bly and James Hillman in a feminist volume by changing men titled *New Men, New Minds: Breaking Male Tradition*.[27] It is particularly telling that precisely from such men an analysis is forthcoming that claims that those '60s and '70s men who have approached their own feminine side have made an invaluable discovery, appreciated both by themselves and by the women they love, and who love them. But something is wrong. Something further, a next step seems necessary, and this fact is intuited by both the men and the women companions. Making contact with the wildman at the bottom of the pond is the step the '70s and '80s men have not yet taken.

When the male looks into his psyche, not being instructed what to look for, he may see beyond his feminine side, to the other side of the deep pool, to the bottom of his psyche wherein lies the instinctive, the sexual, the primitive. This figure is even more frightening than the interior female, who is scary enough. Who's got the golden ball? In the '60s, males were told that the golden ball was the feminine, in their own feminine side. They found the feminine and still did not find the golden ball. The step that men are beginning to undertake now is the realization that you cannot look to your own feminine side because that is not where the ball was lost.

> After looking for the golden ball in women and not finding it, then looking into his own feminine side, the young male is called upon to consider the possibility that the golden ball lies within the magnetic field of the wildman. Now that is a very hard thing for us to conceive the possibility that the deep nourishing and spiritually radiant energy in the male lies not in the feminine side, but in the deep masculine. Not the shadow masculine, the macho masculine, the snowmobile masculine, but the deep masculine, the instinctive one who's been under-water for we don't know how long. Young men are not meant to kiss frogs. The women's movement has helped women learn to throw the frog against the wall, but men haven't had this kind of movement yet. The kind of energy needed is not the same as macho, brute strength which men already know enough about; its forceful action undertaken, not without com-passion, but with resolve, to make the passage into their in-stinctive male energy.[28]

The job of modern males is to go down into the psyche and accept what is dark down there, including the sexual; the cour-age to go down into the pond and accept what's there, which includes the hair, the ancientness, the rustiness. Some haven't gotten the water out of the pond yet, they haven't left the collective male identity and gone into the wilderness alone, into

206

the unconscious. You've got to take a bucket, several buckets. You have to do it bucket by disciplined bucket. Then you have to ask for the golden ball back. The parents must be away. A break is in the air. That the key is under the mother's pillow has nothing to do with incest, but with ancestral strength—under her pillow resides the secret of the mother's strength: her ambition, drive, fantasies for her sons, her forebodings and hopes, fantasies from ancestral roots, their ancient claims on life arising again into life through her dreaming head on the pillow.

There are several possible arrangements in life that a male can make with the wildman. The wildman could go back to his pond, so the split happens over again; the male and the wildman can exist together in a civilized place, like a courtyard, with the wildman in a cage, and they can carry on a conversation with each other, which can go on for a long time. But apparently the two can never be united in the courtyard, the boy cannot bring the wildman with him into his home. When the wildman is freed a little, when the young man feels a little more trust in his instinctive part after going through some discipline, then he can let the wildman out of the cage. And because the wildman can't stay with him in civilization, he must go off with the wildman. That is where the break with the parents finally comes. As they go off together, the wildman says, "You'll never see your mother and father again," and the boy has to accept that the collective thing is over. He must leave his parents' force field. He enters into the instinctive male world, far beyond his personal father and into the moistness of the swampy fathers who stretch back century after century.[29]

Gay men have unfinished emotional business with other men—scary, promising, troubling, absorbing business. Whether this is identically true of lesbian women with other women is for them to say, whether in stories as above, or in some other manner. If we are to have serious lesbian/gay contributions to sexual theology and ethics, it is crucial that we do collaborative work, speaking out of our respective experiences, as having equal importance, even though such experiences need not be identical, much less need be "complementary." In the perspective that gender "otherness" is the highest kind of otherness, and that more otherness is presumably always better than less otherness, an erotic relationship between an aging wealthy white man and a young, poor black woman might contain an especially large amount of otherness, and so be judged more than usually mature and courageous. Perhaps even more if he only spoke English and she only spoke French? There is no otherness more other, I would submit, than the otherness between any one person and any other.

Perhaps I can best open up the issue of needing to speak out of your own experiences by briefly raising the question as to whether sexual norms are identical across heterosexual and homosexual lines, indeed, identical for gay men and lesbian women in every way. I cite friendship as an illustrative arena for scrutiny. In the small amount of writing on the question of identical sexual norms, theologians like John McNeill,[30] or ethicists like Margaret Farley,[31] address the question briefly and answer in the affirmative: "the norms of justice . . . respect for autonomy and relationship through requirements of mutuality, equality, commitment and fruitfulness . . . the Christian community will want and need to add . . . faithfulness . . . forgiveness . . . patience and hope." Mary E. Hunt suggests six qualities that emerge from the lesbian experience: friendships that are mutual, community seeking, honest about sexuality, nonexclusive, flexible, and other-directed.[32]

I do not know if these elements are identical with those of gay men in friendship, nor do I need to know. My proposal is precisely that the gay male community find out for itself by self-consciously deepening and reflecting on its own experience of friendship, and see what ethical wisdom emerges. Speaking as a sex therapist, for a moment, I rather suspect that these qualities from lesbian friendships will not be identical with those from gay male friendships, although they may well converge. I suspect that something qualitatively different happens between man and man, woman and woman, man and woman—not better or worse, but different in texture. But we won't know unless we generate sexology, data, in same-sex communities, and in so doing generate a sexosophy, a wisdom about sex, that can mirror the variety and diversity of the authentically human.

Sexually active heterosexual single people generally have a wider sample of sexual experience than married heterosexual people. Gay men may very well have more sexually active experience than most single people of whatever orientation, although that is neither all they do nor all they know. Ours is not at the moment to decry that sexual activity, but to tap that experience, such as it is, to see if it suggests new perspectives on the nature and values of human sexuality in general and of heterosexuality in particular. Beyond a tedious ethics of rights, we might start hearing about an ethic of the good—that gay men saw that they were naked and "saw that that was good." Moreover, that they rejoice in being naked, rejoice in the immediacy of vigorous male-to-male sexual activity, relish their immersion in desire, excitement, arousal, pleasure, eroticism.

Gay men know a lot that might be usefully shared about the ambiguities and multidimensionalities of sexuality, its myriad motivations in the service of the many meanings it can carry in general, and in its specifics—motivations and meanings that do not disappear on an AIDS diagnosis, but may indeed get only more complicated and more necessary and useful. Gay men know about sexuality's polyvalent, polymorphous nature, its pluralistic modes, its relative plasticity and malleability, its range of sexual triggers, the variety and variability of sexuality's functions. If really engaged in dialogue, gay men know a great deal about sexuality's complexities of intentionality, nuances, shades, textures, delight, and shadows. All this could help fill out a phenomenology of sexuality, a catalog of what people do, their sentiments, their ways of needing and wanting. Not an anatomy of something hidden, but a recognizable description of what is; not simply a matter of statistical accounting, but a detailed description of the movements and desires that name our lives.

It is precisely the delicate ties of desire that bind gay men together that frighten society and that are the real source of bitter attack, whether from the Moral Majority or anguished liberals. Yet without the foundational sexological data we need for sexology, there will be no sexosophy. We need to throw the net wide enough to hear expected and even unexpected testimony that "their eyes were opened and they saw that they were naked—even in a time of AIDS—and they saw that it was good."

As a gay man and a professional theologian within the lesbian/gay community, I have accepted the challenge of this Canadian

Consultation to do theology and ethics on sexuality, and to grapple as more than a one-eyed cyclops. Literally incredible sexual theological traditions necessarily throw us back on ourselves in uncertainty and anxiety to be radically suspicious of bankrupt sexual traditions and wooden gods. Our radical suspicion of unambiguous religion's compulsory reality, compulsory androcentrism, and compulsory heterocentrism, and radical suspicion of unambiguous sexuality's drives, bursting dams, rudderless boats, and wild horses move us on with fundamental trust to search out abandoned pieces of track, *topoi*, as our lesbian/gay theological foundations for an embodied sexual theology beyond dualisms, a sacramentally embodied theology beyond splits of orientation/behavior, and a truthful account of our lives and loves beyond the claustrophobia of closets.

The "sacrament of coming out" extends Word and Sacrament into education and community, providing lesbian/gay criteria for a New Reformation in sexual ethics. Even more radical than sixteenth-century Reformation questioning is the contemporary question as to whether faith and theology are even possible After AIDS. Nonetheless, individual and communal responsibilities and consequences in a time of bankrupt sexual traditions lead us to search for the discernment of emerging ethical wisdom in the moral geography of the lesbian/gay community's own understanding of informed consent, relative autonomy, and a fraternal friendship that attends to the necessity of confronting "the hairy man lying at the bottom of the pond."

Notes

1. World Council of Churches, Church and Society Documents, *AIDS and the Church*, March 1987, No. 1 (Geneva: World Council of Churches, 1987), pp. 21–26.
2. W. Dwight Oberholtzer, "Subduing the Cyclops: A Giant Step Toward Ethics," in *Is Gay Good? Ethics, Theology and Homosexuality*, ed. W. Dwight Oberholtzer (Philadelphia: Westminster Press, 1971), pp. 11–73.
3. I am indebted for this use of the bankruptcy metaphor as originally applied to historical biblical criticism by Walter Wink, *The Bible in Human Transformation: Toward a New Paradigm for Biblical Study* (Philadelphia: Fortress Press, 1973), pp. 1–15.
4. Quoted in the *Village Voice*, June 9, 1987, p. 19.

5. Karl Rahner, "Uberlegungen zur Methode der Theologie," *Schriften zur Theologie* 9:81–95. Also: "Orthodoxy and Freedom in Theology," *Concilium* 6 (June 1971): 99.

6. Paul Ricoeur, *The Conflict of Interpretations: Essays in Hermeneutics,* ed. Don Ihde (Evanston, Ill: Northwestern University Press, 1974), pp. 148ff.

7. Harvey Cox, "Theology: What Is It? Who Does It? How Is It Done?" in *Theologians in Transition,* ed. James M. Wall (New York: Crossroad, 1981), pp. 151–60.

8. Paul Tillich, *Systematic Theology,* vol. III (Chicago: University of Chicago Press, 1963), pp. 98–106.

9. Charles Davis, *Temptations of Religion* (New York: Harper & Row, 1973).

10. John J. McNeill, *The Church and the Homosexual* (Kansas City: Sheed, Andrews and McMeel, 1976), p. 189.

11. Elizabeth Schussler Fiorenza, *In Memory of Her: A Feminist Reconstruction of Christian Origins* (New York: Crossroad, 1983).

12. Elizabeth Schussler Fiorenza, *Bread and Stone: The Challenge of Feminist Biblical Interpretation* (Boston: Beacon Press, 1984), pp. 43–63. Also "Emerging Issues in Feminist Biblical Interpretation," in *Christian Feminism: Visions of a New Humanity,* ed. Judith L. Weidman (San Francisco: Harper & Row, 1984), pp. 33–54.

13. Gregory Baum, "Sexuality and Critical Enlightenment," in *Dimensions of Human Sexuality,* ed. Dennis Doherty (Garden City, NY: Doubleday, 1979), pp. 79–94.

14. Ethel Spector Person, "Sexuality as the Mainstay of Identity: Psychoanalytic Perspectives," in *Women: Sex and Sexuality,* ed. Catherine R. Stimpson and Ethel Spector Person (Chicago: University of Chicago Press, 1980), pp. 36–61.

15. Philip S. Keane, *Sexual Morality: A Catholic Perspective* (New York: Paulist Press, 1977), pp. 3–19. Also John Timmerman, *The Mardi Gras Syndrome: Rethinking Christian Sexuality* (New York: Crossroad, 1984), pp. 29–49.

16. George S. Klein, "Freud's Two Theories of Sexuality," *Psychological Issues* 9, No. 4, Monograph 36 (New York: International Universities Press, 1976), pp. 14–70. First published in *Clinical-Cognitive Psychology: Models and Integrations,* ed. L. Berger (Englewood Cliffs, NJ: Prentice-Hall, 1969), pp. 136–81.

17. Ibid., pp. 40–41.

18. Ibid., pp. 38–39.

19. Johann Baptist Metz, *The Emergent Church: The Future of Christianity in a Postbourgeois World* (New York: Crossroad, 1981), pp. 48–66.

20. Gabriel Moran, *No Ladder to the Sky: Education and Morality* (San Francisco: Harper & Row, 1987), pp. 142–43.

21. John Macquarrie, "The Idea of a Theology of Nature," *Union Seminary Quarterly Review* 30 (Winter–Summer 1975): 69–75.

211

22. Harvey Cox, *Religion in the Secular City: Toward a Postmodern Theology* (New York: Simon and Schuster, 1984), pp. 262–68.
23. Gordon D. Kaufman, *Theology for a Nuclear Age* (Philadelphia: Westminster Press, 1985). Also Richard Rubenstein, *After Auschwitz* (Indianapolis, IN: Bobbs-Merrill, 1966).
24. Gustavo Gutierrez, *On Job: God-Talk and the Suffering of the Innocent* (Maryknoll: Orbis Books, 1987). Gutierrez's liberation perspective on Job further elaborates my earlier analysis of Job and the problem of evil as experienced through AIDS, "Religion, Moralizing and AIDS," in *Homosexuality and Social Justice*, The Consultation (San Francisco: The Consultation, 1986), pp. 215–19.
25. Walter Brueggemann, *The Creative Word: Canon as a Model for Biblical Education* (Philadelphia: Fortress Press, 1982), pp. 67–90.
26. Simon Schama. *The Embarrassment of Riches: An Interpretation of Dutch Culture in the Golden Age* (New York: Alfred A. Knopf, 1987).
27. Keith Thompson, "What Men Really Want: An interview with Robert Bly," pp. 166–81, and James Hillman, "The Wildman in the Cage: Comment," pp. 182–86, in *New Men, New Minds: Breaking Male Tradition,* ed. Franklin Abbot (Freedom, CA: The Crossing Press, 1987).
28. Thompson, p. 170.
29. Thompson, pp. 171–72.
30. McNeill, p. 176.
31. Margaret A. Farley, "An Ethic for Same-sex Relations," in *A Challenge to Love,* ed. Robert Nugent (New York: Crossroad, 1983), p. 105.
32. Mary E. Hunt, "Lovingly Lesbian: Toward a Feminist Theology of Friendship," ibid., pp. 153–55.

212

14

An Invitation to Rethink Sexuality: A Christian Feminist Liberation Perspective

Dr. Mary E. Hunt

AIDS is shaping Christian sexual ethics at a time when many questions remain to be answered and many voices remain to be heard. Christian denominations develop ethics for themselves, but they spill over into the larger society as well. Thus it is incumbent on those of us who belong to these faith communities to develop ethical reflection and ethical methodologies that are adequate and meaningful in the face of the health crisis occasioned by AIDS.

My purpose is to approach the task from a Christian feminist liberation perspective (which I will spell out shortly). I am concerned that we move beyond debates over the morality of *particular sexual activities* to a serious consideration of *the very way in which we as communities come to such decisions.* Only by shifting assumptions and power dynamics in the very *doing of ethics* can we expect to achieve any insights into appropriate sexual ethics.

In this essay I will set the context and spell out certain presuppositions that shape my perspective. Then I will turn my attention to the need to broaden and deepen the parameters of ethical reflection, using insights from a Christian feminist liberation perspective. I will sketch some of the aspects of the Christian tradition that can be reappropriated. Finally, I will offer some first steps in the development of renewed sexual ethics. I hope that participants of the Consultation and other readers will, in turn, add next steps as we engage in a communal model of "doing ethics."

Context

AIDS is an impetus for Christian ethicists to rethink fundamental categories of sexuality. High-risk groups have not shifted dramatically since the early diagnosis. Sexually active gay men, intravenous drug users, and hemophiliacs are the groups most directly involved. But numbers are such that by the turn of the century most of us will know someone with AIDS, and some of us may even have it ourselves.

The so-called Coolfont estimates, released by the U.S. Public Health Service in 1986, suggest that by 1991 at least 179,000 deaths (or roughly 54,000 per year) will be attributable to AIDS. Medical care costs will be between $8 and $16 billion dollars annually. This is simply in the United States. When the statistics are projected worldwide, experts agree that we are looking at a medical problem unparalleled in the contemporary period.

For ethicists, the issues take human form. The age-old tendency to blame the victims takes on new meaning. Gay men are accused of murder when they infect one another. Intravenous drug users are ostracized even by those who might help them. Children with hemophilia are banned from schools and, in one tragic case, even had their home burned. These are social consequences for which carefully thought out ethical analysis is crucial if we are to live faithfully in the face of AIDS.

Much of this backlash, or at least the scandalous silence that has accompanied it, has been fueled by religious assumptions about just punishment for "unnatural" acts, the wrath of God, and the mysteries of the cosmos. A recent statement by Archbishop John Foley, on the eve of the pope's visit to the United States, was a classic in this genre. He suggested that AIDS was a "sanction" against so-called sexual immorality.

In an airborne press conference on the way to the United States, the pope himself left room for ambiguity. When asked to comment on Foley's claim that AIDS is divine retribution for homosexuals, the pope responded that it is hard to know the mind of God. With this kind of confusion and, in some cases, malicious warping of the basic Christian message of love and justice, renewed ethical reflection is urgent.

Presuppositions

Every ethical claim is based on certain presuppositions. I assume, for example, that every ethical formulation emerges from a partial, limited, and contextual perspective. I identify mine as a Christian feminist liberation approach. I do not expect that all readers will share it, nor that they will even admit to its relevance. But I articulate it in order to stress the need for ethical claims to be accompanied by an equally clear expression of the writer's starting point. This is a step toward an adequate ethical methodology, one in which no single perspective can claim to represent the whole.

Naming one's starting point is an effort to break down several problems in the field of ethics and in the Christian community. There is a shift from an imperial model that has one truth claim to a model in which competing claims are held in tension. This shift is difficult for those who favor the former view.

The first problem is the notion, still held by some, that there is a definitive Christian ethical position for all times and places that simply needs to be discovered. Contemporary moral theology is a highly differentiated science. Complex social, cultural, economic, and political factors combine to produce myriad nuanced situations in which we take moral stances.

But contemporary Christian moral theology is also a highly refined art. The ethicist must ferret out that which is essential from that which is extraneous, that which permeates from that which only embellishes. For example, as Krister Stendahl makes clear in a careful look at Pauline materials, there are times when one must allow the triumph of love even over integrity.[1] In short, contemporary moral theology is an activity for which flexibility and humility are essential. Final answers are few, but human compassion is paramount.

The second problem is that claims made from a *particular* perspective are often written off by those who hold positions that purport to represent the whole. They contend that attention to particularity amounts to advocacy, that ethics should be pure. I contend that there is no such thing as "pure ethics," rather that there are competing ethical claims even within the same (Christian) faith tradition. The contemporary challenge is to develop ways to live with the tensions and ambiguities that accrue from taking particularity seriously.

These presuppositions will not persuade those who reject the notion of ethical pluralism. But I hope that the methodology I present takes their critiques seriously without capitulating to them.

A Christian Feminist Liberation Perspective

My perspective is *Christian* insofar as it emerges from lifelong location within the Christian community. It is in continuity with the concerns of those who claim that the life, death, and resurrection of Jesus represent a prototype of human redemption. It is rooted in the assumption that the Christian community ought to be about the praxis of love and justice.

It is *feminist* in that I understand how women's moral agency has been denied by patriarchal religion. This has meant that women, and by extension other marginalized people, have not been part of the shaping of the Christian ethical tradition. This becomes painfully obvious when sexual issues are under consideration. It is a mistake that we need to avoid when dealing with AIDS.

Even though most persons with AIDS are men, many women are at high risk as well. Prostitutes, intravenous drug users, and/or any women who have had heterosexual relations without condoms with intravenous drug users, gay or bisexual men, or hemophiliacs since 1977 risk exposure. This includes hundreds of thousands of women. But more important, the shaping of sexual ethics is an activity for the whole community, not only for those most directly influenced. Women's moral agency and women's bodily integrity, as articulated by Beverly Wildung Harrison, demand as much.[2]

Focusing attention on the gay male community as it struggles with AIDS can be an unconscious way of passing over the thousands of women and children who have been infected. However, commenting ethically about female (or male) prostitution ignores the fact that prostitution is a business and not a life-style or a sexual preference. Patriarchal economic conditions and cultural assumptions about the use of bodies combine to make prostitution a viable industry. It is no wonder that prostitutes are disproportionately represented in women who have AIDS. So many cultural messages brand them as expendable.

My approach is simply to urge a preferential option for women, always aware of the systematic inequities that plague. Likewise, any Christian ethic will pay special attention to the needs of children who have had no role in shaping the culture in which they live. Their nurture and protection are predominantly women's responsibility, although efforts are made to share it with men. This is the essence of a feminist perspective.[3]

My perspective is in the *liberation* stream insofar as I incorporate much of the method and content of Latin American liberation theology into the doing of moral theology in North America. Three aspects of liberation theology inform this task. First, a "preferential option" is given to the struggling poor, those who have been marginalized but who lay just claim to their inclusion in society. They are the most deeply affected by the results of such struggle, and in most instances they have little to lose.

For lesbian and gay Christians this is evident in the formation of denominational groups like Dignity, Integrity, Affirmations, and the Conference of Catholic Lesbians, among others. Although the reception is not always a welcome one by church bodies, lesbian and gay Christians have nothing to lose. Such witness is an important clue to the faithfulness called for to be a lesbian/gay Christian in the face of church-fueled persecution.

Second, the social sciences are an important tool for doing ethics insofar as sociology and psychology have become important aids in the reading of the data of revelation. Reading the "signs of the times" is key for the doing of ethics. For example, psychology and sociology have revealed that homosexuality is perfectly natural for at least 10% of the U.S. population. Likewise, we have learned that there are millions of lesbian and gay people living healthy, productive lives in this country. Such data are part of what is used to evaluate the morality of sexual issues, without in any way doing ethics simply by consensus.

A third aspect of liberation theology that informs contemporary ethical reflection is the hermeneutics of suspicion. Hermeneutics is the framework in which a text or doctrine is interpreted. Suspicion arises when texts expected to be used for inclusive building up of the community are used to exclude, to judge, and to ban. Either the text itself must be rejected, or the way of looking at the text comes under scrutiny.

A hermeneutics of suspicion assumes that scriptural and theological sources have not been read with an eye toward promoting lesbian and gay people, for example, in the face of institutionalized heterosexism and homophobia. Such a hermeneutics of suspicion is useful for developing alternative views of Christian ethics that are explicitly oriented toward the whole community, beginning with those who have been marginalized.

These three aspects of liberation theology lead me to conclude that a renewed sexual ethic must begin with the experience of sexually active gay men and those women who are at high risk. From a Christian feminist liberation perspective, I claim that as society's scapegoats, they must be among ethics' agents. Note that the very term "doing ethics" comes from the Spanish *hacer teologia,* to make or do theology. Likewise, we "do ethics" when we engage in the communal activity of holding one another accountable.

Expanding Sexual Ethics

AIDS is an equal opportunity killer even though high-risk groups exist. Sexually active gay men bear the brunt of the blame. Susan Sontag, writing about tuberculosis and cancer, concluded that long after a cure is found for society's dread diseases, certain groups remain ostracized. Society tends to project its anxiety over the reality of evil on those who suffer from the most difficult of diseases.[4]

The problems of homophobia and heterosexism are far more complicated than Sontag's analysis reveals. But Sontag provides a useful start in helping us to understand what fuels the virulent anti-gay attitudes and activities that hold sway in our society. They are, finally, ways to put at a distance the reality of evil, regardless of what we know scientifically about homosexual people.

There is an inherent danger in focusing on sexuality, since it may reinforce this blaming posture when the origin and causes of AIDS remain unknown. Nevertheless, the Christian ethical tradition has been part of the problem because of its teachings on homosexuality. A renewed Christian sexual ethics is needed to be part of the solution to a problem that goes deep into our social fabric, that is, discomfort with our bodies and dis-ease about sex. Thus my emphasis is both on ethical method and on the need to shift the content of some ethical positions on sexuality. This is a two-pronged effort to expand sexual ethics.

For human beings, sexual activity is highly symbolic behavior, albeit with very concrete, physical results. It is the way in which we "say" certain things about ourselves and one another. A brief review of sexuality in the Christian tradition reveals that misogyny and homophobia have unfortunately been components of even some of the most enlightened positions. Little is gained from rehearsing these, except to highlight how culturally conditioned and time bound sexual ethics have always been. From Augustine to Luther, from Calvin to Fletcher, sexual ethics have reflected the prevailing view of the body.

The advent of effective birth control and the recognition by the American Psychiatric Association that homosexuality is not a pathology are key social scientific facts that inform renewed sexual ethics. More significantly, people talk about sexuality in polite society in ways that a generation ago would have been considered unacceptable.

We simply do not know if actual sexual practices have changed as significantly as some data seem to suggest. But we do know that people discuss their sexual practices and expect to be accepted in society without regard for sexual preference. This is a new moment in Western history that the churches have yet to recognize. This is the cultural backdrop for the AIDS crisis, although it must be understood that such liberated ways about sexuality are more prevalent in the cities than in rural areas, and are usually more accepted among well-educated people than among less-educated people. In short, while progress has been made on this front, it would be an overstatement to say that most people in the United States are as comfortable with sexuality as selected New Age publications might suggest.

Nevertheless, this context suggests four essential elements of a Christian sexual ethics, which I will outline. Then I will respond to the elements I have outlined, using AIDS as the controlling factor.

First, *participation* is demanded in the shaping of Christian ethics. For most people, sexual ethics are part of the handed-down wisdom that they receive from their biological and faith families. Myths abound. Changes, no matter how pastorally progressive, do not come about by fiat, but through the participation of those most directly involved. Fiat is a singularly inefficient way to communicate a decision.

Real participation is the antidote to the liberal sense that people simply need continuing education. Education alone does not change the power equation appreciably, since people are simply told what those who make the decisions think. Those who make the decisions can just as quickly change their minds.

For example, in Roman Catholic sexual ethics, a slight shift took place after Vatican II to change the "end" of marriage from procreation, to procreation and companionship. Hardly any married Roman Catholics know this, since it was a decision made by a group of celibates and not effectively communicated. Of course married Catholics know why they married, but the sad irony is that they do not realize how in line with church teachings they really are.

Participation of those most deeply involved means not simply being interviewed, or read about, or watched on television. Rather, participation means being part of the decision-making body. Participation, in the liberation sense, includes those who are struggling to be heard. It includes special attention to people who are very young, elderly, disabled, or ill, all who would be left aside when the "normal" net is cast. This is perhaps the strongest challenge to renewed ethical exploration. It means exercising a fundamental trust in the experience of those about whom experts have heretofore pronounced.

This is a call, in the Roman Catholic Church, for a radical restructuring of the Vatican, something that is far beyond the scope of this essay. But for Protestant and ecumenical efforts it means encouraging widespread consultation and participation in drafting ethical theory. It means including the marginalized at the table, better, moving from the table to the streets and hospitals, where such people are. This is what it means to change the power equation.

Second, no ethical reflection begins in a vacuum. The Christian *tradition* is particularly rich with trends and movements that have informed generations before us. Not even the most outrageous preoccupation with what Daniel Maguire calls "pelvic theology" can be considered constant teaching of Christianity. *Deo gratias.* Natural law, while long outdated, had its own genius. But so, too, does the contextual method that flows from feminist and liberation approaches.

This approach reflects the need for more nuanced arguments to coincide with the complexity of our technological time. Still, what has endured throughout the Christian tradition is an effort to reflect gospel values of love, justice, inclusivity, and mutuality in everyday life, and a recognition of the tentativity of all human efforts in cooperation with divine workings.

Third, *social and physical sciences* are essential to Christian ethics. No longer the also-ran of theology, the sciences are integral elements of sound ethical reasoning. That is why no moral theologian can work without close cooperation with colleagues in many cognate areas.

While such cooperation may seem so obvious as to be banal, there are those who refuse to admit the inestimable contribution of the sciences to the doing of ethics. A subtler form of the same tendency emerges when some of those who admit the sciences do so with so many caveats (e.g., that science will dictate ethics, or that the sciences ought to be taken into account, but that the laws of God transcend "mere" human laws) that scientific advances are effectively barred from ethics.

This attitude has given moral theologians or ethicists a bad name. It has increased the distance between us to the point that many scientists simply write off ethical reflection as counterproductive. This achieves just the opposite of what serious ethicists intend. Mutuality between science and ethics will take time. And ethicists should not shrink from the task of critical reflection on scientific possibilities. But the olive branch must come from ethicists, since hard and often unfair criticism has come from our corner at times when scientists have been about the work of enhancing the human condition.

Finally, putting together an ethical method that invites widespread participation, maintains a faithfulness to the tradition, and incorporates the social/physical sciences still leaves ethics with a demanding job. This is the work of *concrete, daily choices,* living the moral life. The "moral choice" is ever a dance between informed judgment and divine grace.[5] Certainty eludes even the sharpest moral detectives. But painstaking research yields insight. Case-by-case evaluation, erring on the side of human frailty and presuming human goodness, will take us a great distance toward the ever receding horizon of truth.

Let us look at these elements of an ethical method, using AIDS as the case study. The question of *participation* begins with gay and lesbian people. Note that lesbians (at least those who do not have sexual relations with high-risk men and do not use intravenous drugs) have a negligible rate of AIDS infection. Nevertheless, because homophobia and heterosexism control both women and men, and because many lesbians have close gay male friends, lesbians have been deeply involved in the struggle against AIDS.

Stereotypes and laws, Supreme Court decisions, and church polity contribute to a climate of fear and repression. In my judgment, these mitigate against the possibility of a healthy sexual ethic, since such an ethic is for the whole community, regardless of sexual preference. This is especially ironic when some of our churches' "best and brightest" are gay/lesbian. When Roman Catholic priests die of AIDS, and ministers from several denominations have succumbed, people are beginning to realize that gay/lesbian people are everywhere.

As communities discard their fears and listen to gay men and lesbian women, they are hearing the life stories of their brothers and sisters. Likewise, when Christians consider the data on the dreaded child abuse, they are finding gay/lesbian people noticeably absent. So why all the residual homophobia and heterosexism standing in the way of a healthy sexual ethic? Unfortunately, aspects of the *Christian ethical tradition* must be faulted here.

Two reasons predominate. First, gay/lesbian people make an implicit statement about the fact that life need not be the way churches have taught (i.e., marriage is not necessarily the norm for all). If all lesbian/gay people were presumed to be healthy, good, and natural, rather than simply permitting an exemplary couple here and there to live without censure, then there would be a new cultural norm. The churches, ever the guardians of a culture's mores, are reluctant to let this happen.

I expect that Christians will eventually claim that all lesbian/gay people are good by reason of being created in the image and likeness of God/ess, and are to be judged like heterosexual people on the basis of their relations. But this implies that there are more ways to be fully human than we had previously imagined. Unfortunately most people operate out of a theory of scarcity rather than a theory of plenty; if gay/lesbian is good, then heterosexual is bad. Why not assume that gay/lesbian can be good, just as heterosexual can be good? The value then is placed on the quality of love involved and not the gender makeup of the people involved.

It takes time for this possibility of plurality to take root. Much economic, political, and ecclesial clout is tied up in the heterosexual ideal. Many people fear that part of them which is attracted to people of the same sex, even if they choose not to act on their attractions. These are powerful reasons to enforce heterosexism.

Second, lesbian/gay people represent, both actively and symbolically, a thorough embracing of sexual expression for pleasure and not for the procreation of children. This strikes at the heart of the Christian tradition, insofar as lesbian/gay sexuality is oriented toward deepening friendship and not toward reproduction. Admittedly, this is one gay/lesbian ideal and not shared by all. Likewise, there have been excesses. Promiscuity and anonymous sex are not the practices I have in mind here, although some gay men assure me that even these activities can have redeeming social and spiritual value.

Rather, I suggest that even before AIDS the challenge of

sexual experience without the possibility of children was anathema. Strains of punishment for sex linger in our society, probably because they have been a subtle part of churches' teaching. Pregnancy is the prime example of punishment, with the disproportionate burden of this cultural pathology falling to women. Anti-abortion virulence is a case in point. For example, opponents of choice make a distinction between protected and unprotected intercourse, usually favoring abortion in the face of contraceptive failure, but not when human error is involved. The burden that this places on women leads me to reject it outright. And it shows why homosexual sex is outside of the perverted pale that such reasoning represents.

Moreover, punishment for sex offends my Christian sense that sexual expression is a language in which consenting adults have right to communicate provided that some "rules" and "grammar" of accountability are followed. It is these rules and grammar (i.e., ethics) that need refining. And this can happen only when those who are most intimately familiar with the language can express themselves.

Thus heterosexism and homophobia are the catch-22 of Christian sexual ethics. Lesbian and gay people cannot share their experiences without real fear of censure, especially within their religious families. The miracle is that these people have any interchange with religion.

It is important to point out that gay/lesbian people have engaged in selfless efforts to provide for persons with AIDS (without regard for sexual preference). Attention to these extraordinary efforts may help to bridge the gap between Christian ideals and actual practice. The irony of those who are excluded actually taking leadership in roles that the churches stress is not lost on anyone.

Resources abound in the Christian tradition for dealing with AIDS. Previous plagues have found their heroes and heroines in the religious sphere, and AIDS is no exception. Christian care for the sick and dying is legend. AIDS is, finally, a disease, not divine retribution for life-style choices that some do not accept.

Reports are that some Christian organizations currently providing care for persons with AIDS have been proscribing certain practices (i.e., preventing lovers from visiting their dying partners, etc.). This is simply unacceptable in the face of sick persons who deserve compassion and care, and the right to die with dignity. In this medical sense there is nothing special about AIDS. It is simply another way that people die.

But to get to such clarity requires negotiating the crowded waters of sexual variety, accepting the mystery of sexual difference, and rejoining in the goodness of embodied human love. This is not easy for those who would confine their window of acceptability to monogamously married heterosexual people. But for the vast majority of believers, Christianity provides the ethical elasticity to embrace the exile. This is the challenge of lesbian/gay people to the churches.

The *sciences* are our biggest help in the face of AIDS. Much work needs to be done. But we now know how it is spread, although not how it began. We now know how much of it can be contained, although not how to eradicate it. This is the legacy of tireless scientists who have risked infection for the sake of medical knowledge. It seems that we who "do ethics" can risk the contamination of our professional reputations as we deal with the unpopular and wrestle with the unresolved.

Science has also contributed to society's ability to live with AIDS unafraid. Ethicists have the responsibility to educate, especially within the parameters of a faith tradition. We need to begin with sex education, so that children know and can say the names of body parts and sexual activities just as they are learning what it means to live and love responsibly. This will help to check the spread of AIDS.

It is up to ethicists and, by extension, pastors and church officials to be sure that such communication gives a positive impression of sexuality. For example, condoms, while not 100% effective in preventing AIDS, are rapidly becoming an accepted part of healthy heterosexual and gay male sexual activities. Imagine a generation that grows up with this experience, that grows up putting condoms in the same grocery cart as milk and eggs. This is part of a healthy integrated sexuality for which church workers must assume some responsibility. We must communicate that sex is good, a part of creation, something to be enjoyed and shared responsibly. If the only messages children get from the churches are warnings, then the separation between secular and sacred, between bad and good, will be exacerbated.

No scientific facts will substitute for careful consideration of *concrete ethical claims*. Nor will promise of a cure for AIDS comfort those who will die before it is readily available. Here the churches have no choice but to begin to transform their dismal track records into histories of leadership in a difficult moment.

Many Christians have encountered roadblocks to their faith when their churches' positions have condemned homosexuality. Many Roman Catholics, for example, are deeply discouraged by the recent Vatican letter that called the tendency toward homosexuality (as opposed to homosexual acts themselves, which had previously been condemned) "morally disordered." Other denominations, while normally more polite, have made equally dubious theological assessments. The legitimate question raised by lesbian/gay people is why bother with such a tradition, why try to change it when the position is so clear?

My answer is that such questions challenge the churches to the very ethical reconsideration that this essay purports to undertake. I turn then to those aspects of the Christian tradition that can be used to move beyond the current situation to a "discipleship of equals" in which such questions would not have to be asked.

Rescuing Christian Sources for Ethics

The two major sources of Christian input for ethics, scripture and the theological tradition, contain elements that can be useful for a renewed sexual ethic.

Christian scripture is more properly the subject of another essay in this series. But I turn to the work of Elisabeth Schussler Fiorenza for insights on how to appropriate scripture, using a critical feminist hermeneutics of liberation, in the face of anti-lesbian/gay sentiments. Her brilliant volume *In Memory of Her* has set the exegetical pace for contemporary theology.[6]

Schussler Fiorenza claims that the hermeneutical task must be oriented toward "a critical evaluation" of texts in order to "uncover and reject those elements within all biblical traditions and texts that perpetuate, in the name of God, violence, alienation, and patriarchal subordination."[7] These, then, are simply to be left aside.

It must also "recover all those elements within biblical texts and traditions that articulate the liberating experiences and visions of the people of God."[8] This approach to scripture, although largely untried by biblical scholars working on gay/lesbian issues, holds great promise for developing a renewed sexual ethic. Otherwise, we are left with the unhappy and inefficient approach of proof texting, reinterpreting difficult, contextually bound materials. Schussler Fiorenza's challenging approach allows us to deal with frequent scriptural arguments against lesbian and gay people in a creative and decisive way.

Similar breakthroughs in systematic theology are less spectacular. But the insights of feminist theologians provide some keys. For example, it is generally assumed, after the pioneering work of Rosemary Radford Ruether, Elisabeth Schussler Fiorenza, and others, that women's experiences have been left aside in the doing of theology.[9] Similar claims are being made by church historians like John Boswell and Judith Brown when it comes to understanding how gay/lesbian themes influence the doing of theology.[10]

Beverly Wildung Harrison's work is probably the closest ethical analogue.[11] Her focus was on abortion, but her claims for the priority of bodily integrity and women's moral agency have their parallels in lesbian/gay experience. Sexual preference is part of bodily integrity. The ability to choose how to relate with one's body, whether genitally or otherwise, is a basic human right. Surely Christian ethics will look different as this becomes a shared belief.

Likewise, moral agency cannot be stolen from lesbian/gay people simply because some do not approve of our sexual preference. Moral agency, or the right to make contextual decisions based on concrete cases, is another basic human right. What is called into question is the "top down" decision-making style that would presume to leave social values in the hands of a few.

There is a paucity of resources here for a genuine reconstruction of the Christian ethical tradition. But at least there is some precedent for our efforts. At least there is interest on the part of those who have been deeply hurt and alienated by the churches' behavior in the past to try to rescue parts of the tradition for future generations. It is the task of my generation of theologians and ethicists to do the constructive work on the basis of lesbian/gay experience.

Toward a Renewed Sexual Ethic

The work of criticizing or discarding a particular ethic involves a responsibility to try to replace it with something more useful. Otherwise, critical work is simply destructive. My intention is to pave the way with the foregoing for some initial thoughts on a renewed sexual ethic, confident that the more refined ideas will emerge from shared discussion.

In the case of AIDS, perhaps the most urgent challenge is to keep sex, especially gay male sex (and by extension gay men), from having a bad reputation. There is nothing wrong with sex per se just because some people die of a deadly disease that is spread, in some cases, by some forms of sexual expression. To the contrary, sex is one of life's great pleasures and one of relationship's great benefits. This should be the churches' first and most frequent message. It applies equally to everyone.

I realize that this is the hardest message to elucidate, but let me suggest four aspects of sexual expression, understood from gay/lesbian experience, that I think lead to a renewed Christian sexual ethic. Note that the same could be done from a heterosexual point of view. In fact I would encourage that. But for my purposes this less understood and more feared perspective provides just the impetus we need to really renew ethics, not simply to add on to or readjust what exists already.

The four aspects that ground a renewed Christian sexual ethic are vulnerability, pleasure, accountability, and generativity. Exploring each of these in turn will provide insight into the project at hand.

Vulnerability is part of every deep human relationship. It is an essential ingredient in the "fierce tenderness" of friendship.[12] The link between vulnerability and sexuality is what ethicist Karen Lebacqz, writing on sexual ethics for single people, calls "the precondition for an adequate sexual ethic."[13]

228

Vulnerability, according to Lebacqz, is to be valued as a part of sexuality. "Sex, eros, passion are antidotes to the human sin of wanting to be in control or to have power over another."[14] It is part of the biblical sense that human intimacy or "knowing" one another involves great risk. It takes great responsibility to protect and nurture the beloved who is vulnerable.

In the case of gay/lesbian sex, the usual interpersonal vulnerability is magnified by the social risk of being "known" as that which society at large rejects on the basis of whom one loves. How odd, from a Christian perspective, that love itself is the cause of inappropriate, unprotected vulnerability. Thus vulnerability not only names the stance that friends assume when sexual expression is integrated into a relationship, but also describes the point at which the Christian community needs transformation.

Further, the specter of AIDS and other sexually transmitted diseases makes some forms of sexual expression riskier than others. Vulnerability is not an excuse for unsafe sexual practices. But it is a powerful reminder of the mutual responsibility that sexual relations involve if, tragically, one's partner is afflicted.

Pleasure is a second aspect of a creative sexual ethic. I do not mean here a hedonistic glorification of pleasure for its own sake, although I do not oppose it. Rather, I mean an honest reveling in the pleasures of the body that are part of the created order and meant to be enjoyed.

One of the most damaging dimensions of Christian ethics has been the all too successful effort to rob people of the few natural, inexpensive, and (in most instances) legal delights left in the world. Sexual pleasure is one of them. Women have an especially difficult time undoing social and ecclesial conditioning in this regard. Women wonder if we are deserving of what we enjoy; guilt abounds.

Thus pleasure must be rescued from the jaws of oppression and returned to the sexual realm. Then we can claim that the divine intention in creation is fulfilled as we enjoy ourselves and one another. For lesbian and gay people this "pleasure principle" is a powerful antidote to the pain that is inflicted by society. Yet revenge is not pleasure, and ought not be construed as such.

Sexual pleasure is not the only kind there is. Nature, food, art, sports, music, children, etc., all provide pleasure. I am simply suggesting that pleasure, which has been banned by the somber debates that usually accompany such discussions, ought to reclaim its place in Christian sexual ethics. Lesbian/gay people do this implicitly, and, as I have noted above, this provides a challenge to a heterosexist society.

Pleasure's balance comes from *accountability*. A renewed sexual ethic need not abandon time-tested virtues of this sort. But it must expand the notion of accountability from a private to a communal sense. Actions are not simply acceptable or unacceptable on the basis of their impact on one's partner. Rather, they must be seen in the largest possible context in which neighbor is understood as those both near and far.

Accountability is what ethics is all about. But it is not meant to be the brakes on the engine of change. Rather, it is intended to be a way of seeing behavior in a larger context than the local setting. It is a way of claiming kinship and acting in solidarity with others. It is a way of breaking down the tendency to think of oneself and one's family rather than of all of us and those we do not yet see. More than ourselves are affected by sexual expression.

This leads to the final factor, *generativity*. I do not mean this as a synonym for procreation. Such theological sleight of hand has no business in ethics. Rather, I mean that all love relationships, hence all contexts for sexual expression, generate something beyond the relationship itself. This need not be a child. In fact, in the case of most lesbian and gay people it is not a child.

It may be a deeper, broader sense of community, of welcoming the stranger, of developing a home where others feel welcome. It may be that sexually expressed love inspires great art, a tasteful garden, fine poetry, a well-tuned auto, even, with a little luck, good ethics. The lover is often the muse, May Sarton reminds us. The point is that generativity is available to everyone, regardless of marital status or procreative possibilities. Generativity is another name for divine-human cooperation.

230

A sexual ethic that combines vulnerability, pleasure, accountability, and generativity is a good start for renewing our thinking and living in the face of AIDS. It will not cure the disease, but it will encourage us to live in a more humane way in the meanwhile.

Implementation

The move from contemporary sexual ethics to the broad framework that I have described is not as difficult as it might appear. I realize that for many denominations, and especially for my own Roman Catholic Church, it is difficult to move beyond the parameters of traditional ethics. More so, it is hard to let the stranger in, to extend the ethical frontiers to include the marginalized.

However, two guiding principles may be helpful. The first is that although I have founded this ethical discussion on lesbian/gay experience, it is not only for lesbian/gay people. Such a juxtaposition (i.e., usually a lesbian/gay ethic is derived from heterosexual experience) may actually help some people to see how close our various experiences are.

Second, I would stress the need for church groups to begin with discussion of actual people's experience. It is far too easy, following an analysis of this sort, to remain on a level of abstraction and theory as a convenient way of never grappling with the fact that those who have AIDS have names and faces, families and lovers. My analysis arises out of such concrete pastoral experience, and I suspect that it will deepen best in conversation with more of the same.

A renewed sexual ethic for Christian churches, one that is firmly based on participation, tradition, social/physical sciences, and real moral choices, and measured by vulnerability, pleasure, accountability, and generativity, will be a welcome contribution in the face of an unwelcome disease. Then, as in the resurrection of Jesus, we will be able to say of AIDS that once again new life comes to the Christian community after unspeakable tragedy.

Notes

1. Krister Stendahl, *Jesus Among Jews and Gentiles* (Philadelphia: Fortress Press, 1976).
2. Beverly Wildung Harrison, *Our Right to Choose* (Boston: Beacon Press, 1983).
3. I have named mine a feminist perspective, aware of the fact that black women, especially Delores Williams, speak of theirs as a "womanist" perspective. The womanist perspective takes account not only of the ways in which women are systematically oppressed in society, but what Williams calls "demonarchy," the social forces which prevent women from providing for themselves and their dependent children.

   My understanding of feminism has been expanded to include these concerns, yet I continue to call it feminist so as to underscore that it emerges from the experience of a white woman who is indebted to black women like Williams for their useful insight.
4. Susan Sontag, *Illness as Metaphor* (New York: Farrar, Straus, Giroux, 1978).
5. Cf. Daniel Maguire, *The Moral Choice* (New York: Winston-Seabury, 1979).
6. Elisabeth Schussler Fiorenza, *In Memory of Her* (New York: Crossroad, 1983).
7. Ibid. p. 32.
8. Ibid. p. 33.
9. Cf. Rosemary Radford Ruether, *Sexism and God-Talk* (Boston: Beacon Press, 1983) and Elisabeth Schussler Fiorenza, ibid.
10. Cf. John Boswell, *Christianity, Social Tolerance and Homosexuality* (Chicago: University of Chicago Press, 1980); Judith Brown, *Immodest Acts* (New York: Oxford University Press, 1986).
11. Harrison.
12. Cf. my forthcoming *Fierce Tenderness: Toward a Feminist Theology of Friendship.* To be published by Harper & Row, San Francisco, 1989.
13. Cf. Karen Lebacqz, "Appropriate Vulnerability: A Sexual Ethic for Singles," *The Christian Century,* May 6, 1987, pp. 435–38.
14. Ibid. p. 437.

15

Biblical Revelation and Human Sexuality

Dr. Gerald T. Sheppard

Our current moment is characterized by anxiety over the quantity of "information" at hand and by the loss of a "modern" confidence regarding its significance. Our deconstructive agility is more impressive than our vision of how to move forward. If we are "post-modern," we should remember that the prefix post denotes the equivocal sense of "ahead" in time but "behind" in space (e.g., post-axial). The very ambiguous promise of a post-modern future allows for the awakening of older, lazy legalisms and prejudices that modern Christianity and a secularized modernity temporarily had laid to rest. Within this climate the churches need to have a certain sound, a clear voice.

Among the implications of AIDS for sexuality is a bitter resentment, expressed popularly by an essay in *Toronto Life*. As a refrain throughout the article, the author announces, "The party's over."[1] He pines the fate of a younger generation that will not be able to experiment sexually without fear. The traditional association of love and death (cf. Song of Songs 8:6) reasserts itself in a cruel and unexpected fashion. When the guests at a party begin to die because of their participation, that party indeed should be over. The imagery of "a party" itself may betray a certain equivocal assessment of the sexual revolution. Greater sexual experimentation may, in fact, not be synonymous with enhanced pleasure, personal affirmation, or even more "fun" at a party. Real "love" and "good sex" (as Dr. Ruth alone can pronounce correctly) are treasures as well as pleasures. Ethical reflection about them honors that recognition. If sex belongs only among the cheap favors and perishable decorations at a party, then the party that is ending was not much of one anyway. The crisis of AIDS will force us to think about sexual practices. Expressions of intimate sexual love have suddenly become more demanding of our careful reflection, thoughtful precaution, and genuine appreciation.

At the moment, I am pessimistic about the prospect of strong positive leadership or a common voice from most Christian churches on the subject of human sexuality. Churches have proved better at learning to wink at some previously condemned sexual behavior than at finding ways to discuss affirmatively ethical implications of the same. In general, churches have only barely started to seek a fresh understanding of what would constitute a Christian freedom to act in the light of the current possibilities of sexual expression. Moreover, a failure to address profoundly a matter so basic to our existence and life together must weaken the constructive influence of the churches in contemporary society and, in theological terms, betrays a blindness to signs of the reign of God among our own prophets, priests, and sages. What I have to say is, in that sense, only some ophthalmological notations to be shared among my colleagues. My strategy will be to explore some implications of changes both in our understanding of human sexuality and in our use of scripture as the principal witness to Christian revelation for a Christian ethic of freedom, love, and justice in all human relationships.

The New Possibilities of a Modern "Sexual Liberation"

Why are there genuine new possibilities in the area of human sexuality that require a new response from the churches? On the one hand, people in our society can expect to experience an extended life span. We also experience the protraction of dating before a postponed age for marriage, new developments in birth control, medical cures for sex-related diseases, a different socio-economic interpretation of "family," and a clearer understanding of human sexual functioning so that older taboos, laws, and wisdom must be revised to respond to a more precise taxonomy of sexual dispositions and practices. On the other hand, these developments are but one manifestation of a larger technological revolution. Equally pertinent and related possibilities include artificial insemination, utopian procreative proposals, genetic engineering, and other medical and surgical advances.

Our increased openness to a new variety of possibilities that touch on the area of human sexuality may, in fact, be far more the result of technological advances than the consequence of enlighted moral reflection or sexual liberation. Sexual liberation can easily be confused with the willingness to try anything technologically made safe or feasible, as though the exercise of every low-risk sexual option were a sign of freedom. The ethical implications are further complicated by an awareness that there is great variety in the ethical potential of one's actions. An action in one context will be significant, and in another, trivial. Some will be considered good and life-affirming, others evil and destructive. How the sexual revolution can really contribute to human liberation, in an ethically positive sense, remains a major matter of concern for the churches and for caring people everywhere. If new technology has unleashed new possibilities that we have tried to enjoy for the benefit of all, AIDS is a frightening reminder that we can no more control everything in territory related to sexuality than we can manipulate the environment without the risk of catastrophic surprises of nature. What may be low risk today could become high risk tomorrow, and our technology may not be able to respond quickly or effectively.

At a minimum, the new possibilities in the area of understanding human sexuality force a fresh set of questions on the churches and may nuance some sexual matters in a way that opens once closed issues in Christian ethics. Here I include questions about birth control and artificial insemination. Even the more ordinary issues of human sexuality may appear different to us. For example, churches have now become adept at trying to distinguish and to evaluate ethically a hierarchy of sexual expressions in prolonged dating that could lead to sexual intercourse (kissing, holding hands, light petting, heavy petting).

Another significant change has been that most of even the more conservative churches now accept the position that one may have a same-sex orientation that derives from early childhood and is not a matter of personal choice. My point is that such a shift in perception necessarily implies a new set of questions in response to modernity and just as necessarily seeks some new guidance in biblical revelation for contemporary Christian ethics. If these churches simply cite older formulations of church law, they will do justice neither to the gift of this moment within the history of God's creation nor to the profundity of God's revelation regarding how we can be free within it.

New Possibilities for Understanding the Bible in Relation to Christian Ethics

Before considering major issues in a Christian ethical response to the current possibilities of human sexuality, some basic stance must be assumed about the nature of scripture and the presumption of biblical revelation within Christian faith. My aim here is to focus on one fundamental issue: What is a biblical text and how does such text offer minimal clues about how it can be read biblically? A clear answer to this question will not solve a number of equally significant problems for ethics, but it will at least venture some discrete vision of the Bible so that one may discuss what new possibilities arise for the modern or "postmodern" interpretation of it.

The position I am espousing has gained momentum in the past few decades, principally among biblical scholars and theologians. My own version draws on both traditio-historical and comparative religious modes of expression. From a comparativist approach, we see that particular pre-scriptural traditions or texts may eventually attain the status of "scripture" within most world religions. Although the nature of these scriptures varies considerably, the phenomenon itself remains a familiar one. As in Judaism and Christianity, the presence of such a scripture need not preclude the importance of extra-scriptural authorities or canonical traditions (e.g., Christian creeds, or the Oral Torah). A "modern" and, therefore, "new" contribution of traditio-historical investigations has been the discovery that most of the traditions retained and preserved within the scriptures of world religions were not originally composed to be scriptural texts. Rarely does a religious founder intentionally write such a text; the final context of a scripture reflects almost universally the effort of later believers to give some definitive shape to older traditions. This general feature of scriptures in world religions applies well to the cases of Judaism and Christianity. A great variety of emphemeral traditions are eventually collected in the final form of Jewish scripture. Christianity proves to be exceptional among world religions because its scriptures are a composite of another religion's scripture that has been expanded and altered in its semantic import ("Jew scripture" transformed into "Old Testament") through the addition of another canon of scriptural books, the "New Testament."

Implications for Christian ethics from a comparativist perspective include a new appreciation for similarities and differences among religions on a topic such as sexuality. It may be argued, for instance, that Christianity is the only major world religion that from its inception defended monogamy as the only proper social context for sexual intercourse.[2] Christian ethics uses the "Old Testament" in a manner quite distinct from the Jewish reading of Hebrew scripture. If the Torah is the central subject of a Jewish interpretation of Hebrew scripture, the gospel of Jesus Christ is the primary subject of the Old Testament within Christian scripture. Both Judaism and Christianity recognize that Torah, Prophecy, and Wisdom are major idioms of their shared scripture, but Christianity understands these idioms in the context of a new "gospel" revelation, often in a manner quite distinct from what is found in Jewish interpretation. My interest is not to suggest the superiority of Christian interpretation, but rather to challenge the all too common assumption that a Christian ethicist should principally seek to read the "Old Testament" as Christian scripture detached from the New Testament and, therefore, as a neutral source of moral rules or unifying ethical themes of equal significance to Jewish and Christian believers. Such generosity does justice to neither Judaism nor Christianity and usually depreciates the specific context in Judaism of normative Oral Torah (Mishnah, the Talmuds), as well as the genius of midrashic interpretation. Chris-

237

tians in conversation with Jewish interpreters on matters of ethics in human sexuality need to respect these differences, just as they do in conversation with other religions.

Traditio-historical investigations of the Bible in the modern period have raised other problems for how ethicists appeal to scripture. Using modern historical criteria, scholars could deconstruct the Bible into its older "genuine" units of traditions or sources. Through speculative reconstruction within the biblical theology movement, scholars sought to find some unifying elements within the diversity of tradition or some relatively constant factor supposedly at work in the history of pre-biblical traditions. In these scenarios the value of traditions found in the Bible could be determined by how well one could recover their original social or historical contexts. The danger here is that historical criticism can seem to solve problems by first establishing the ethical past as an antiquarian moment and then distilling some significance from it through a philosophical theory of historical transcendence. The temptation is to choose a pious reading of a reconstructed history rather than a historically informed interpretation of a constructed, scriptural text.

Consequently, Christian scripture is not the result of an endeavor to provide historically accurate impressions of the antique ethical "life worlds" from ancient times. Rather, in the words of Brevard Childs, "it is constitutive of the canon to seek to transmit the tradition in such a way as to prevent its being moored in the past."[3] The formation of scripture suggests less an idealization of history or a sacrifice of ethical concreteness than a revelation or rendering of reality. The vehicle of biblical revelation remains a human witness presented in scripture through a densely edited variety of both historical and non-historical traditions. One cannot make scripture more biblically alive or valid by repairing traditions within it so that they correspond with more fidelity to specific moments in the history of the ancient world. Conversely, the mere fact that some ethical teaching in scripture conforms to socioeconomic conditions no longer common to later generations does not, in itself, remove the force of its authority. The present tense of scripture demands other interpretive responses than those typically used in simple, modern confrontations with traditions mired in the concreteness of their own historical references.

238

If an ethicist insists that the significance of the Bible must lie in its capacity to exhibit actual ethical actions within a specific historical context, then it is true that the Bible may prove disappointing. The Bible is only a modest resource for case studies in the ethics of pre-biblical times. While, in fact, certain contexts of Jewish and Christian scriptures show high regard for historical sequence, others just as often conjoin earlier traditions anachronistically in order to establish some other topical orientation or inner-biblical connections. So, David is integrally associated with the psalms despite the presence of a psalm of Solomon (Psalm 72), while the link with Solomon establishes certain books as biblical "wisdom" with minimal historical setting. The effect, however, is to transform an ancient hymnbook into a prophetic commentary (cf. 2 Sam. 23:1–2) and to establish a characterization of biblical wisdom as distinct from, although not contradicting, the Mosaic Torah (cf. Ecclesiastes 12:13). Although there may be only limited concern with a modern desire for distinctive historical contexts of ethical action, the interpretation of the Bible as torah and wisdom bears directly on other matters unquestionably of central concern to a modern ethicist.

Such a fresh appreciation of the canonical context of scripture for Christian ethical interpretation changes how we conceive the relation of the Bible to sexual ethics. Instead of atomizing the Bible and reconstructing its parts into a scheme of "salvation history" or into a thematically related cafeteria of "biblical theologies," the biblical text itself is sustained as a common text open to interpretation between pulpit and pew, classroom and work place. Historical criticism denotes a variety of deconstructive methods of investigation that may illuminate the biblical context by clarifying systemic vagueness, sharpening our perception of contextual ambiguity, illuminating realistic elements, heuristically helping our recognition of how traditions and books attained a scriptural context, and heightening our perception of unresolved differences retained in the biblical text from its etymological past. One of the characteristics of scriptural literature is an unharmonized or uninterpreted dimension that evokes rather than settles the possibilities of interpretation. For example, there are different sets of laws written in the Torah (pentateuch), in the prophets, and a post-biblical Oral Torah, yet only one torah that each generation seeks to hear and to do in its own time. There are four Gospels, Pauline letters, James, and post-biblical ecumenical confessions, yet only one gospel of Jesus Christ that each Christian reader seeks to express in her or his own time.

Koinonia Ethics and Wisdom Ethics

How the Bible remains pertinent as a norm in Christian ethics, including the ethics of sexuality, is a continuing question. In the recent past a major problem has emerged regarding the relation of Christian ethics both to modern views of anthropology, whether social scientific, medical, or psychological, and to practical reason. This problem has been exacerbated by positions that have become commonplace in dogmatic and biblical theology. Friedrich Schleiermacher's incisive theological proposals provided the paradigm of a liberal theological effort to start with modern scientific, rationalistic, and psychological criteria for defining the nature of humanity. Neoorthodoxy arose as a criticism of these liberal conceptions of "anthropology." Karl Barth compellingly objected to the use of modern anthropology as a point of departure for theology. In his sharp no to Brunner, he made a further case against any effort to argue for a "natural theology" distinct from special revelation. The identification of the nature of humanity with the image of God could be ascertained only though an analogy of faith and not by an analogy of being. Without denying the value of the social sciences, one can argue that a theological anthropology can only begin with the testimony of scripture and especially with the revelation of humanity in the crucified Christ.

The rejection of the primacy of social scientific insights for theological anthropology corresponds well with a key theme in the biblical theology movement. By placing emphasis on revelation through testimonies about historical events or even "history as revelation," scholars often stressed the essential message of the Bible as "salvation history." The effect was to marginalize biblical traditions that could not be located in specific moments of history, including especially wisdom such as found in the Solomonic books or even in the Psalms. Gerhard von Rad, a premier Old Testament scholar of this period, tried to describe

240

the Psalms and wisdom literature as a timeless "response" to salvation history.[4] Other scholars suggested that wisdom literature offered an alternative secular or humanistic perspective to the prophetic assumptions about God's historical revelation in word and deed. Because wisdom literature seems persistently anthropological in scope, the question of how an ethics so concerned with theological anthropology should relate to anthropology generally, both in the Bible and outside of it, became increasingly ambiguous. Particularly with fresh insights from a canonical approach to scripture, a reformulation regarding the role of scripture in Christian ethics is needed. Moreover, because so many features of the sexual revolution pertain to new knowledge in sexology, new technology, and new sources of practical reason, the relation of the social sciences to Christian ethics deserves reexamination.

My constructive proposal for ethics is twofold. First, I think we should continue to reject an anthropocentric theology, one that starts from modern social scientific knowledge of human nature, and we should continue to defend the primacy of divine revelation in a Christian understanding of anthropology. Furthermore, I am sympathetic with Christian ethics that looks to scripture for a revelation of that *shalom* and *koinonia* that provides a context from which to evaluate the ethical potential of our actions.[5] Second, I would recommend that a Christian approach to ethics take seriously the presence of biblical wisdom in both the Old and the New Testament. In the context of the Old Testament, the Solomonic wisdom books offer a guide to the obedient life distinct from the revelation of laws and realistic narrative depiction in the Torah. While the Torah in its written form of a pentateuch is associated with Moses, the prophet par excellence, the books of Proverbs, Ecclesiastes, and the Song of Songs are associated with Solomon, the sage par excellence. In the narrative and literary context of wisdom books a correspondence is established between wisdom and torah. Wisdom in scripture is clearly not the same as revealed law. As von Rad brilliantly articulated, wisdom literature in scripture presumes a self-conscious bracketing out of most of the key elements in the confession of the religion (covenant, the Exodus, revealed law, prophetic interpretation). However, if Solomon is to be a righteous king before Yahweh, he must accompany his renowned wisdom with obedience to the laws of God epitomized in the Mosaic legislation (cf. 1 Kings 3:14). This interplay between wisdom and law is carried over into the New Testament. It is present, for example, in the tension between the Pauline expression of the gospel and the wisdom teaching of the book of James. Wisdom is not so much "a response" to the historical claims of biblical revelation or "salvation history" as it is an alternative way of self-consciously participating in the international endeavor to circumscribe the world God has made and the nature of human life within it.

In a wisdom ethics, a self-conscious effort is made to bracket out vocabulary ideosyncratic to the religion, while affirming a "fear of God" resembling that of believers in other religions. Although not abdicating to any purely secular or merely rational descriptions, Christian wisdom uses mundane logic to identify wisdom and foolishness, right conduct and wickedness. At the same time, it overtly values the pursuit of pleasure, success, hospitality, and social justice. Biblical wisdom comes the closest to *resembling* a "natural theology" or a "world theology" because it maximizes the family resemblance between what it knows through the advantage of revelation and what others in the world may know also through various means. It invites the possibility of borrowing wisdom from the rest of the world and of competing with the sages of every nation and religious conviction. In its highest moments it enduces the Queen of Sheba to come to test Solomon with riddles. Because it values and draws boldly on the knowledge of the world, its expressions seek to grow in precision over time. The riddles that test it become increasingly subtle both for the world and for the Christian believer in pursuit of a free, just, and loving life in the world. The wisdom mode of expressing ethics derives neither from an admission of a failure in Christian revelation nor from a reluctant turning to better, secular, and social scientific descriptions of humanity. To the contrary, it is because of our faith in God and because we have experienced God's love revealed in scripture and in our lives that we, "in the fear of God [Prov. 1:7]," value the discovery of new wisdom wherever and by whomever it is found in the world.

242

Christian Ethics and Sexuality: Specific Responses

Because I have concentrated on more general hermeneutical issues, my suggestions here will necessarily be succinct. I will offer a series of suggestions without endeavoring to be systematic. In the area of sexual ethics, Christian ethics in the light of the gospel seeks to know how one can be free rather than captive to legalisms or prejudice. This freedom is a freedom to be faithful, to experience koinonia that is analogous to God's love for us, and to live without condemnation.

1. We should recognize that "ethics" is not an internal biblical category, and a distinction between "Old Testament ethics" and "New Testament ethics" almost inevitably misconstrues the relation between the testaments as part of Christian scripture. While the law, prophecy, and gospel obviously make ethical claims, so does wisdom literature. Wisdom literature encompasses much more than ethics, but it also takes up many concerns of ethics. In Proverbs alone one can find undifferentiated demands or appeals to wise and right conduct suggestive, for instance, of contemporary distinctions in deontological, perfectionist, teleological, prescriptive, and consequentialist approaches. Ethics as a Christian discipline defines its task properly in a post-biblical form and in a response to post-biblical questions and conceptions of differentiation.

2. Using categories I have suggested, much of the advice sought about sexology, psychological dimensions in sexuality, safe sex practices, birth control, and issues related to abortion belong to a Christian wisdom ethic. However, many other decisions regarding the morality of birth control or abortion belong to reflection based on a koinonia Christian ethic, based on a full confession of the gospel. Wisdom brackets out many of the concerns of a Christian view of koinonia in order to make observations about what actions are "better than" others; wisdom recognizes a relativity to the ethical potential for certain possible actions being foolish or wise, moral or immoral. Because one can be wise without always knowing or obeying the law of God, wisdom ethics allows for significant public discourse that rivals

and borrows from wisdom found anywhere in the world. As another example, a Christian wisdom ethic, in my view, must include psychological and social scientific understandings of homosexuality, same-sex sexual practices, safe-sex precautions, and the social abuse experienced by gay and lesbian people. I would think that applying Christian ethical wisdom, one would support human rights for such people, equal opportunity in employment and housing, and laws against social homophobia.

There is an overlap in *some* ethical positions in the Bible between the central revelation and wisdom. For example, proverbs in the book of Proverbs as well as the law in the Mosaic Torah have condemnations against moving a boundary stone or using unfair weights in measuring goods. So, a wisdom ethic can reject pederasty, same sex and opposite sex, simply as an imperative without a full koinonia defense, while practical reason in the world regarding the psychosocial destructiveness of such relations may be sufficient support for the same imperative among non-Christians. However, the ethical decision about whether people are gay only as the result of divine wrath in response to their prior acts of sin or because of their disbelief is a different kind of theological issue and specifically pertains to an understanding of Christian koinonia. Such a decision is not resolved solely by social or psychological evidence, although it ought to be *informed* by such wisdom instead of the foolishness of uncriticized prejudice.

3. Advances in a Christian wisdom ethic must necessarily affect how one frames questions and elicits ethical answers based on biblical interpretation and an understanding of koinonia. A wise observation of slavery has changed our perception of it socially and psychologically over time. Concurrently the institutions of slavery have also changed. Here we borrow from and contribute to social scientific information, political analysis, and even the personal accounts of slaves. Both Christians and members of society at large form ethical opinions about the wisdom and rightness of slavery. However, Christian ethics must ask another question: Does slavery as we now know it violate koinonia under terms of the gospel? Even if slavery is tolerated and sustained by many statements in the Old and New Testa-

ment (cf. 1 Timothy 6:1–5), we may condemn it, as we can know it in wisdom, as an unbiblical violation of koinonia according to the claims of the gospel. We do not condemn slavery simply because we are now better informed, but because greater precision in wisdom naturally invites a new precision regarding the ethical terms of koinonia. This position does not advocate a postbiblical, progressive revelation, but rather the search for a more precise understanding of how the claims of the gospel ethically pertain to contemporary life. It is not a neutral hermeneutical exercise in pure reason for it seeks to illuminate through the power of the Holy Spirit the relation of the testimony of scripture to its proper subject matter. The potential differences between the biblical witness to the gospel of Jesus Christ and occasional laws in the Bible that implicitly support slavery by making it more benign are heightened so that they become for us an either/or. Either the gospel or slavery! In this form the koinonia ethic for Christians may actually become less tolerant than the prescriptions of wisdom.

How the Bible can be used as a norm regarding the subject of homosexuality moves in a similar direction.[6] On grounds of Christian wisdom, fresh questions have been raised about same-sex-oriented people. Conservative and liberal churches alike already have recognized a new possibility, that most gay people neither chose their orientation nor is it the result of God's wrath against their sin or unbelief. For these reasons self-styled "evangelicals" now recommend that for Christian koinonia, it is permissible that one admit to "being" homosexual as long as that person remains celebate. This position in a koinonia ethic exceeds explicit statements of scripture by raising a more precise question to the claims of the gospel. However, I would argue further that, as in the case of our views about slavery, the biblical injunctions against same-sex sexual practice demand a more precise response in the light of a proclamation of freedom in support of koinonia that is integral to the gospel. Despite no explicit biblical evidence in support of same-sex sexuality, the gospel warrants its moral potential under these more precise theological and sapiential definitions. Of course, accepting the positive moral potential of same-sex sexuality does not spell out either the terms of Christian koinonia governing it by which such sexual activity is to be encouraged, treasured, and celebrated. Not everything that is possible has the potential for ethical affirmation, and anything potentially affirmed ethically also has the potential for foolishness and evil. How the churches will respond to the gift of a new precision in our understanding of same-sex-oriented people will have at stake both how the world perceives the wisdom of the church and how well the church understands its own gospel.

4. The concept of koinonia should invite greater creativity regarding the nature of "family." Without withdrawing support for traditional families, the prevalence of more single adults, single parents, second marriages, stepfamilies, alternative communal living arrangements, and so forth deserve fresh attention. Too often sexuality has been considered only in the context of a traditional family so that this form of family becomes idealized and is assigned a burden of representing an idealized morality that it cannot bear.

5. It should be unnecessary to say that the subject of AIDS pertains principally for me to the matter of Christian response to disease and that the ethical issues surrounding it most often belong in the realm of an ethics of Christian wisdom. The implication of the gospel surely means that churches should seek to go beyond the wisdom of this world in compassion, to struggle for better care for persons with AIDS, and fight against any homophobia that might be evoked by its occasional predominance among gay men. AIDS is not a gay disease. Although it evokes life-threatening circumstances where new ethical decisions must be made, it contributes nothing new to a Christian understanding of human sexual morality.

Notes

1. Paul Roberts, "Sex and Death," *The Toronto Life*, August 1987, pp. 28–33, 45–50.
2. Cf. Edward Geoffrey Parrinder, *Sex in the World's Religions* (Don Mills, Ontario: General Publishing Company, 1980).

3. Brevard S. Childs, *Introduction to the Old Testament as Scripture* (Philadelphia: Fortress Press, 1979), p. 79.
4. Cf. Gerhard von Rad, *Old Testament Theology* (New York: Harper & Row, 1962), vol. 1, pp. 355ff.
5. I find particularly helpful Paul Lehmann's presentation of a koinonia ethic in his *Ethics in a Christian Context* (New York: Harper & Row, 1963).
6. For further discussion on this matter, see my "The Use of Scripture within the Christian Ethical Debate Concerning Same-Sex Oriented Persons," *Union Seminary Quarterly Review* 41/1&2: 13–16, 1985.

16

Report from "Sexuality" Stream

AIDS: We Are Not a Throw-Away People

I. God calls us as a people, a whole people, and no one is expendable. It is unacceptable, indeed sinful, for Christians to act as if any one or any group is expendable. We are called to bear witness to the good news of the gospel that *no one* is a stranger or an outsider, that division and separation have been broken down, that in the life, death, and resurrection of Jesus there are no longer the "pure" and the "impure." In the face of the world-wide crisis of AIDS, we are especially called to be *one* people.

II. AIDS has no religion, no nationality, no gender, no sexual orientation. AIDS is a disease, a disease that confronts our prejudices and our bigotries, which in Canada and the United States have shown themselves in systematic neglect and individualized violence against gay men, prostitutes, people of color, and intravenous drug users. We have willingly maintained a state of ignorance about AIDS in continents other than our own.

III. We confess that in Canada and the United States our churches have been almost totally silent. Recent history painfully reminds us that silence equals death. Our deeply seated fear of sexuality and our ancient habit of excluding men and women whose lives or words threaten us have made us accomplices in the bigotry and violence we now must end. We have often contributed to the pain of persons with AIDS and those who love them by not embracing them as our own. We have turned our backs on our neighbors from other continents as well as the gay neighborhoods of Canada and the United States. We recognize that the churches have historically misunderstood and perpetuated false teaching about the sexuality of men and women and have, accordingly, been guilty of gross abuses and inhumanities. We call the churches to a vigorous program of sex education and to a fresh celebration of the variety of our sexualities, without easy moralizing on illicit or permissible sex. Had we recognized the validity and the diversity of our sexual lives and loves, we would then have been bodily present to the pain of AIDS of all people.

IV. All around us men, women, and children are dying of AIDS. We must act now. We commit ourselves to eradicating the bigotry and hatred that are feeding this disease. Therefore, we call the churches to more than empty gestures and token actions. From our immense institutional, personal, and financial resources the churches must provide effective support to persons with HIV infection and all those affected by this crisis.

V. We urgently demand that government at every level be held accountable to the persons already diagnosed with AIDS and those infected. These number currently, respectively, about 50,000 and 1,500,000 in Canada and the United States and equal or greater numbers in the developing world. The churches need to challenge the governments and the medical community to assure the right to care of all people and need to provide legal challenges to assure the same.

The churches need to prophetically challenge themselves as well as speak truth to power and demand from the governments' massive funding for research and care focused more then hitherto on the determined maintenance of health of the millions of people already infected, who indeed are not throwaway people. We must end the deplorable state of their neglect in North America and other continents.

VI. We, the churches, need to take up the challenge to participate in and provide leadership to bold education on sex and prevention of AIDS so that the epidemic will be stemmed. In so doing, the churches need to enter into partnership with the medical community, local action groups as well as churches in the developing world so that the resources of knowledge and science can be shared timely to the benefit of all people.

VII. Rather than simply taking care of ourselves, our faith demands that we take care of one another. As a Christian community, we reject any description of AIDS as punishment of God for sinful behavior or even an act of revenge by nature for acts claimed to be "unnatural." *God calls us as a people, a whole people, and no one is expendable.*

17

Reflections on "Sexuality" Stream

Screaming for Help

Mr. Chris Glaser

One evening, a man screamed for help as an assailant stabbed him. He managed to break away and bang on a neighbor's door for assistance. The neighbor, frightened by the commotion, did not open the door. A few minutes later the attacker returned and stabbed the man again. By the time things quieted down and the woman worked up courage to open the door, the victim had just enough life to crawl into her home to die. Police and paramedics arrived too late to help.

Many people in the Sexuality Stream felt like the person under attack in this true story. We urgently needed help for our friends, parishioners, clients, and, in some cases, ourselves in the attack of AIDS. We were angry about governmental resources that failed adequately to protect and assist us. We felt impatient with the church's timidity in opening the door and providing sanctuary. We wanted to shout for help, yet feared our screaming would keep the church's door shut. We knew that in the North American mind AIDS is associated with sexuality, a mystery as fearful as the shadows of night.

All Streams of the Consultation were called to consider the church's response to the crisis. Other Streams were charged with addressing its medical and social dimensions. Our Stream was challenged to shed light on sexuality.

The man under attack in the opening illustration did not have the leisure to consider the beauty of the night. Neither did we experience the leisure of considering the beauty of sexuality. The neighbor inside, if she were to save the man, did not have the leisure to indulge her fear of night or lack of trust in her neighbor. Likewise, we felt it was time for the church to overcome whatever fears of sexuality and homosexuality it has and learn to trust its neighbor (and its neighbor's experience).

Of course there is a wisdom of self-preservation in the neighbor's choice not to open the door. After all, women are frequently subject to men's violence. And sometimes people *do* unnecessarily cry "Wolf!" to exploit or attack. Here the analogy breaks down. The church's wisdom of self-preservation at the expense of the neighbor is made foolishness by Jesus' commands to risk life and possessions to find life in God's commonwealth (kingdom). The church's wisdom to play it safe, avoiding ritual impurity (as did the priest and Levite who passed the wounded) is made foolishness by Jesus' parable of the good Samaritan (his response ultimately to a question about eternal life).

The twofold urgency the Sexuality Stream experienced had to do with God's biblical admonition to choose life: choosing life for persons infected with HIV and those who could become exposed, and choosing life for the church, which risks losing its soul and vitality by ignoring this crisis.

Because it was this emergency we felt compelled to address, a leisurely stroll through the garden of earthly delights (reflecting on sexuality) gave way to a dash for help. As one participant observed with discomfort, we shifted from a discussion about sexuality to an argument for justice regarding sexuality.

That may have been the appropriate strategy. Three days of consultation could hardly gestate a prophetic stance on sexuality that might dissuade the church from centuries of limited knowledge and numerous theological/ethical misapplications regarding sexuality. At most we could call the church to such a task, while protecting sexuality from one further "bad rap," that of being associated with death imagery and AIDS. Acknowledging that AIDS is primarily a sexually transmitted disease, we nonetheless did not view AIDS as any divine retribution for sexual expression, homosexual or heterosexual, any more than it is God's response to hemophiliacs, drug users, or babies of infected mothers.

However strongly we believed the church needed to discuss sexuality, we also wished the church would leave such discussion open-ended and not feel the need to conclude it with a proclamation of judgment. As one person put it, "it's time for the church to pray for the gift of ears rather than the gift of tongues." Sexuality has not been adequately, openly, and honestly discussed in the church for fear of such judgment.

While encouraging judgment-free discussion of sexuality, the church may yet be able to take a life-choosing position by educating its membership and the broader community as to how to avoid infection with the HIV virus, whether in abstinence *or* sexual expression. The church's previous counsel of abstinence until marriage is inadequate in the face of the AIDS crisis for several reasons: marriage is no safe haven, as the partner may be infected and thus safer sex practices must be known and practiced; homosexuals are denied the option of church- or state-sanctioned marriages; and single heterosexuals and homosexuals alike frequently ignore such counsel and enjoy sexual encounters. Surely preserving life is of higher value than the often futile attempt to limit sexual expression.

Two ironies occurred to me in our discussions. The public still has the misperception that homosexual people endanger society's youth, and thus discrimination against gays and lesbians is justified and dissemination of safer sex materials is viewed suspiciously as encouraging homosexual expression. But it is the homosexual community that, in sounding the alarm about AIDS, is trying to *protect* the next sexually active population likely to be affected: heterosexual and homosexual adolescents.

The second irony is that the advent of the lesbian/gay rights movement is perceived as a factor in the deteriorization of everything from the family to the community. Yet the AIDS crisis reveals that gays and lesbians have created families and communities to support their own when biological families or ecclesiastical and societal communities have refused to do so.

Concepts in the papers (received and read before the Consultation began) provoked our discussion, but the basis for most of our conversations was the diversity of our respective traditions and experience. The papers for the Sexuality Stream addressed systemic problems related to biblical, theological, ethical, and ecclesiastical concerns. Although we believed the system retarding the church's ready response to AIDS needs reform, we did not believe ourselves adequate to the task in our brief Consultation. Indeed, some of us were not convinced we could or even should write a brief statement of conclusions. But our deeply felt urgency for the church to respond to AIDS and to sexuality needed *some* voice.

We were not representative of the church at large, although this should be viewed less as our liability than as an indictment of the church. For most of us had had some experience of caring for persons with AIDS, an experience not common in the church. Those on the forefront of such care are homosexual themselves, so a disproportionate number of us were gay or lesbian. Those on the frontiers exploring the relation of sexuality and spirituality are nongay women, lesbian women, and gay men; thus we experienced a disproportionate number of these. Finally, those struggling on behalf of marginalized people are a minority in the church, so there was also a disproportionate number of social justice advocates.

Still another way in which our Stream was not representative, for which the church at large and we as a Consultation must bear mutual responsibility, is that we were all white. Although persons of color experience AIDS at twice the rate of their proportion in society, their only voice within our Stream came from a white woman, Dr. Cécile De Sweemer, a presenter on the AIDS crisis in Africa, who joined us for part of our deliberations. Then, of course, her voice could not represent North American latinos and blacks.

Our process of discussion was open, but with fifty persons in the Stream and shortness of time, perhaps a dozen with passion and/or insight spoke regularly. This weakness was overcome by small-group discussion from which ideas were reported to the whole. And although some speakers dominated, I believe the group gave them permission to do so because most were in agreement with them. A few felt their views were unrepresented; one went so far as to dissent in a plenary of the full

Consultation. The rest of us (including another dissatisfied participant) felt offended that he hadn't bothered to dissent within the Stream itself, instead choosing not to attend several sessions. The one time he spoke within the whole Stream attracted only a stunned silence and no commentary, not because what he said was untrue, but because it was perceived as insensitive in context. In his public dissent he took exception to someone inflating a condom during a break in the proceedings, viewing it somehow as representative of homosexuality (which the perpetrator did not), and objected to "obscenities" that, in truth, were infrequently used slang referring to sexual partners and the sexual act.

Given the cacophony of voiced concerns related to sexuality and to AIDS within our Stream, I believe it was truly a work of the Spirit that two small writing groups harmonized our opinions into a brief, lucid statement with which the vast majority of us could concur. I felt deeply moved as the final product was read to the Consultation's plenary, proud to have been associated with the process that led to it.

At one point a participant reflected the feeling of our deliberations by suggesting we sound in the church a call to arms for a holy war against AIDS. Recognizing no war should be dignified with the adjective "holy," and believing violence begets violence (even verbally), we refrained from such language. We feared frightening the neighbor whose door we wished to open, whether of heart or of home or of holy place. So, in a sense, we chose to call the church to a *holy peace* that could embrace persons with AIDS and, at the same time, allow and encourage those whose sexuality varies from church norms to share their experience within the community of faith. If the church has ears to hear and eyes to see, we can learn much from all of them about life and death, suffering and joy, spirituality and sexuality. And perhaps we might also prove a good neighbor to the person crying for sanctuary.

Process and Panic

the rev. barb m. janes

O Christ, the healer, we have come
to pray for health,
to plead for friends.
How can we fail to be restored
when reached by love that never ends?*

The hymn ended, we began to pray, and in that prayer we were invited to call out the names of people we knew who had died of AIDS. Jeffrey. Layton. Richard. Rod. Finis. Larry. Walter. David. Michael. Susan. Charles. Owen. Matsuko. Mark. Karl. Paul. Casey. Gary. Beulah. Joseph. Nathan. Evelyn. Stewart. Albert. Raul. Stephen. Robert. It was a prayer to wring the very heart of God.

We had gathered in Toronto to grapple with the theological and ethical issues arising from the AIDS crisis. We were preachers and chaplains, doctors and hospice workers, academics and activists—and persons with AIDS. Each of us had come with our own distinct, individual agenda, and each of us came with a common agenda: to face death and to face life.

And me? What could a parish minister in rural northwestern Ontario possibly have to do with AIDS? i had come because i had caught myself saying, "i don't *yet* know anyone who has AIDS." The "yet" points to a false luxury of time, a luxury i won't have for long if the virus gains ground as rapidly in the future as it has up until now. But those are reasons of the head, and the heart has its reasons that reason cannot know. AIDS threatens to put the fight for the rights of lesbians and gays back to the days before Stonewall, to reinforce the idolatry of the (male-dominated) nuclear family, and to confirm a social structure in which

---

*"O Christ, the Healer" was written by Fred Pratt Green. Words copyright © 1969 by Hope Publishing Company, Carol Stream, Illinois 60188. All rights reserved. Used by permission.

some groups of people simply don't matter a damn. AIDS has become the threshing floor for sexual and religious politics. As opportunistic bigots ride the wave of AIDS, the net they cast is a broad one. Gay men are the catch, but lesbians, feminists, intravenous drug users, persons of color, pro-choice advocates, and sex educators end up in the same net. My heart is on the left; i am in the net.

My heart is also on the *Christian* left, which makes the demands of the struggle more rigorous than mere partisan politics. As a Christian, i am moved by the God incarnate who broke bread with prostitutes—sexual outlaws—as often as with his own followers. This means Jesus breaks bread with me in my status as a sexual suspect if not outlaw, and i am called to share my bread with other outlaws. But as a Christian, i am also warned against self-righteous posturing. i am called not just to speak truth to power, but also to speak the truth in love, as one sinner to another. This does not negate or undercut what must be said, nor ever alter its tone; rather, it alters the speaker.

The AIDS crisis shows us what we really are, and our Stream on Sexuality quickly reached an important consensus: AIDS has legitimated society's sinful tendency to regard certain groups as throw-away people. In the United States and Canadian contexts this primarily refers to gay men, other groups with AIDS such as intravenous drug users, persons of color, and weaklings who need transfusions already having been dismissed. The throwaway people concept is a helpful one, as it most strongly points out the rampant homophobia in our cultures and in our church.

It is no secret that the church has never been a friend of gay sexuality. As one of the chief propaganda agents for the nuclear family, alternate life-styles have been traditionally viewed as a threat rather than as a cause of celebration. One has only to look at the token roles generally assigned to women, children, and ethnic minorities in the church to reach the conclusion that white male heterosexuality was the law and norm.

In the Sexuality Stream, white male homosexuality was the law and norm, and perhaps we were guilty of what Dr. Cécile De Sweemer called a "righteousness of marginality." Gay men made what were, to this woman's ears, some rather outrageous statements. For instance, "I hope the lesbians have been paying attention to the Gay Liberation leaders because someone will need to take over when we have died of AIDS"—as if lesbian women are sitting at home tatting revolutionary slogans for the banners in Gay Pride Day marches while the gay men are doing the real work of the struggle. The AIDS crisis cannot be abused by gay men as an excuse not to deal with their sexism any more than we can allow the church to continue on its merry, homophobic way, pleading it is busy with "other issues."

But the split in the Stream was not only male/female; it was also a split about process. Each Stream was given the task of creating a statement, and in the lust for the goal the process was often trampled. The goal, though, was ill-defined. Were we writing the statement to shame the church into action or to gain media attention? Or were we creating an academic paper to be included in this book, which in turn will be marketed to a limited audience? Do we use the buzz words of academic theology ("hermeneutics of suspicion," for instance), or do we need to be as forthright in our religious talk as we are in our safer sex education programs? The AIDS crisis is throwing the spotlight not only on those sinful silent churches, but also on the vested interests of those engaged in the issue. There were no persons of color in our Stream, and few at the Consultation itself. Our Stream consisted of white, privileged, upper-middle-class people. Although there were a significant number of women in the Stream, as a group, women were largely silent/silenced. So unfortunately were the persons with AIDS. While we grandstanded over tactics and wording, we did not take the time to ask the very people to whom we had said we were accountable. Perhaps we would have been further ahead to name the tensions we were so gleefully fueling: male/female, academic/unschooled, media wise/media-inexperienced, worried well/persons with AIDS, denominationally faithful/denominationally rebellious.

It is tempting to say so what? to the above, recognize that time is the enemy, and get on with the work. Resource person Mary Hunt suggested a vision of the church as an "unlikely coalition of justice-seeking friends." At the time this seemed like a fine statement, but with 20/20 hindsight, there is something troubling here.

A coalition is a group of disparate organizations and/or individuals who come together to achieve a common goal, such as the recently defeated proposed return to capital punishment in Canada. Labor unions, church groups, feminists, professionals joined together in that common struggle, but once the goal was met, the coalitions dissolved and we returned to the same old bickering among ourselves (professionals are really management incognito, churchwomen are vapid sellouts of the feminist cause, etc.). A coalition is a *temporary* grouping that ends when the goal is achieved.

Friendship contains elements of coalition, and more. And it is the "and more" that makes us the church. Among friends, the process takes priority over the goal; the "how" we do things is at least as important, if not more so, as the "what." The work of friendship is much more difficult and demanding than the work of coalition—and much more nourishing in the long haul.

We need, like friends, to cling to each other as Ruth clung to Naomi, pleading, "Entreat me not to leave you." When we bicker and struggle, we need to wrestle as openly as Jacob and his angel, holding each other into right relation, grunting, "I will not let go until you bless me."

This honest wrestling was missing from our Stream. At one point in our time together, an academic theologian made a statement that left us slack-jawed in stunned silence. The next speaker began by saying, "I don't want to even respond to that." Neither did the rest of us, despite the prominence of a T-shirt that read "SILENCE = DEATH." If we are to be more than a coalition, we must break silence and not sidestep the power of anger in the work of love, to use Bev Harrison's phrase. Then when we say to each other "I love you," it will be a trembling statement that is never routine, for we will not take the returning of love lightly or for granted.[1]

We joked a fair bit that although our Stream was entitled Sexuality, we seemed singularly reluctant to talk about sex. In our cultures it is more acceptable to call a stupid person an "asshole" than to refer to that part of your anatomy with that very precise term; the bugger has virtually disappeared from everyday speech, yet it remains the act that offends the church. Our hesitance to speak frankly out of our experience even in that open group is a frightening sign of the times. When one of the several people who mentioned that the church needs to take lesbian and gay sexuality seriously as data of revelation went on to note how expensive that data are, we collectively—and silently—nodded.

Justice is the precondition for frank talk about sex, and so our Stream chose to talk about justice rather than sex. It was not an articulated choice so much as an evolution; perhaps it was simply safer ground. But when one of our Stream's persons with AIDS said that it is his sexual loving expression that is keeping him alive, it would have been good for us to have listened more attentively to the link between sex and life.

Note

1. Jane Rule, *Memory Board* (Toronto: MacMillan of Canada, 1987), p. 77.

Part 5

Reactions and Reflections

18

What the Churches Must Do About AIDS: Service, Prophecy, and Communion

Dr. Tom Sinclair-Faulkner

"Fear" is the word that echoes through my mind as I consider how we churchpeople are responding to the AIDS crisis. Here in Nova Scotia the first skirmish occurred in the fall of 1987, when Eric Smith, a high school teacher in a small coastal town, tested positive for the AIDS virus and the community rose up to oppose his return to the classroom, supported by their clergy and—to read the newspapers—challenged only by a few of Smith's friends. In the end the provincial government defused the confrontation by appointing Mr. Smith to a royal commission on AIDS. It was a solution that can only work once.

So I was pleased when the World Council of Churches and others invited the North American churches to send their best front-line people to a three-day consultation at the Toronto School of Theology to consider the crisis of AIDS. Billed as a follow-up to a world consultation in Geneva in 1986, it brought 130 persons together in Toronto October 23–25. With the exception of half a dozen laypeople like myself, they were all AIDS experts of some sort: nurses and physicians, chaplains and pastors, and persons with AIDS themselves.

I went to Toronto recognizing how terrifying AIDS is: an infection that may lie undetected for years before being transmitted in ways that stir deeply seated moral passions, and then turning into a disease that is always fatal. Furthermore, I know how weak and marginalized the churches are in our society. Nevertheless, I returned to Halifax persuaded that there are useful and important things that our churches can do to respond to the AIDS crisis. As a result, a local pastor, a chaplain from a regional hospital, and myself were able to propose some projects to the churches of Halifax that churches elsewhere in North America might consider for themselves. The results have been mixed so far: on the one hand, many Christians and some churches have responded positively; on the other hand, I have been receiving obscene mail from as far away as Saskatchewan charging me with undermining the Christian civilization.

The AIDS Consultation in Toronto had no embodiment outside the three-day meeting, but we residents of Halifax were able to distill proposals for three kinds of action from the discussions. So we sponsored a public meeting at the Atlantic School of Theology (an ecumenical seminary of the Catholic, Anglican, and United Churches) and advertised widely through mailings from the Pastoral Care Department of the Victoria General Hospital. Seventy persons from our metropolitan community of 200,000 turned out, and most of them were church or health care leaders. Here is what we set before them.

First, governments must be mobilized to provide adequate health care and research into AIDS. It is not enough for churches to write letters pressing governments to do this. The churches must commit significant portions of their admittedly slim resources to showing governments what is possible and what is urgently required. By *doing* good instead of merely calling for it, the churches may indeed move governments to commit their vast resources to dealing with AIDS.

For example, the United Church of Canada might link up with appropriate churches and agencies in Africa to identify those hospitals where blood banks are not tested and where one or two hypodermic needles are serving the needs of the entire hospital, over and over again. A North American church can afford a few thousand dollars to test blood banks or to purchase supplies of disposable needles and then call a press conference to say, "If we can save lives with so little, what can Washington and Ottawa do with so much?" Concrete gestures of this sort are needed, particularly in the face of the American government's reduction of assistance to the World Health Organization.

In North America one of the greatest needs is hospice care for persons with AIDS. Many persons with AIDS are ostracized by family and friends, and health care institutions are often eager to turn persons with AIDS out to fend for themselves rather than take up space in hospitals. In a city like Toronto the local council of churches could undertake a needs assessment to see whether a coalition might purchase a few houses and staff them with trained hospice workers. Recently the Catholic archdiocese of Toronto opened such a house, but the Toronto Committee on AIDS says at least half a dozen more are required. Once such hospices are opened, the churches may speak with authority to governments, saying, "Now you must do your duty as well; adequate and fair treatment for persons with AIDS is their right."

In establishing such local support, the network of about 250 Metropolitan Community Churches is a valuable and indispensable resource in the United States and in Canada. With their deliberate welcome to gay men and lesbians, these Christian congregations have become focal points for efforts to build support systems for persons with AIDS who have been rejected by mainstream society because of their sexual orientation. Those who contract the disease through other means need hospice care as well, but there is no reason why the local initiatives of the Metropolitan Community Churches or by the gay community itself cannot be taken as a useful starting point for care that may then become available to a broad spectrum of persons with AIDS.

Another concrete gesture that the Christian churches may make is to publish straightforward information about how to prevent the spread of AIDS. Specifically, the churches must publish information about how to use condoms and how to sterilize needles. The position of the Catholic Church is most frequently cited by public health officials as a formidable barrier to the publication of such information by governments, and here in Canada, Catholic institutions have generally resisted pro-

265

posals to distribute information about safer sex. For example, last September the two Catholic universities in Halifax refused to accept free condoms offered by the Metro Committee of AIDS for distribution to first-year students. But an editorial in *Commonweal* (November 6, 1987) asserted that it would be better for the Church to risk misleading people about its position on chastity and birth control than to place barriers in the way of frankly presented information about how to hinder the spread of AIDS—the only practrical method of containment discovered to date. And the bishops of the Catholic Church in the United States announced in December 1987 that they are prepared to see such information distributed.

This is one of the few instances in which the Catholic Church in the United States has proved more liberal than the Canadian wing. Other churches may and should go further, however; they should become publishers of useful information about safer sex themselves, just as the United Church of Canada did in the 1960s when it was illegal to distribute birth control information as we do today.

The *second* proposal that we made was that the mainstream churches must challenge what the media understand to be the "Christian" position on AIDS, that it is God's punishment for social and individual immorality. The news reporters who attended the Toronto Consultation constantly returned to this point, their body language shouting disbelief whenever someone suggested that most Christians are reluctant to adopt this deuteronomic position. Some see the media's bias here as another example of their never-ending search for sensational confrontation, but I think that it also has to do with the failure of mainstream churches to challenge directly those who imply or flatly argue that persons with AIDS deserve what they get.

For example, a paper prepared especially for the Toronto Consultation by theologian Mary Hunt recorded that reporters asked the pope during his recent visit to the United Sates what he thought of Archbishop John Foley's statement that AIDS is God's sanction against sexual immorality. The pope's low-key response that "it is hard to know the mind of God" would scarcely be construed as a stiff rebuke.

Some members of our audience in Halifax felt that we had exaggerated the strength of Christian opinion that AIDS is God's scourge, but I continue to think that the North American public is hearing little else from the churches. For example, in the November issue of *Faith Today,* a handsome magazine published by the Evangelical Fellowship of Canada, editor in chief Brian C. Stiller cautioned his readers not to subscribe to the view that AIDS is God's judgment on homosexuals alone. Instead, he argued, "it is a message to the world that humankind cannot violate God's laws without repercussions." Such theological efforts to fix the blame in God's name necessarily reinforce the impatience of health care workers with those whose behavior puts them at risk with AIDS. That impatience—often a thin disguise for paranoid fears—reduces their willingness to heal and support persons with AIDS. Church leaders ought to be inviting nurses and doctors to serve persons with AIDS courageously, not providing them with excuses to neglect such persons on the grounds that they are justly being punished. To pretend to read the mind of God in such detail is to range ourselves with the comforters of Job who "have not spoken . . . what is right [Job 42:8]."

Our churches need to reconsider the ethics of prophesy on another count as well. In my view prophesy is courageous when Nathan confronts the king and says, "You are the man" (2 Sam. 12:7]," but it is bullying when it condemns people who lack power and standing in the community, as Jesus knew when the woman taken in adultery was brought before him for condemnation (John 8:2–11). The task of Christians is to heal and to comfort; to announce that AIDS is God's vengeance is to usurp God's role.

This means that local councils of churches ought to feel obliged to refute publicly the false prophets who feed civic fears and encourage official neglect by blaming AIDS on its victims. They must do more than say that it is hard to know the mind of God; they must speak forcefully in favor of loving and just care for those afflicted, and they must do it whenever one of the false prophets captures the ear of the media.

Speaking up in a timely way in this manner might make the mainstream churches of the western province of British Columbia a force for good in the debate there over whether to quarantine persons with AIDS against their will. Such a scheme has all the merits of the decision to send Japanese Canadians to concentration camps during World War II. We certainly need to hear from the churches in Nova Scotia, where the attorney general advocated in January 1988 that the law be changed to permit him to force persons with AIDS into quarantine.

The *third* course of action that we commended to the churches of Halifax at our open meeting was one that draws on their *symbolic power*—surely the one power that churches possess in a special way. When persons with AIDS are identified in North American communities today they are usually ostracized: their jobs are taken from them, they are banned from their schools, their families disown them, and health care professionals who bravely handle highly infectious patients such as those suffering from hepatitis scramble to refer them somewhere else. Local congregations—not denominational executives—have the power to challenge such inhumane behavior.

The power lies in one of our central rites: the eucharist, symbol of our common life in Christ. When a person with AIDS is identified in a public way in my community, my congregation should immediately and publicly invite that person to join us in the Lord's Supper. Naturally this is a policy that would have to be explored and adopted well in advance, since our experience tells us that communities react fearfully and thoughtlessly when a person with AIDS is actually discovered to be among them. But consider the powerful witness of a congregation that has thought the thing through before it happens—consulting expert medical opinion and asking prayerfully what a Christian congregation ought to do in such a case.

I would have no more hesitation about inviting my spouse, my young children, and my friends to join a person with AIDS at the communion table than I had in breaking bread with and embracing persons with AIDS at the Toronto Consultation. This is not a matter of bravado; it is a matter of medical knowledge and Christian faith, both of the most elementary sort.

Service, prophesy, and communion: these are the three things that the churches must do about AIDS. Will they do them?

I am hopeful but not optimistic. Despite the fact that AIDS is not a "gay" disease, the great barrier to church action on AIDS is our traditional understanding of sexuality. To my surprise, even the Toronto Consultation failed to deal adequately with this issue. The 130 participants were divided into three working groups that worked more or less independently, and midway through the three-day meeting two of the groups foundered on the shoals of sexuality. Some of the division was expressed directly: "Being gay is part of God's gift." "No; homosexual activity is inherently sinful." Sometimes the division was expressed indirectly: The statement "If you can't handle my being gay, I don't want you as my chaplain" was met by the reply, "I came here to talk about AIDS, not about being gay."

B.J. Stiles of Washington, D.C., and I had the assignment of drawing up a consensus statement for adoption by the final plenary session. We succeeded in one respect only; the plenary session rejected our draft and came to the consensus that it did not have sufficient time to produce a common statement. The consultation was left with statements from each of the three working groups, and recognition that our failure to produce a synthesis of the three was due in part to continued division over sexuality.

The participants in the AIDS consultation were relatively sophisticated about sexuality, yet they failed to rethink the traditional Christian position on gays and lesbians. What prospect is there that local churches will have better success? My sense is that the prospect is poor, yet it is urgent that we make the effort. The three-point program of service, prophesy, and communion does not depend on rethinking our position on gay sexuality, but it would be immeasurably strengthened if we were to do so.

I want to suggest a strategy similar to the one that led to the abolition of slavery—an institution that received support from the Christian tradition in the past just as homophobia receives support today. We cannot reasonably expect denominational executives or even local pastors and priests today to lead the way in such a controversial rethinking of the Christian position. We can expect the ones oppressed by the tradition to lead the way; just as persons of color spoke out against slavery in the past, so gays and lesbians are finding their voice today in the struggle against homophobia. But we can also expect to hear from laypeople who are "straight" or heterosexual. Our clergy see themselves as mediators bound to keep congregations together, "facilitators" eager not to be accused of clerical domination. And—let us speak frankly—they generally owe their livelihood to the congregation that pays their salary. I do not expect the clergy to lead the Christian churches in their rethinking of our understanding of sexuality.

Laypeople who play active roles as Sunday school teachers, elders, trustees, choir members, etc., also are in a position to speak up forcefully and effectively in support of gays and lesbians. Now that gay Christians are speaking up in public (see, for example, "A Gay Witness to Pope John Paul II," *The Christian Century,* October 7, 1987), it is time for some straight Christians to join them—not in a patronizing way, but in the hope that their own children will be able to grow up in a world free of homophobia. Like William Wilberforce and his friends in the Clapham Sect, they may be labeled and challenged, but no one will be able to deprive them of their pay check and few will dare to say that they are not loyal members of the churches. When they begin to speak up, the stuttering debate over our common understanding of sexuality will acquire some of the coherence that it currently lacks.

In the meantime clergy and laity alike will find plenty to do in meeting the challenge of AIDS together.

19

Reflections by Participants with AIDS/HIV Infection

Response to Theological Consultation on AIDS

The Rev. Mark Mosher DeWolfe

When I first agreed to attend the Consultation, I knew I would be wearing many hats. First, I was asked to attend because I am a person living with AIDS. But there was also the hat I would wear as a parish minister, albeit in a denomination (Unitarian Universalism) that has only observer status with the Canadian Council of Churches and the National Council of Churches of Christ in the U.S.A. And unlike some parish ministers, I am one who enjoys taking part in theological dialogue. I came as a kind of inside-outsider: a person comfortable with theological dialogue yet representing a minor denomination, and, as the rules for doing liberation theology would have it, as one of the metaphorically poor invited to be at the discussion table. So the first question that came to mind was, how do I hold in balance all those different roles?

I approached the Consultation with a specific fear: that the traditional homophobia of churches would cloud the discussion, hanging in the room unnamed, causing us to wrangle without clarity over issues of ethics. If we left unnamed the role played by people who claim the heritage of Jesus in promoting hatred of those peoples in North America most affected by AIDS, nothing we accomplished would be credible to the people we hoped to address: churches, persons living with AIDS, the wider community.

Wearing my persons-with-AIDS hat, I worried that our presence might be only token. Would we really be listened to? Or would preconceived notions of who we were and what we needed reduce our role to a mere token gesture? I knew the Consultation planners had worked hard to find persons with AIDS who were both well enough and interested enough to spend a weekend with people whom many consider to be the enemy. Would there be tension?

I took part in the Sexuality Stream, in part because I came with deep questions about how AIDS challenges our attitudes on sex. After reading the papers, I was hopeful that what we might produce would be of true value to those thoughtful people in the religious community who are courageous enough to consider AIDS. It seemed that the theologians were ahead of their churches in their willingness to be open to the experience of the communities affected by AIDS. People whose lives have been touched by AIDS, whether it is themselves or someone they love who is infected, are caught between the churches' unreadiness to provide pastoral support and the leadership of these theological voices calling us to truer ministry. My hope was that when theologians are ahead of their churches, they can be a voice of hope that the church is not closed to those who have need of ministry.

The discussion eased my fears about the Consultation's willingness to hear the experiences and opinions of persons with AIDS. The response to my presence was one of warmth and support, and sincere interest in my views. It was heartening to find so much good will.

In the deliberations of the Sexuality Stream, the atmosphere in the room was one of urgency from Friday night through Saturday. The tone had been set by Mervyn Silverman's description of how persons with AIDS are being denied medical care by physicians and surgeons who fear infection. The tone was taken up by Kevin Gordon, who in his opening remarks to the Stream emphasized the massive size of the problems in the United States: how society, including the churches, continues to abandon persons with AIDS, and how meager the responses from the churches have been to date. Our discussions became centered on how the homophobia of the churches is at best a silent partner in this genocide. As a result, we left unanswered larger questions of sexuality and sexual ethics.

The story was told in our Stream of a woman from a rural community whose son had died of AIDS. She traveled a great distance to attend a bereavement group offered by a community-based AIDS organization in the nearest major city. She did this because in her town there was no one she could talk to about the fact her son had died of AIDS. Where was her pastor? Where were her beloved fellow congregants? Hiding behind fear and rejection, they were unable to minister to her. Clearly the challenge to the churches is to be open to the pain of people whose lives have been touched by AIDS. Yet we cannot do that if we remain associated with the harsh judgment pronounced by those who blame the victims, and whose vision of God's love ends with the kind of love God visited on the Egyptians in Exodus. To maintain that association, all we need do is remain silent.

In retrospect, I am almost glad that we did not try to pass over easily the question of justice for persons with AIDS. Had we moved too easily from that into questions of sexual ethics, we would not have properly prepared ourselves for the kind of thinking that needs to be done. If we left the homophobia and erotophobia of the church tradition unchallenged, AIDS could too easily push us into a simplistic ethic that begins with sexuality as dangerous and death-dealing and proclaims celibacy as the only safe and moral Christian position, and leaves everything else—like marriage—as second best. Isn't this how we often hear Paul's "it is better to marry than burn" interpreted? We cannot forget that in some corners of the popular imagination sex is still associated with punishment for the sin of Adam! AIDS could too easily burn out the hard work of the past few years of sex research and ethical thinking, by using fear to propel us away from an understanding of sex as a gift from God, of eroticism as a good part of human nature, of sexual acts as not intrinsically evil, but subject to ethical evaluation. Any ethical statement about sexuality that did not accept and apologize for the churches' responsibility in promoting hatred of those groups most affected by AIDS would be hollow. Those who most have need of our ministry would not be listening to anything we said. In essence, the Toronto Consultation took the first step. But it has left so many questions unanswered.

Because of the unanswered questions, which have their own urgency for all of us struggling with AIDS, I hope there will be more theological consultations on AIDS. We have not even begun the work needed to address the questions AIDS provokes for churches and for the society in which we minister. Let me tell you some of the questions that still lie before us.

The AIDS Committee of Toronto sponsors self-help groups for persons with AIDS, one of which I attend. Two men who also attend my group come to mind when I think of unanswered questions left for us to explore. One found himself unable to enjoy his sexual feelings because he blamed them for his illness. Another considered himself a walking murder weapon because his sexual activity could deal death to another. How do we bring a healing ministry to people who consider their sexuality an agent of death? These men provoke in me questions deeper than simply what is ethically acceptable sexual behavior in the age of AIDS. How do we encourage a healthy attitude toward self in people who believe something as fundamental as their sexual feelings are responsible for their suicide, or for making them murderers? Surely these men will not find healing when they feel burdened with guilt for a virus they did not consciously contract!

In a speech to our Pacific Central District Unitarian Universalist Association in September 1987, I described what I believe to be the unspoken element in AIDS hysteria. AIDS is spread by blood and sexual fluids, symbols of life. It is by sexual fluids that life is first conceived; it is by blood transfusions that we give life to each other. As an expression of love, sex is a means by which life is enhanced. AIDS is a reminder of how interconnected we all are, that the blood that flows in our veins is the same from one to another. AIDS, then, is a reminder of how vulnerable we all are—for the symbols of life can so easily become the vectors of a death-dealing virus. The question AIDS provokes in my mind that we have left unanswered is how we live with faith in the power of life borne in blood and sexual fluids when we know that openness to life leaves us open to death. How do we celebrate our wonderful interconnectedness without being naive?

The list could go on. How do we encourage loving, complete relations when AIDS provokes so many to reactions of suspicion, fear, and self-righteousness? What moral and ethical criteria do we use to evaluate sexual relations? And how do we answer God's call to reconciliation in an arena in which the human family is so broken?

There must be further consultations, for the work is only begun.

(Editor's note: Mark DeWolfe died in July 1988.)

Reflections

Mr. Nicholas Gray

Larger than the decisions that were arrived at, or the statements made, it was the encompassing personal experience that for me made this conference a success. I was revitalized in my journey, talking with people that cared and finding out how they did it. How they kept up the good fight. Their ideas and perspectives renewed mine. In session rooms and over dinner ideas were exchanged. It excited me to know that the organizers had been willing to invite such a variety of experiences and ideas to intermingle

I had arrived at the conference caught up in the seeming futility of my own work/fight with AIDS. Weary and strained, I was reluctant to believe that these discussions would make a difference. I was unsure of how my concepts and experiences would fit. I felt inadequate to do the job requested. In early discussions I hesitated, certain that all that would come of this weekend was yet another statement that could be ignored by those that it was meant to enlighten. Would we actually be able to do the task we had set for ourselves?

Slowly, the limited personal perspective I had brought with me from Vancouver gave way to a larger picture. Rebellion stirred in my soul as I was overwhelmed by the global crisis. The gentle, reflective words of Dr. Cécile De Sweemer moved me, and placed the African AIDS crisis in a very disheartening light. What can we really do to help a nation that is already so devastated by this and numerous other health crises? How can we make a difference in a land that has no mechanics in place to accept the help that is offered? Rather like fighting a forest fire with a single bucket, the futility of our current efforts created such a negative picture. I could not comprehend a solution. That there exists a concurrent North American reality was underlined by the words of the Rev. Carl Bean. I have seen the proverty-riddled communities of which he spoke. I know they exist. Here, in two of the world's richest nations, nations that have the time, money, and knowledge to fight and educate, we are faced with willful ignorance of a major crisis. We ignore our brothers and sisters. We lose ourselves in meaningless dialogues about condoms and morality. We ignore the disease as it stares us in our faces, when it lives next door. Facing an AIDS caseload that grows daily, British Columbia can still reject concepts of education and assistance. The current costs are nothing compared with the cost and damage we will experience farther down the road.

AIDS organizations are currently asking for minimal assistance to create maximal effect, and they are being turned down. What can our governments be thinking of? Where is our responsibility? And what of the public? As part of that general public, I always expected that help would be there if ever I needed it. Not always the case. In our own communities it is sad. Globally it is pathetic.

We are experiencing the health crisis of the century. We do not have time for procrastination. We are living in a war zone. We must assault the enemy head on. In times of combat, rules of society become expendable. When the enemy is other people, we fight to the death. Why do we hesitate against this weak little virus? Is the battle not real? The body count certainly is. This is our generation's Vietnam. Think about it. Do you think I care if I offend someone if the result is that lives are saved? We are hearing an urgent call, to which we must respond.

"It's your fault!" As a people we like to place blame. Find a scapegoat. What is the point? Does it help anyone live longer? When it was just the gays, or Africans, or junkies, the public at large could feel safe. They should not. This virus knows no morals. There is no hierarchy of suffering, and we should not create one. The Haitian woman, or Sengalese child, or the Manhattan junkie, all are equally oppressed when it is their lives that are being taken from them. This is an urgent issue. We have to face the challenge and come together as a world community—with no segregation. We must care for and respect equally all people—and allow each to be whoever we are culturally, nationally, or sexually.

In 1937 the churches did nothing to stop the Holocaust. We will not have the luxury of saying, "We didn't know" this time around.

Responsible action must be taken, but what?

As religious/spiritual bodies, we have to come to terms with AIDS. We need to have the answers when the questions arise in our communities. We must know and understand the "word" that we are spreading. Is it laced with understanding, knowledge, and hope? I believe "the people" would rather be protected from the virus than from the words. They are demanding accurate information. They are put off by the long-winded rhetoric about funding and morals and celibacy. We know the impracticality of these concepts and we need realistic guidelines. We need the truth, to the extent that we know it. Sex is not going to go away. Unfortunately neither for the moment is the virus. It enrages me that our authority figures—the leaders, doctors, teachers, and clergy—are so resistant to providing what the people really need. We, the people at the conference, are the liberal faction. If we do not speak out, who will? We must take the knowledge and experiences shared here, and take it back to the grass roots. It is our responsibility to create local dialogues about the AIDS crisis. We must search for our own solutions.

As persons with AIDS, we were there to give a face to the disease. We were a living reality for some that only knew AIDS theoretically. Our presence made it clear that we were not society's cast-off children. Instead they saw that we were vibrant, life-filled men from Vancouver or Edmonton or Toronto or Los Angeles or Seattle or even the house next door.

When AIDS appeared to be just an African problem, we denied it. As it moves into the fabric of North American life we cannot. Those of us with HIV infections are not expendable. We are your brothers and sisters, cousins and lovers. We are many people and we touch many lives. In time no one will remain untouched. We must all "deal" with it.

And how must we do that? There was a call for "civil and ecclesiastical disobedience" that struck a chord with me. I have buried too many friends, and now I share the journey with so many more. I would scream out, but who would hear? When our governments resist the efforts I am making to save my own life, such disobedience seems totally in line.

But what will get the world's attention? People are dying on a daily basis, and still we are able to ignore. What will be noticed? How can I be civilly disobedient in a way that will build awareness? That will cause action and growth. I am aware of the world crisis surrounding this virus. I am aware of the inaction of most of the Western governments. I feel the hesitation in the medical community. I know the economic pressure we will soon be under. How can I expect to cause movement when all this reality has done so little? What can I do that will not be ignored?

I don't know. How could I? I do know that I must continue my quest, to do my piece. Somehow, with all the other good soldiers, we shall overcome. We will come together as a community and do battle. With time, we will win. We must find our strengths. The churches must help us. The job is immense. It is more than healing. You must help us to prepare for the next step.

The spiritual odyssey a person with AIDS faces on diagnosis is considerable. Our spiritual leaders must be there to help. Life becomes a microcosm of itself, compressing into a short time a journey I felt I would have much longer to complete. This quickening of the pace often speeds our questions and increases our need for guidance. As a guide you must remain open to all that I may ponder. Don't try to sell me a set concept of life and death. Listen to me. I must make my own peace with my life and my death. If you can listen, you will be able to help. Your ears and hearts and minds must remain open to things that may not be in your comfort zone of theological leanings. You must listen to us now, when we are well, as we may not be able to hear you when we are sick.

The church must have the compassion to hear.

Many of us currently dealing with AIDS are also dealing with the sexual issues surrounding the infection. Was my sexuality the root cause of my illness? Am I being punished? I must believe that my sexuality is good. Although it holds with it the possibility of death, it also embraces life. It affirms it and extends it. It is my humanity, my vulnerability. Sex, sexuality, is a crucial element of human life. Those of you in the position to teach, do not discount this need. We must all know it, accept it, and work with it.

We must teach. We must stop moralizing about sex, or how those desires are expressed. We must give the children the knowledge so it can make a difference in their lives. We must teach them intimacy. How to be close. How to love. And we must teach them quickly. Sex is a reality for most teenagers. If the virus gets loose in the youth of America, it will go crazy. Each month there are 1 million unwed pregnancies. And you can only get pregnant three days out of the month. The HIV virus is always there. As always, it is the youth that feel invincible. We must teach them how to be. Screw "morality"; we're talking about mortality. Nothing is more immoral than letting the children die of ignorance.

We must take responsibility. We must be accountable. We must care for one another. Come together as a community. Persons already experiencing AIDS are waiting. We are the liberal wing of the church. If we do not speak, who shall?

In community there is healing. The gay community has been healing itself. We should follow their lead on a world scale. Our brothers and sisters are learning to love one another. Trust is necessary.

We must find treatments. We must move our governments to act. We must learn from the whole experience—from the dying, as well as the living that surrounds it.

And we must see beyond AIDS. The community of humankind. Our history. That will continue long after us.

Reflections

Dr. Gary K. McClelland

When I was first asked to attend this Consultation on grappling with the theological and ethical issues of AIDS sponsored by *"the church"* I was somewhat reluctant to even file my application. On the one hand, I did feel qualified to speak to some of the issues as a physician, a gay Christian, a person with HIV infection, and the director of an active AIDS ministry in Los Angeles. On the other hand, the idea of meaningful dialogue with prominent members of the institutional church—so long condemnatory of my personhood, so slow to respond in a meaningful way to this frightening health crisis—seemed almost futile, a sop to satisfy the conscience in a token way. I finally decided to attend because of a small flutter of hope that always seems to be within me that perhaps this was an honest beginning, a slight opening of that door closed and tightly locked for so long.

Leaving the conference I have mixed feelings. I think the Consultation was superbly organized and run, with the exception of not having enough time to accomplish the work. And I certainly met a large number of honest, open, spirit-filled people anxious to get on with the task ahead and to examine new possibilities in their theologies. I was in the Stream on Illness and Health, and it was reassuring to be in a group where there were other persons with AIDS as well as health care providers. Our early sessions were tense and closed as participants "staked their territory" and quite verbally made known their particular agendas. This was especially true over including issues of sexuality in our Stream—an issue most felt was impossible to separate from health care given to persons with AIDS. A dramatic example of the homophobic roots of the problem was discussed in the empathetic care given to a woman, an infant, or a man acquiring the infection from a blood product versus the perfunctory care often given the gay male infected by the exact same virus. In the end, when our group position paper was presented to the entire Consultation, it was accused of being too soft and nonfocused. I think this was due in no small part to our attempt to accommodate the wide variation in sensibilities within the group.

It was not until we subdivided into smaller groups late Saturday morning that meaningful dialogue began to occur—that barriers were lowered and trust developed. In any future Consultation I would suggest some sort of exercise early on that would "break the ice" and open communication earlier. In the end I think we had a really good group that was willing to talk, to listen, to exchange, and to create.

I found the result of the Consultation quite good as far as it went, but as a person living with HIV infection I have serious doubt about how quickly recommended changes will be undertaken, and am not sure the group really understood the sense of urgency we implied. Given the difficulty in concurrence among the participants—who after all have demonstated their openness to the issues simply by registering—I have serious doubt about how quickly any radical transformation will occur at the congregational or grass-roots level, which is much more resistant to change and is, after all, where we live.

It is my hope and my prayer that this report will not be put on the shelf to collect dust, but will be widely and rapidly distributed and implemented at every level of the church. It is also my hope that each participant in this Consultation has been touched in a special way and has been empowered to return to their home to implement some of the many action steps recommended. The AIDS crisis has created a church in crisis, one that does not live what it preaches, whose salvation will be a return to the principles of *unconditional* love and of Matthew 25:35–36. I do think that the door has been opened just the tiniest bit this weekend, and I can't wait for the day it is flung widely open and *all* of God's people are invited in.

Report on the Bi-National Consultation

Mr. Patrick Morin

Preparation. The time for reading and digesting the ideas in the papers was inadequate.

Papers. The range of faith views and belief systems ran from liberal to conservative but did not include the fundamentalist voice (so that we could be in dialogue with that perspective).

People. There was a lack of diversity of people, and the low number of church representatives was disappointing. This underscores the problem that even the liberal church continues to have difficulty dealing with AIDS. The number of people from AIDS organizations was laudable, but few were church-related, so that they brought only a societal view to the Consultation.

Time. Considering the difficulty that churchpeople have in dealing with AIDS, the time together in the Consultation was too short by at least one day. If one of the goals of the Consultation was to allow the groups to learn how to work together effectively, then more time was needed.

Task Focus. There was pressure on the production of a statement too quickly. After ignoring AIDS for years, the church seemed more focused on making a statement almost overnight with no attempt at working on more concrete tasks that could bring the churches into being prophetic and giving leadership in pastoral care and hospice work, and so on.

Structure. The Consultation's format and direction were more than open—it was loose, so that participants wasted time and energy finding focus or task orientation. They took too long discovering why they were there and what they were to do as well as what they wanted to say or accomplish.

Process. All Streams were interrelated, but people were not clear that they were encouraged to discuss anything that might duplicate what might be addressed in another Stream. In the Illness and Health Stream there was little talk about either. It did deal with social consequences of the AIDS crisis and the attitudes of the church and of the society. It should have focused on health and the production of a statement defining "health," then discussing how AIDS underscores society's disease (illness, brokenness) in failing to deal with this sexually transmitted or drug use-related disease (and to some extent, race-related disease.) The final report of the Illness and Health Stream did not reflect the amount and the importance of the discussion on death and dying of AIDS. For instance, during the Stream process someone pointed out that they had observed many instances in which when death was raised in the discussion, talk about death and dying was avoided (probably unconsciously) by people changing the topic. Yet in the Stream it was stated that having a "healthy" attitude toward death led to having a healthy attitude toward life. Constantly avoiding (denying) the reality of our mortality is the root of society's dis-ease in dealing with sex and AIDS. I pointed out to the Stream participants that one of the problems that gay men have in dealing with AIDS is that the church has so constantly stated that their life-style is damned and that death would bring them only to hell, that they have often refused any pastoral care offered. (Most of the homosexual population have left the church—Metropolitan Community Churches are the exception.) It was at this point that sexuality became an integral part of our discussion. Since that was the focus of a separate Stream, we felt that we should not discuss it, but the persons with AIDS in the Stream felt that a discussion of sexuality was important to bring out what persons with AIDS thought was health and what was a healthy attitude toward sex.

I felt that there was a lack of cohesion for the first day and a half. Most of Friday and half of Saturday the Stream spent getting to know one another and getting clear on the topic (task). That seemed to use up an inordinate amount of the allotted time. I think that this time could have been reduced if the Health and Illness Stream had been given more focus as to the specific topics it was to address. More time for work after community building had been achieved was needed.

During the process of decision-making those groups representing nonchurch, gay-oriented groups, I felt, were uncomfortable doing God-talk. The idea that theological statements were
being formed seemed to be difficult for those members who
wanted to make social statements. There was a highly defensive
posture from the gay and AIDS-supportive people. The AIDS-
supportive people felt that they were going to be undermined or
ignored—that their work was going to be unrecognized and that
the church was going to take over their care work and service
and claim it as the church's own. Some of the gay men and
AIDS-supportive people felt that the church was coming into the
situation late, and they resented the lack of compassion that this
tardiness represented. Also the gay men and AIDS-supportive
people pointed out that it was the churches' teachings on sexual
orientation (promoting heterosexism) that has largely formed
society's intolerance toward nonheterosexuals and largely or
solely made homosexuals resistant to pastoral care. They feel
that their dying would be best among the comfort of other
homosexuals and those whom they feel certain will be nonjudgmental of whom they loved. I felt that many of the church
representatives were being defensive as well because of their
feelings of guilt about the slow and weak response of their
churches and their failure or tardiness in countering the fundamentalist view that AIDS was God's curse on homosexuals because of whom they loved. Some have belatedly stated after
much agony of decision processing that the love ethic of Jesus
Christ reflects God to us more accurately than the disease-
punishing image of God (punisher-by-disease) so that the voice
of the church that was heard by society at large and by the gay
community was for too long a condemnatory voice, not a compassionate and healing (restoring) voice.

Underscoring the problem is the fact that the church responds
slowly even in the best of times; the underlying sense of urgency
that is felt by the AIDS-supportive community and the speed
that the church normally takes in making decisions reminded
me of trying to mix oil and water—it is accomplished only in an
agitated state or with the presence of a surfactant that breaks
down the surface barriers. This Consultation started such a
barrier-breaking or reducing process, but my greatest fear

around this Consultation is that it was an expensive public relations exercise by the church toward the AIDS-supportive groups, but that the churches will not change either their teachings or their statements. Those churches that do feel that change is inevitable face a task that may take decades to accomplish, yet the urgency that AIDS presents does not allow that slow a response.

I found it depressing that there was a lack of prayer within our Stream. I believe that reflection (meditation) would have been useful at the beginning of each Stream session.

The closing worship was a healing highlight that gave appropriate closure to the Consultation. It seemed that the Holy Spirit was there (I felt it), but people were hesitant to acknowledge the Holy Spirit's presence by mentioning it.

I felt that throughout the Consultation many of the participants (especially the Roman Catholic representatives) were feeling an inner conflict, since their Church's teachings on homosexuality and the AIDS crisis as it is developing were in conflict. It seemed that some of the people involved in the Consultation were having an emotional battle in dealing with statements from their church's hierarchy that did not seem to match the work that they felt was required. They were almost behaving as if their personal faith was guiding them more than any dogmatic statement from their church. Some were faced with the situation that their church's teachings were in direct conflict with the health and emotional situation (e.g., the use of condoms and the reality of recreational [nonprocreational] sex activity) as well as with their personal faith; this was causing them turmoil and creating a rift between those from their same church (faith community) who held conservative versus liberal views of their faith. The biggest difficulty was in dealing with safe sex. Some people recognized that safe sex practices had to be taught while their churches refused to teach anything other than abstinence. This was not explicitly expressed, but was an underlying current recognized by almost everyone. AIDS has made sexual behavior more than a moral responsibility; it is now a life and death responsibility.

Continuing Challenge. I feel that the Consultation was a useful experience but that unfortunately it was difficult to prepare for everyone. The challenge of AIDS is large and complex because many ideas and issues have to be dealt with simultaneously. Death and sex have been taboo topics of discussion between churches and society, and yet they are key areas for any work on AIDS by the church. The question that keeps coming to me is, How do we get the churches to deal with these topics and become prophetic and lead society through this crisis? Must we wait until AIDS becomes the general population's epidemic, and even then will the church have its theology ready?

Thanks. I thank the Consultation organizers for bringing me and others in my situation together. The work was stimulating, tiring, and even painful but useful. I appreciated the quiet resting place that was made available to persons with AIDS because it kept us able to participate as fully as our energy allowed, knowing that we would not have to leave the Consultation site in order to restore our energy.

Reflections

The Rev. Ron Russell-Coons

Is it possible for the church to move beyond an "us and them" world view long enough for all people to lovingly journey through the AIDS crisis together? Weeks before the event the little child within me began to anticipate the Consultation on AIDS. What a marvelous opportunity to celebrate our common humanity and focus on the togetherness of God's people. Serendipity will be our experience, I thought, as we discover ways that the church can mobilize in the face of AIDS. All the while, my critical parent ego-state was negating the possibility of mutuality within the universal church. That part of me was saying, "AIDS will only further divide us."

Like a well-syncretized transmission, we shifted into the "us/

286

them" mode as the Consultation got under way. Sometimes "the other" or "them" was defined as AIDS patients. There were moments when I (being a person living with AIDS) looked on the healthy participants as "them." In group dialogue we discussed what "us/the church" could do for "them/the marginalized persons of the global AIDS crisis." Our language and thought processes demonstrated that humanity is divided into tiers. If this structure exists, someone is relegated to be at the bottom. Experiencing the dynamic of the Consultation, I wondered what it might take for People of Faith to begin seeing humanity on a horizontal, level plain. Is it possible that AIDS will ultimately be the force that calls us to oneness, to "we-ness"?

Throughout the weekend I felt anger that we could not trust one another any more. Dr. Cécile De Sweemer noted that we were a room full of nonbreathers. For whatever reason, people practice shallow breathing when they are afraid, uncomfortable, or distrustful. It was true. As I glanced around, it was obvious by our breathing that we were afraid of one another. Some of the distrust came from our denominational differences. Yes, we were all God's children, but far-removed, distant cousins within God's family. We were also aware of the complexity of sexuality and life-style issues. When those issues surfaced, the "us and them" became more pronounced.

My specific participation was in the Illness and Health Stream of the Consultation. Dr. Abbyann Lynch encouraged us to begin grappling with questions such as, What are the differences between illness, pain, and suffering? We could not enter into a discussion of such poignant questions because we lacked trust (trust in ourselves and trust in one another). AIDS, like other epidemics, moves people to redefine their theologies and look for meaning in the midst of crisis. We missed the moment. While we exhausted ourselves being self-protective, while we spent our energies on keeping up walls, we let the rich moment pass us by. It was a moment to be real, to be vulnerable, and to offer permission to the church to question and search for truth. We left Toronto without ever touching on some of humankind's most enduring dilemmas. In that moment, the gift of three days together, we made a choice. Our choice was to be distant and to generalize. The moment is gone.

287

Some of us attending the Consultation are persons living with AIDS. We're forced to ask questions and find answers—quickly. There may not be another moment for asking or seeking. In New York, in Toronto, in Regina, in Paris, in Nigeria, and in Seattle, women and men are appealing to the church to show them how to search for answers during the siege of AIDS. It will be hard to show anyone the way to truth if we have not dared to journey there ourselves.

In many ways, my critical parent was correct. We went to Toronto, we met, we eyed one another from a distance, and we left. We weren't certain in leaving if we had really said anything. If something was said, was it heard?

My inner child did find a transient point of unique celebration in the midst of the Consultation. For a brief, fleeting segment of the program I felt *us* encounter what it means to be *we* on this globe. As a person with AIDS, I was somehow linked to persons with AIDS in Zimbabwe. On Friday evening when Dr. De Sweemer shared with us her powerful summary of the AIDS crisis in Africa, I believe we all became persons living with AIDS. Although it was a brief moment, we had no walls between us . . . we had no sense of a *them*. I think that we could have trusted one another. Believing that, my child rejoiced.

We are witness to one of history's nightmares. Most physicians agree that the worst is yet to come. When I was growing up, it was reassuring to have someone come into my room and comfort me after a nightmare. The comfort was in knowing that I wasn't alone. We confronted the bad dream together. We—all of God's children on this planet—are together in the AIDS crisis. There's no time to learn to trust. We simply have to trust.

Next time . . . next time *we*'ll make it!

The Healing Church

Mr. Stephen Schell

The call to be a healing church for persons with AIDS emerged as one of the central themes of the Consultation. While undoubtedly an important first step, I fear that this call may become misdirected insofar as producing any tangible benefit for those it is intended to help. I would therefore like to highlight an approach for dealing with persons with AIDS that I believe must underpin our more general recommendation. This approach has been largely shaped by my own experiences as a gay man diagnosed with AIDS for the past year.

First, I think it is keenly important that the church is able to separate its relating to the problems of someone with AIDS from its relation with the actual person. In other words, I am a person with AIDS, which is a disease. I am *not* the disease. I am the equal of anyone who reaches out to me or anyone who cares for me. If all the church can see are my problems, however, then they are diminishing me as a person and turning me into nothing more than a victim or a medical case.

When making this separation, the church must also begin to see people as living with AIDS rather than dying. I believe that most persons with AIDS are able to live with their condition when they can still enter into peer-type relations with other people, not self-pitying relations. As such, the church must aim to create an environment in which someone with AIDS can still be committed to her or his personal growth and to cherishing his or her identity. This is an environment in which a person does not have to despair about how little time might be left, but rather rejoice in what time there is.

This approach also requires that the church accepts the person's sexuality if it is to bring any healing. More specifically, a homophobic church can no better minister to a gay man with AIDS than a racist church can minister to a black man with AIDS (or a misogynist church to a woman with AIDS). I suggest that the homophobes within the church spend their time trying to deal with their own prejudices and leave the pastoring to someone else.

For me, my sexuality is especially important at this time because of the additional strength and encouragement I receive from my partner during a period of illness. Yet it is at this very time that some within the church wish to deny my partner's existence, or at least the fact that he is male rather than female. Churchpeople would rather have me die without the comfort that this loving relationship brings, so that they can continue to live within their own narrow religious dogma.

Given the avoidance of homosexuality by some in the church, I am not surprised to find so many gay men with AIDS finding their Christian support in places other than the church. I seem to be less troubled about this than others at the Consultation. In fact, there was a sense among a few participants that if we do not reach out to persons with AIDS, they will somehow die without God. On the contrary, God has never deserted me, nor have I seen God ever desert anyone else with AIDS. The fact that I might die without the God promoted in some churches is not of great consequence. I am only saddened that these churches have yet to find the God of love and acceptance, the God who appreciates our sexuality as much as our spirituality.

20

Comments by Other Participants

In Our Reaction to AIDS Lies an Authentic Confession of Faith

Dr. André Guindon

The reports from all three Streams of the Consultation on AIDS point to the fact that our confession of faith is being tested in the way we react, by words and deeds, to persons with AIDS. The Stream on Social Consequences expresses this idea well when it states that "the attempts to link the AIDS crisis with the wrath of God . . . misrepresent the character of God." For the churches, this is perhaps the most crucial aspect of our reaction to AIDS. The issue at stake is, Who is our God?

Peter Berger writes that "inductive faith moves from human experience to statements about God, deductive faith from statements about God to interpretation of human experience."[1] Traditionally, Christian ethics has relied on "deductive faith." We have been busy trying to figure out what the gospel statements about God teach on human behavior. This approach, though, is easily deceptive. Gospel statements about God, in effect, necessarily make use of human speech. Yet human speech makes sense only to the extent that the receiver relates what is said to her or his own experience of reality. As central a gospel statement as "God is *abba*," for instance, would not mean the same thing to the two protagonists of Chaim Potok's novels *The Chosen* and *The Promise* because of their different experience of filiation. Reuven Malter's warm, intelligent, familiar, caring, confident relationship with his father would enable him to be in contact with a divine Reality named "abba" in a way that would not be immediately accessible to Danny Saunders, whose relationship with his father is one of cold respectfulness, mutual incomprehension, and intellectual rivalry. Both could call God "abba," but beyond language, the perceived reality would be different. When we abstract from "deductive faith," statements about God are mere formalities.

Contemporary research on moral and religious development[2] is documenting the fact that the real-life issue concerning the human content given to images of God is not one of "deductive faith," but one of "inductive faith." If the formal notions we are taught about God have a certain influence on the way we conduct our moral lives, the quality of our moral vision and of the way we involve ourselves in the world with others has a greater influence on the existential quality of our faith. The God in whom we effectively believe is not necessarily the One we confess with the "right words." She/he is the One about whom we speak (to ourselves as well as to others) as we interrelate with others in our community. This real-life language, according to Matthew's scenario of the Last Judgment (25:31–46), will be the test of faith: not whether we have used the "right words" when we speak about God, but whether our gestural language speaks about the "right God." Do we feed the hungry, clothe the naked, assist the sick, and support the prisoner? When we do these things, we proclaim the good news of the gospel, that our God is one who loves unconditionally, with no strings attached, one who does not take offense as we human beings are so prone to do, one who causes the sun to rise and the rain to fall on everyone alike, independently of their sex (John 4:5–27; Luke 8:1–3; 10:38–42), their age (Mark 9:33–37; 10:13–16), their nationality (Matthew 21:43; 28: 18; Luke 7:1–10), their morality (Matthew 9:9–10; 21:31–32; Mark 2:3–12), and even their religion (Luke 10:29–37; John 4:1–42).[3] This is the specific perfection of the God revealed in Jesus the Christ (Matthew 5:45). Anyone who does not have the human experience of the sort of love that liberates others and lets them be themselves fully cannot bear witness to the specific perfection of our God. He or she recites texts or pronounces the right words but does not confess the God revealed in Jesus.

We churchpeople, lay and cleric, confess our faith when we react in words and deeds to AIDS. To say the right words of "deductive faith," that "God is love [1 John 4:8, 16]," yet to make real-life-related statements suggesting that God might have something to do with the human evil of AIDS is to proclaim the bad news that ours is a threatening God, a "perverse God" who is waiting to "get us,"[4] that God prefers the company of people living in a "nice neighborhood" and behaving nicely, to the company of those people whom society marginalizes because they do not measure up to the conventional definitions of nicety.

Pope Paul VI said appropriately that "modern man listens more willingly to witnesses than to teachers, and if he does listen to teachers, it is because they are witnesses."[5] Our teaching concerning the good news of a God who loves "no matter what" will be credible to the extent that we are witnesses. In our reaction to AIDS lies indeed an authentic confession of faith.

Notes

1. Peter Berger, *A Rumor of Angels* (New York: Anchor Books, 1975), pp. 71–72.
2. See, e.g., Ana-Maria Rizzuto, *The Birth of the Living God* (Chicago: University of Chicago Press, 1979); James W. Fowler, *Stages of Faith: The Psychology of Human Development and the Quest for Meaning* (New York: Harper & Row, 1981).
3. See, e.g., Claude Ortemann, *Le Dieu gratuit de Jésus-Christ* (Paris: Desclée, 1986).
4. See Maurice Bellet, *Le Dieu pervers* (Paris: Desclée de Brouwer, 1979).
5. Paul VI, *Apostolic Exhortation "Evangelii Nuntiandi,"* Dec. 8, 1975, paragraph 41.

Comment re "Social Consequences of AIDS" Stream Recommendation

Dr. Abbyann Lynch

"We recommend that . . . churches must encourage the dissemination of AIDS-related information even when it relates to behavior that may be in conflict with church teachings, in order to save lives." In any effort to stem the spread of AIDS, we must observe both the rules of reason and a respect for the conscience of others. The recommendation cited is deficient on both counts.

It is one thing to ask Christian churches to consider changing their teaching regarding "behavior" (in this context, read "condemnation of certain sexual activity"). That many disagree with such teaching may be a legitimate ground for making such a request. When such teaching is perceived to counter human well-being, or even to present risk to life, the ground for making such a request appears very strong indeed. It is quite another thing to ask anyone, including Christian churches, to profess what is not believed. While support for the first request should be widespread, support for the second request (i.e., the substance of the recommendations cited above) should be nil. To endorse the recommendation as it is proposed is to endorse irrationality as a rule for determining conduct. Second, the recommendation implicitly trivializes the role of conscience; it overlooks the deference to be shown toward the conscience of others insofar as that conscience is fundamental to all truly human endeavor. Finally, if it were possible to enforce the recommendation, the outcome of such enforcement might well be counterproductive in terms of the struggle against AIDS. To allow this recommendation to stand as is is really to dis-value those very characteristics of human living that make the struggle against this lethal disease worthwhile. With respect, then, let the recommendation be changed to read: "Christian churches should reexamine their stance on dissemination of AIDS-related information whenever it appears that such a stance contributes to the loss of life. If the original stance should be re-affirmed, Christian churches have an obligation to provide public education regarding the positive basis for such a stance."

A Statement

Dr. David G. Roy

In the beginning was the Word . . .

The word is being spoken in the experience of those who have AIDS and, especially in North America, in the experience of those who live forms of sexuality that have been long condemned by the churches.

We are being called to hear and ponder the message:
Sexuality is sinful, not because it is homosexual or hetero-sexual, but wherever it expresses domination and betrayal of human beings, or their trivialization, rather than libera-tion and fidelity.

All of the churches are being called to consider:
We cannot really say that we accept people as human beings while rejecting the sexuality that constitutes a central dimen-sion of their own personal identity and being.

Many persons with AIDS are demonstrating that death is *not* the greatest evil. That evil rather is to be found in the abandonment of suffering people by those of us who are complacent in the conviction of our moral superiority to those whose behaviors we reject, and in the conviction of our social superiority to those who, because of their color, poverty, or life-style, we consider marginal and helpless.

A Statement

Fr. Bela Somfai

I am a Roman Catholic priest, a professor of moral theology at Regis College, Toronto School of Theology, and a member of the Society of Jesus. In one of these capacities I was invited to the organizing committee of this conference; now I wish to have my name removed from this list.

I participated in the Sexuality Stream. I find myself in substantial agreement with the first two reports on Illness and Health and Social Consequences, but I cannot accept the one submitted on sexuality and AIDS.

As a Canadian, I cannot accept the blanket condemnation of our health care system that provides full coverage for AIDS victims at the expense of other worthy needs. As a Roman Catholic, I cannot accept the blanket condemnation of past and current church positions on homosexuality.

What I am bringing home to my community as a Roman Catholic is the advice that prevention is easy and effective; let us put our resources behind this effort and continue to serve those who are suffering from AIDS. At the same time, however, I also have to urge my fellow Catholics to have nothing to do with those who, on one hand, claim that AIDS cannot be used to condemn homosexual orientation, and at the same time use the tragic occasion to justify homosexual practice and orientation. For myself at least, and I believe for the whole Roman Catholic Church, the decisive criterion on the morality of homosexual orientation is missing, but I am certain that it cannot be found in the context of discussing the tragedy of AIDS.

Finally, for the Canadian social and political context, I have one more observation: increase in gay militancy will carry certain social consequences for which those will pay who are already wounded by a deadly disease.

I submit this with the request of publishing it among the comments and documents of the Consultation.

Part 6

Concluding Comments from Closing Plenary

21

Personal Statements from Some of the Participants in the Final Session

Comment: I am a person with AIDS. One of the things that struck me when coming and, I think is still striking me, is the fact that we all know there's a sense of urgency. I know that the body of the church works very slowly and I also know that the work we do here will not help me because I probably won't be around!

I also know that the work we do may help the next generation of persons with AIDS. Those people who won't have to suffer in the same way that I have. Who won't have to worry about having money. Who won't have to worry about dying alone and without their God. It's hard to realize that there are going to be people tomorrow, tonight, today who are going to die without their God. But the work we do here is to try to bring that God to them. To others, the people who need God.

Comment: I've been very aware in these last moments of not only our indebtedness to our planning committee and the groups that supported this event, but to all the real work that was done in the communities primarily by the gay community years before the church began even to acknowledge this issue. We would not have been able to gather or come where we've come in these past two days without that work. I hope acknowledgments and documentation reflects that indebtedness of what we've been able to celebrate in our work here today.

The second thing is, I'm also very conscious that as the community gathered we experienced divisions and differences. They are real, and they are not resolved in our two days of gathering. Also at the same time we've been able to celebrate some breaking down of our hard-held barriers of one another and a little bit more fluidity between those labels that we dearly hold and carry, whatever they are. I give thanks for that. I think that will be reflective of what we face when we go back to our own home communities. Thank you.

Comment: I, too, would like to express my thanks to the steering committee and all who made this event possible. I think it's been extremely helpful and extremely eye-opening.

I would like to see perhaps some thought given to the next steps. I think we have opened up a lot of things. I think all of us in the various Streams have felt overwhelmed by the amount of material and information we tried to process, understand, reflect on, absorb, and then reproduce in some kind of a statement that could call ourselves and our church communities to take some action.

I have one particular area of interest I would like to see some further work on. I don't mean to indicate that this is the only area because I think there's so much here that needs to be developed further. Maybe it's my own Presbyterian background, but I would like to see more scriptural study. I think that so much misuse has been made of the scripture on this kind of issue, and I think that is something we could contribute to. I know Professor Sheppard, whom I've known for years, had a paper on "Bible Revelation" in the Sexuality Stream, and I thought that was very helpful. We did not have anything of that nature for our Stream, and it seems to me that, with all the diversity we have, and we have many different theologies and communions, we have to deal with some of these basic questions of what in fact is biblical revelation? What is Christian tradition? What is historic theology? If for nothing else, I think we have to give a witness in a situation in which I think there's some real demonic use being made of the symbols and bases of our faith.

Comment: There was a term that was bandied about a fair bit and has been a big part of this conference. It didn't get into our

300

document, and that's the word trust. I have learned a greater measure of trust of some of those who are different from what I am. And I think that's a big part of the personal learnings that for me come out of this Consultation.

I just took a quick glance through the documents and I think there is one area that we've overlooked. That's people like me: pastors of specific congregations. We've been very ready to point the finger at doctors who may shy back from people with HIV-related conditions, but what about those of us pastors who through neglect are not fulfilling responsibilities? One of the things that I must take back with me is my own personal responsibility within that context and out of the trust that I have had enhanced at this gathering.

Comment: When I first thought about coming to the conference, I was very interested in becoming part of the Stream on Illness and Health. I wanted to be part of that Stream because my main responsibility to my community, which is largely the gay community and my own parish, is to provide pastoral care to AIDS patients and their partners and their friends. But I changed my Stream, largely because of Kevin Gordon's paper. He raised a lot of questions that I thought the Illness and Health Stream ought to have raised. The whole business about whether we will speak well or ill of God after all of this, and the kinds of questions that, of course, you all know are so radically raised in the book of Job.

One member of our Sexuality Stream said at one point that many AIDS patients have been sanctified and sanctify those around them. I see that happening all the time in the kind of bonds that this kind of disease has created and the many, many good things that really have come about. There are many others like me, I think, who feel a tremendous responsibility as a representative of a healing God to bring people to the realization that not to be cured is not necessarily not to have been healed. That's a very difficult task for anyone, be they theologian, priest or minister or whatever in a world that is so riddled by disease in so many forms. I would like to have seen the Stream on Illness and Health struggle with that because I think that those are real theological issues that perhaps we couldn't have raised

301

here now, but I think are very important for us to raise in the future. I was glad to hear our friend with AIDS witness to the people who tried to bring him their—for want of a better word—system of spirituality. I hope that in doing so they've always brought something of themselves because the healing really takes place in us first and then we, I think, help to bring it about. I think we need some help to do that. I certainly need some help to do that. I'm profoundly interested in the really serious theological questions that real healing raises in the context of AIDS. I don't have a lot of support. I don't read a lot of things that have been very helpful. I'm a little disappointed that that hasn't happened here, to some extent, although again, I think the things that happened in my Stream on Sexuality have been of some help to me. I do want personally to proclaim or witness to you how important Kevin Gordon's paper has been to me.

Comment: I want to say many things that are fighting for priority in my mind. But let me maybe give you a couple of paradoxes. On the one hand, I'm very happy that I got up from the sickbed and got to Toronto. I think from a personal point of view, I feel quite encouraged having met many of you. On the other hand, I feel a creative dissatisfaction with where we are. There are two things that I think I feel most as things I would have liked to have had here, and so far haven't seen very much here. One is passion. I grew up in a Roman Catholic country and I happen to think that one of the great gifts from Roman Catholicism to the world is art and passion, even though I am Protestant. I wish we could feel, think, act with a little more passion.

You cannot live without passion and neither can you die that way! AIDS demands that we live and that we learn to die, and that we don't spoil life with death and that we don't spoil death with life. I think, I hope, that not only have we started breathing a little bit more normally, which I think we did, but that we dare to let the fire of passion come. It's not going to destroy us! We cannot believe in the Spirit if we cannot believe in passion. Why can't we give ourselves freedom to be passionate? Maybe we would cry at moments that are embarrassing but so what? It doesn't matter, let us be human beings, first and foremost. Not gay or straight, not oppressor or victim, but human beings who can be passionate about this with all that we have. I hope in the months and years to come we will become freer and freer to be passionate.

The second thing may sound very paradoxical. Yesterday someone in a distracted moment asked me what I would like people to pray about and I said, "First thing is, let us not take ourselves so seriously." I think we take ourselves damn seriously, if you excuse my language. And we have no reason for it. The AIDS crisis is here; we can either be part of the problem or part of the solution. But neither are we *the* problem nor are we *the* solution.

We are players. I'm not underestimating how important or unimportant we can be, but you should not take yourself so terribly seriously that you are totally unable to truly play your role. So let us hold our differences lightly. Let us hold our opinions and our feelings lightly. Let us be able to concentrate on what is the real problem and truly play our role, however important or unimportant that role may be, given lots of opportunities and lots of chance effects.

I heard the sister talk about the church and her feeling that yes, we need to challenge but no, we don't need a break-up where things no longer flow and communicate. We need to be prophetic, but prophets were also people who sang and danced. They were also people who were able to be joyful with the community, to reach out to the community with all their passion. I'm sure if there ever were passionate people, it surely was the prophets of the Old Testament. With all their passion, they also had a sense of humor and a sense of taking themselves lightly. I hope we can do that because there's a tremendous temptation in this situation, a tremendous temptation to be now the ultimately self-righteous because we stand up to the self-righteous, and it's not going to help. A Pharisee multiplied with a Pharisee still remains a Pharisee. What we need instead is to be able to be passionate but also compassionate with those with whom we differ in opinion. To be able to feel their pain of their particular limitations in accepting others because there is pain in that, and to be able to try to help them. I think many of our friends who have been able to say, "I'm gay" or "I'm gay and I have AIDS," have done the first step, which is to recognize that I'm here, I'm a human being, and this is what you might label me.

I think the second step is the willingness to invite to real interplay, not just recognize me but recognize me and let us celebrate life together, and eventually, when the need is there, let us celebrate death together.

Appendixes

Appendix A

AIDS and the Church as a Healing Community*

The Executive Committee of the World Council of Churches, having received a report on the Consultation held in Geneva in June 1986 "AIDS and the Church as a Healing Community," wishes to call the attention of the churches to the urgency of this issue.

We call on the churches to respond appropriately to the need for pastoral care, education for prevention, and social ministry as called for by the Consultation.

The Executive Committee also asks the General Secretary of the WCC to plan for appropriate follow-up of the recommendations of the Consultation by the sub-units on Church and Society, Family Education and the Christian Medical Commission.

The Medical Background

The Consultation provided important medical information, including the following:

The rate of spread of AIDS and its high fatality is frightening. AIDS is a viral infection which recently appeared, being identified only five years ago. It is sometimes considered to be the plague of the 20th century.

According to reports from the World Health Organization,

---

*January 1987 meeting of the Executive Committee of the World Council of Churches.

AIDS is present on all continents where it is contracted by men, women, and children, regardless of socio-economic status, education, culture or religion. The number of people ill is increasing geometrically, doubling every 10-14 months. At this time, the world has about 30,000 persons with AIDS (24,000 in the USA, 2600 in Europe and 1000 reported cases in Africa.*This number is probably underestimated, as many countries have not been able to give complete information. The number of persons infected by the virus who have no clinical manifestations (so-called carriers) is unknown. It probably numbers in the millions. It appears that a great number of people are infected annually. The rate of infection may vary significantly from one place in the world to the next.

In Africa the illness is contracted primarily by a heterosexual population; in Europe, North America, and Oceania primarily by male homosexuals and intravenous drug-users. Mortality is high, reaching 75% one year after diagnosis and 100% three years after diagnosis. No efficacious treatment has been found. The hope of a vaccine is very uncertain. So far only preventive measures can help to stem the epidemic.

The Church as a Healing Community

The Consultation identified the following theological foundation for the church as a healing community:

In the mysteries of life and death we encounter God; this encounter calls forth trust, hope, and awe rather than paralysis and immobilization. Those we cannot cure we can support and sustain in solidarity: "I was hungry . . . thirsty . . . a stranger . . . naked . . . sick . . . imprisoned, and you fed . . . clothed . . . took care . . . visited " [Matthew 25].

The AIDS crisis challenges us profoundly to be the church in deed and in truth: *to be the church as a healing community.* AIDS is heartbreaking and challenges the churches to break their own hearts, to repent of inactivity and of rigid moralisms. Since AIDS cuts across race, class, gender, age, sexual orientation,

---

*For more recent figures see Church and Society Documents, *AIDS and the Church*, March 1987, No. 1, Geneva: World Council of Churches, 1987.

and sexual expression, it challenges our fears and exclusions. The healing community itself will need to be healed by the forgiveness of Christ.

The Consultation called on the churches to undertake the following:

1. *Pastoral care.*

The people of God can be the family that embraces and sustains those who are sick with AIDS-related conditions, caring for the brother, sister, or child without barriers, exclusion, hostility, or rejection.

Death is a mystery. We are angry and helpless when faced by its reality. We need to acknowledge our helplessness and not deny it. This has particular significance as we share the experience of ministry with persons with AIDS and as we are ministered to by them, as we grow with them in our Christian understanding of death in the light of Christ's death and resurrection.

2. *Education for prevention.*

To assure high quality information on the disease, we invite the churches to participate actively with the health professions, local governments, where possible, and local community agencies in programmes of preventive education. We invite the churches to use the World Health Organization and its network of local resources.

AIDS is preventable. Society must concentrate sufficient resources on its prevention. This will involve measures that should reasonably be adopted by all: carriers, the sick, current high risk groups and the general population, since the latter includes many undetected carriers. It also calls urgently for responsible forms of behaviour by all, and for the improvement of physical and socio-economic conditions in many parts of the world.

Preventive measures and altered behaviour patterns must address the different factors that favour the transmission of the virus; it is necessary, therefore, that the different models of transmission prevalent regionally be clearly described and understood.

3. *Social ministry.*

Given the widely varying valuations of some of the issues related to the disease, member churches and ecumenical councils will have to be rigorously contextual in their response. We affirm, however, certain commonly held values, especially:

1. the free exchange of medical and educational information about the disease within countries and across borders;
2. the freedom to pursue research about the disease;
3. the free flow of information about the disease to patients, their families and loved ones;
4. the right to medical and pastoral care regardless of socio-economic status, race, sex, sexual orientation, or sexual relationship;
5. the privacy of medical records of persons with AIDS or AIDS-related Complex or positive antibodies.

Since AIDS is a global epidemic, effective action by churches and individual Christians must extend not only to the AIDS neighbour closest at hand, but also through effective global collaboration to the stranger on the farthest side of the world.

The Consultation also called on the churches "to work against the real danger that AIDS will be used as an excuse for discrimination and oppression and to work to ensure the protection of the human rights of persons affected directly or indirectly by AIDS."

The Executive Committee also wishes to call to the attention of the churches these further concerns expressed by the Consultation:

to confess that churches as institutions have been slow to speak and to act: that many Christians have been quick to judge and condemn many people who have fallen prey to the disease; and that through their silence many churches share responsibility for the fear that has swept our world more quickly than the virus itself;

to affirm and support the entire medical and research community in its efforts to combat the disease;

to affirm that God deals with us in love and mercy and that we are therefore freed from simplistic moralizing about those who are attacked by the virus.

APPENDIX B

AIDS and Substance Abuse

Mr. David G. Hallman

Dr. Steven Joseph, commissioner of health for New York City, describes New York as the "epicenter of the AIDS pandemic in North America." Since the disease is more advanced there, we should be able to learn certain things from the New York experience that could assist us in controlling the spread of the virus where it is less advanced.

As of April 1988, New York has had nearly 14,000 diagnosed cases of AIDS. Of those individuals, 7,000 have already died. AIDS is the leading cause of death among all men in New York City between the ages of twenty-five and forty-four and the leading cause of death among all women between the ages of twenty-five and thirty-four. It is estimated that there are an additional 300,000 to 400,000 persons in New York who have been exposed to the virus and are HIV positive. By the end of 1991 New York will have had 40,000 cases of AIDS. Put another way, there will be as many people diagnosed in New York with AIDS in 1991 alone as there were during the first five years of the disease, 1981 to 1986.

The disease to this point has primarily affected the homosexual population, and that will probably continue to be the case for some time in many parts of North America. But the New York

---

This appendix was prepared with assistance from Rebecca Porper and Chris Jacques of the New York City Health Department.

situation signals a major shift in the direction of AIDS for the future. In the spring of 1988 for the first time in New York, the number of cases related to intravenous drug use surpassed the number of cases attributable to sexual transmission among gay or bisexual men.

That change may in part be the result of the intensive educational efforts on prevention that have been mounted by the gay community. There are signs that the spread of the virus among gay men is slowing. But the changing pattern is also a clear sign that the virus is spreading in a largely uncontrolled way among a different sector of the population that is extremely vulnerable: poor minority men, women, and children.

Substance abuse is a major factor associated with the transmission of the virus among this population. According to Joseph, the key to the future handling of the AIDS crisis lies in the relation of the disease and drug abuse.

Researchers have identified a relation between an increase in substance abuse, particularly cocaine and crack, and an increase in the prevalence of many sexually transmitted diseases. It appears that the situation will be the same with AIDS. For a virus that lives in blood and blood products, it has become clear that a significant means of transmission is through the sharing of needles when drugs are used intravenously. The infected blood from an HIV-positive person gets passed by means of the needle into the bloodstream of another person.

In addition to needle-sharing, sexual activity is a significant route of virus transmission that is affected by substance abuse. Decision-making capacities are severely impaired when one is under the influence of drugs. When this is combined with the increased sexual drive that seems to accompany the early stages of cocaine or crack addiction, people are less likely to be cautious about the use of protective "safer sex" techniques and more likely to engage in unprotected high-risk activities.

Another factor compounds the problem. Drugs cost money. One way to earn money to support a drug habit is by selling sex. People who are active drug users may find that becoming part of the sex industry is an easier way to make money to buy drugs than other forms of employment. They thus have an increased number of sexual partners with whom they may engage in un-